THE VICAR OF WAKEFIELD
SHE STOOPS TO CONQUER
AND POEMS

OLIVER GOLDSMITH
1728–1774

THE VICAR OF WAKEFIELD
SHE STOOPS TO CONQUER
AND POEMS

Oliver Goldsmith

with an introduction by
C. E. VULLIAMY

original illustrations by
CHRISTOPHER W. BRADBURY

Distributed by
HERON BOOKS

OLIVER GOLDSMITH was the fifth child (the second son) of the Rev. Charles Goldsmith by his wife Anne, the daughter of the Rev. Oliver Jones.

It is now generally accepted that he was born on November 10th, 1728, at Smith Hill, near Elphin, County Roscommon, Ireland. About 1730 his father was presented with the living of Kilkenny West, and moved with his family from the cottage at Pallas which he had occupied as a curate to the rectory at Lissoy, a village situated a few miles from the small town of Ballymahon near Athlone.

Charles Goldsmith was a man of sweet and generous disposition who brought up his children in the love of God and the idea of universal benevolence, but left them ill-equipped to face the realities of a world which did not practise these Christian virtues.

Oliver was sent to school, first with the parish school-master, and then successively to more ambitious establishments at Elphin, Athlone, and finally at Edgeworths-town. In 1745 he entered Trinity College, Dublin, as a "sizar," *i.e.* a student who in return for greatly reduced fees had to perform certain menial duties. His life at university was not happy; he lacked connections, good looks (he was small of stature and his face was badly pock-marked), and above all, he was miserably poor. Moreover, his irregular habits and pranks brought him frequently into conflict with the university authorities. Nevertheless, his talents did not remain unappreciated. In 1749 he graduated Bachelor of Arts.

Having left the university, he lived for a while at home with his mother—his father having died in 1749—waiting to be accepted for Holy Orders. However, his application was rejected. After a short interlude as a tutor to the family of a country gentleman, he decided to study law in London. He set out on his journey with fifty pounds provided by his uncle, but got no further than Dublin, where he lost his money at the card tables. Finally, early in 1752, his uncle having once more supplied the funds, he left Ireland for good to be trained for the medical profession at Edinburgh. He remained in Edinburgh for two winters, concerning himself more with social activities than studies, and early in 1754 went to Leyden (Holland), where he hoped to obtain a medical degree. A year later, being once more penniless, he set out on a tour on foot through Flanders, France, and Switzerland, ending up in Padua and returning via Austria and Southern Germany. He landed at Dover on February 1st, 1756, with a few half-pence and a dubious degree of Bachelor of Physics.

For a time he tried to make a living as best he could, becoming in turn an apothecary's assistant, a physician of the poor, a proof-reader to a bookseller, and an assistant schoolmaster. Around 1758 he began to write essays and reviews for the *Monthly Review*, in which he published a translation from the French: *Memoirs of a Protestant Condemned to the Galleys of France for his Religion*. The same year he was offered—but in the end did not obtain—a medical appointment with the East India Company. Partly with the object of raising funds for his outfit and passage he wrote *An Enquiry into the State of Polite Learning in Europe*, which was published in 1759 and attracted some attention.

He was now launched upon a journalist's career. In 1759 he was commissioned to write the entire contents of a weekly magazine entitled *The Bee* and also became a regular contributor to Smollett's *British Magazine* and to the *Busybody*, another literary periodical. In 1760 he began to write for the *Public Ledger* and created for himself a "feature" with a series of 119 essays which came to be known as the *Chinese Letters* and were later (in 1762) published as a whole under the title of *The Citizen of the World*. It was the turning-point of his fortunes. In 1761 he

6

made the acquaintance of Dr. Johnson, who took him under his protection and introduced him to his circle of friends, which included among others Sir Joshua Reynolds—who later painted a portrait of Goldsmith—Garrick, and Burke. He became one of the first members of "The Club" on its foundation in 1763.

Goldsmith's fame was established with the publication of the poem *The Traveller* in 1765. The following year, through the good offices of Dr. Johnson, *The Vicar of Wakefield* was published, the work by which Goldsmith is known to the whole civilized world. In 1768 came his comedy *The Good Natur'd Man* and in 1770 his second great poem *The Deserted Village*. Finally, in 1773 *She Stoops to Conquer* was performed at Covent Garden. Goldsmith had reached the summit of his reputation.

Unknown or famous, poor or affluent, Goldsmith's expenditure was constantly in excess of his means; on the other hand, whatever he spent he could pride himself on having gained by his pen. So in between writing the works which brought him fame (but little money) he produced laborious compilations for booksellers, compilations which for a whole century became standard works for schools. Among the best known were his *Roman History* (1769 and 1772), his *Grecian History* (1774), his *Abridged History of England* (1771 and 1774), and *An History of the Earth and Animated Nature* (1774).

Overwork (in the constant effort of raising money) and lack of exercise early undermined Goldsmith's health. He died on April 4th, 1774, at the age of forty-six and was buried at the Temple burial ground. A memorial plaque with his portrait in bas-relief and with an epitaph in Latin composed by Johnson was placed by his friends in Westminster Abbey.

H. d. R.

CONTENTS

CONTENTS

CONTENTS

INTRODUCTION

PETULANT and assertive, incorrigibly foolish in talk, and of a morbidly vigilant egoism, Goldsmith combined the gifts of a brilliant versatility with a strange weakness and unevenness of character. "He was not an agreeable companion," said Johnson, regardless of his own disadvantages in polite society, "for he talked always for fame." A more subtle observer would have realized the peculiar situation of Goldsmith in the literary circles of London. He was here living among men who could not always understand or condone the aberrations of a sensitive and irascible genius; he had nothing of the discipline or cold adherence to method which is required by true scholarship; and he strove anxiously, and with invariable failure, to prove himself a man of the world.

He was in many ways unfortunate. He had "no settled notions." The very impetuosity and eagerness of his mind drove him into the most humiliating of absurdities; and there is no humiliation comparable to that of a man who, conscious of his own versatile powers, feels himself at a loss among those who are less gifted, though more assured than himself. He could not endure the massive intolerance or the patronizing benignity of Johnson: he had, as he knew, gifts that were unintelligible to Johnson, a quality of rapid apprehension and response that is rarely found among scholars. Thus, although Goldsmith and Johnson had a precarious liking for each other, collisions, batterings, and repulses were frequent. What Johnson could see and admire in Goldsmith was the extraordinary skill of his writing; what he deplored was his "ignorance." The mind of Goldsmith was essentially volatile and alert; by no means accurate or dependable, or even, in matters of truth, particularly scrupulous. His vanity, his dread of being taken for "an ordinary man," was always conspicuous among his failings and always a source of mental perturbation.

It may seem strange that a man so teased and exhausted by this weakness could have drawn a character so poised and so generously humane as Dr. Primrose, the Vicar of Wakefield. But surely there is no fundamental incongruity in this performance. Goldsmith himself was generously humane, he loved virtue, and he knew something of the simplicity of a good man; a good man with peculiarities, humours, impulses, and occasional passion. He portrayed in Dr. Primrose the qualities which he considered most admirable in human nature; the qualities that were most admirable in Goldsmith himself.

For many years before the publication of *The Vicar of Wakefield* Goldsmith had already exercised his nimble and ingenious faculties in many kinds of writing, and when he died in 1774 at the age of forty-six he left behind him examples (varying greatly in merit) of history, poetry, biography, biology, fiction, comedy, *belles lettres*, essays, and reviews.

But the work which has assured him of a permanent and elevated place among the great masters of English literature is unquestionably *The Vicar of Wakefield*. As a novelist he is excelled by Fielding (to whom he owed much, even if Dr. Adams is not the prototype of Dr. Primrose), but no other writer has excelled him in the writing of pure, harmonious, and lucid prose, or in the charm, subtlety, and humour with which he has drawn the Vicar himself.

The history of *The Vicar of Wakefield* is not always presented with accuracy. The book was apparently begun in 1761 and was finished in 1762, at a time when Goldsmith, in London, was living in circumstances that were precarious and uncomfortable. Some time later he was arrested for debt to his landlady, to whom he owed the rent of his lodgings, and in this distress he sent a message to Johnson. Sending a guinea in advance, Johnson presently arrived at the lodgings, where he found that Goldsmith had already provided himself with a bottle of madeira. "I put the cork into the bottle, desired he would be calm, and began to talk of the means by which he might be extricated." The means were raised by the manuscript of *The Vicar of Wakefield*, which Johnson sold to Newbery the publisher for sixty pounds. The date of this transaction is uncertain; Professor Masson thinks it was towards the end of 1764. It is now known, however, that Goldsmith had previously sold a third share in the book for twenty guineas to Collins of Salisbury, who eventually printed the book for Newbery in 1766.

In addition to literary hack-work, Goldsmith had already published *The Citizen of the World* (1762) and *The Traveller* (1764); and although Hawkins declares that he was still regarded as "a mere literary drudge," his reputation was being steadily consolidated.

None the less, it would be erroneous to say that *The Vicar* was immediately successful, or to allege that Newbery had secured an obvious bargain. The book was published in March, 1766 in two duodecimo volumes at six shillings. Presumably the first edition was not a large one: a second edition was called for in May and a third in August. After this the sales fell off, and the fourth edition was not produced until 1770; and even then the cost of production had not been covered by the profits.

The book made its way slowly among the public and received little attention from the literary magazines. Indeed, the only notice of any considerable length was that which appeared in the *Monthly Review*. "Through the whole course of our travels in the wild regions of romance," the *Review* declares, "we never met with any thing more difficult to characterize than *The Vicar of Wakefield*; a performance which contains beauties sufficient to entitle it to almost the highest applause, and defects enough to put the discerning reader out of all patience with an author capable of so strangely under-writing himself." Goldsmith was accused of deficiency in his knowledge of mankind, but his novel was praised for its "moral tendency." The fourth edition sold but slowly, the fifth did not appear until 1774, and the sixth not until 1779—five years after the death of the author. But several translations had been made in the lifetime of Goldsmith, and *The Vicar's* reputation was beginning to spread abroad. By 1886 there had been at least ninety-six English editions, and the number which has been printed since that date is hardly computable.

No doubt the structure of *The Vicar of Wakefield*, with its machinery of coincidence, its abundance of artifice and wild improbability, may seem awkwardly conventional. But the shrewdness of observation and, above all, the consistent vitality and integrity of the characters are perpetually fresh and endearing. If the events of the novel impose too heavy a tax upon credulity and are seldom plausible, the Primrose family at once establish themselves in the mind of the reader, not as actors upon a conventional stage but as the participators of our common human experience. It is, in fact, this internal reality of character, motive, and action which perpetually delights the reader and which gives *The Vicar of Wakefield* a position of supremacy among English pastoral novels.

Macaulay complained, with characteristic petulance, that the story of *The Vicar* was "one of the worst that was ever constructed," and he asserted that "the latter part of the tale is unworthy of the beginning. As we approach the catastrophe," he continues, "the absurdities lie thicker and thicker, and the gleams of pleasantry become rarer and rarer." Such criticism of the machinery of the novel may be relevant, although superfluous; but Goldsmith never intended *The Vicar* to be a work of undiluted pleasantry, and there could be no misconception more abysmal than to regard the book as primarily a novel of humour.

Indeed, Goldsmith himself was aware of the structural weakness of his book, and had it not been for the importunity of his landlady and the friendly speed of Johnson, it is almost certain that he would have revised and amplified the story very considerably. The literary eye can discern the evidence of makeweight and of padding, there are gaps in the narrative, and the end is hurried and —let us allow—desperately inconsequential. "There are a hundred faults in this thing," said the author in his own advertisement or preface.

As for the story, it has been pointed out very justly that its theme resembles very closely that of the Book of Job: a good and innocent man remaining steadfast in faith and unbroken in courage beneath a series of horribly cruel disasters.

Until misfortune fell upon them the Primrose family lived in comfort and security. Neither Primrose nor his wife desired any change in their condition: "all our adventures were by the fire-side, and all our migrations from the blue bed to the brown." There were six children: George, intended for a profession; Moses, more vaguely destined for "business"; two charming girls, Olivia and Sophia; and two little boys, born "after an interval of twelve years."

The goodness and simplicity of Dr. Primrose do not obliterate his more comprehensible qualities. He could be testy and obtuse, and there is a strange ineffable clumsiness in his endeavours to control or suppress the normal vagaries of the female disposition. He was prosy in defence of principles, and resolutely impolite when his views on monogamy were disputed. But the predominating features of his character are those of cheerfulness, manly courage, faith, loyalty, the true benevolence of an honest heart, an appreciation of learning, and a joy in the simple pleasures of the country scene.

His very whimsicalities are made respectable through sincerity of intention. When he put his wife's epitaph above the chimney-piece (to remind her of her duty), when he tipped the face-lotion into the fire (because of a "natural antipathy" to such things), and when he controversially blazed away at the archdeacon his behaviour

may have seemed a little odd: it was never contemptible.
He is at his best in those charming pastorals when, upon
the seat under the hawthorn hedge, his two daughters
"sang to the guitar" while the Doctor and his wife would
stroll down the sloping field that was embellished with
"blue-bells and centaury," talking of their children and
enjoying the breeze "that wafted health and harmony."
Or should we say that he is at his best when, like John
Wesley, he brought sense and order and the hope of
salvation to the prisoners in the gaol?

It has been suggested that Goldsmith intended Primrose as a portrait of his own father: a notable exception
to the customary treatment of fathers by literary sons.
But no one, so far as I know, has indicated the originals
of the family. Yet the family, and especially the two
daughters, engage our sympathy and interest as fully as
Primrose himself.

Olivia and Sophia are by no means the standard young
misses of the eighteenth century. Goldsmith evidently
saw them very clearly and, within masculine limits,
understood them very well. Olivia, the elder of the two,
had a "luxuriance of beauty" and a romantic warmth of
disposition; Sophia had the allurements of a seductive
modesty. Both were susceptible to the influence of dress:
"A suit of mourning has transformed my coquette into a
prude, and a new set of ribbons has given her younger
sister more than natural vivacity." Both were brightened
and excited by notions of "an approaching triumph"
and both "loved laces, ribbons, bugles, and catgut"
—and those detestable washes that so infuriated their
father. And even Mrs. Primrose, matronly and rather
obtuse, "retained a passion for her crimson paduasoy."
That Olivia should have read *Tom Jones*, without her
father's disapproval, is not a little surprising. What is
more understandable, perhaps, is that Olivia should have
been seduced by Thornhill. But the seduction was quite
as embarrassing for Goldsmith as it was for Miss Primrose, and he leaves her fate unsettled at the end of the

book. As for Thornhill, a defiant and accomplished rascal, he lives in moderate comfort with a relative and spends his time in "learning to blow the French horn."

In the continental adventures of George Primrose, Goldsmith has introduced himself and the circumstances of his early life, when he wandered through Europe playing his flute and wrangling at the universities. Moses Primrose, a simpleton with a little learning, still has the foundation of an honest and original character. He makes one observation concerning Thornhill which is worthy of remembrance: "Thinking freely of religion may be involuntary with this gentleman."

No book surpasses *The Vicar of Wakefield* in subtle and evocative touches of character. Who can forget Mr. Jenkinson who, at fourteen, "knew the world, cocked his hat and loved the ladies"? or the sham æsthetics of the drabs from London who talked of "pictures, taste, Shakespeare, and the musical glasses"? or the state of George when, as a hired companion, he "carried the corkscrew, stood god-father to all the butler's children, and sang when he was bid"?

Thus, whatever its defects may be, *The Vicar of Wakefield* takes a high place, perhaps the highest place, among the smaller masterpieces of English literature. It has, as Washington Irving remarked, "universal and enduring popularity," and its author, in the picturesque phrase of Thackeray, "has found entry into every castle and every hamlet in Europe." Goethe declared that it was "one of the best novels which has ever been written." We shall not dissent from these opinions. We admire in this delightful book not only the exquisite literary skill of its author, but also his goodness of heart, his warm generosity, simplicity, faith, and humour.

C. E. VULLIAMY

THE VICAR OF WAKEFIELD

ADVERTISEMENT

THERE are an hundred faults in this Thing, and an hundred things might be said to prove them beauties. But it is needless. A book may be amusing with numerous errors, or it may be very dull without a single absurdity. The hero of this piece unites in himself the three greatest characters upon earth; he is a priest, an husbandman, and the father of a family. He is drawn as ready to teach, and ready to obey, as simple in affluence, and majestic in adversity. In this age of opulence and refinement, whom can such a character please? Such as are fond of high life, will turn with disdain from the simplicity of his country fireside. Such as mistake ribaldry for humour, will find no wit in his harmless conversation; and such as have been taught to deride religion, will laugh at one, whose chief stores of comfort are drawn from futurity.

OLIVER GOLDSMITH.

THE VICAR OF WAKEFIELD

I

*The description of the family of Wakefield, in which a kindred
likeness prevails as well of minds as of persons.*

I was ever of opinion, that the honest man who married
and brought up a large family, did more service than he
who continued single, and only talked of population.
From this motive, I had scarce taken orders a year before
I began to think seriously of matrimony, and chose my
wife, as she did her wedding-gown, not for a fine glossy
surface, but such qualities as would wear well. To do her
justice, she was a good-natured notable woman; and as
for breeding, there were few country ladies who could
shew more. She could read any English book without
much spelling; but for pickling, preserving, and cookery
none could excel her. She prided herself also upon being
an excellent contriver in housekeeping; though I could
never find that we grew richer with all her contrivances.

However, we loved each other tenderly, and our fond-
ness encreased as we grew old. There was, in fact,
nothing that could make us angry with the world or each
other. We had an elegant house, situated in a fine
country, and a good neighbourhood. The year was spent
in a moral or rural amusement, in visiting our rich neighbours, and relieving such as were poor. We had no
revolutions to fear, nor fatigues to undergo; all our
adventures were by the fire-side, and all our migrations
from the blue bed to the brown.

As we lived near the road, we often had the traveller
or stranger visit us to taste our gooseberry-wine, for
which we had great reputation; and I profess with the
veracity of an historian, that I never knew one of them
find fault with it. Our cousins too, even to the fortieth

remove, all remembered their affinity, without any help from the Herald's office, and came very frequently to see us. Some of them did us no great honour by these claims of kindred; as we had the blind, the maimed, and the halt amongst the number. However, my wife always insisted that as they were the same *flesh and blood*, they should sit with us at the same table. So that if we had not very rich, we generally had very happy friends about us; for this remark will hold good through life, that the poorer the guest, the better pleased he ever is with being treated: and as some men gaze with admiration at the colours of a tulip, or the wing of a butterfly, so I was by nature an admirer of happy human faces. However, when any one of our relations was found to be a person of a very bad character, a troublesome guest, or one we desired to get rid of, upon his leaving my house, I ever took care to lend him a riding-coat, or a pair of boots, or sometimes an horse of small value, and I always had the satisfaction of finding he never came back to return them. By this the house was cleared of such as we did not like; but never was the family of Wakefield known to turn the traveller or the poor dependant out of doors.

Thus we lived several years in a state of much happiness, not but that we sometimes had those little rubs which Providence sends to enhance the value of its favours. My orchard was often robbed by school-boys, and my wife's custards plundered by the cats or the children. The 'Squire would sometimes fall asleep in the most pathetic parts of my sermon, or his lady return my wife's civilities at church with a mutilated courtesy. But we soon got over the uneasiness caused by such accidents, and usually in three or four days began to wonder how they vext us.

My children, the offspring of temperance, as they were educated without softness, so they were at once well formed and healthy; my sons hardy and active, my daughters beautiful and blooming. When I stood in the midst of the little circle, which promised to be the supports of my declining age, I could not avoid repeating the famous story of Count Abensberg, who, in Henry II's progress through Germany, while other courtiers came with their treasures, brought his thirty-two children, and presented them to his sovereign as the most valuable offering he had to bestow. In this manner, though I had but six, I considered them as a very valuable present made to my country, and consequently looked upon it as my debtor. Our eldest son was named George, after his uncle, who left us ten thousand pounds. Our second child, a girl, I intended to call after her aunt Grissel; but my wife, who during her pregnancy had been reading romances, insisted upon her being called Olivia. In less than another year we had another daughter, and now I was determined that Grissel should be her name; but a rich relation taking a fancy to stand godmother, the girl was, by her directions, called Sophia: so that we had two romantic names in the family; but I solemnly protest I had no hand in it. Moses was our next, and after an interval of twelve years, we had two sons more.

It would be fruitless to deny exultation when I saw my little ones about me; but the vanity and the satisfaction of my wife were even greater than mine. When our visitors would say, "Well, upon my word, Mrs. Primrose, you have the finest children in the whole country":— "Ay, neighbour," she would answer, "they are as heaven made them, handsome enough, if they be good enough; for handsome is that handsome does." And then she would bid the girls hold up their heads; who, to conceal nothing, were certainly very handsome. Mere outside is so very trifling a circumstance with me, that I should scarce have remembered to mention it, had it not been a general topic of conversation in the country. Olivia, now about eighteen, had that luxuriancy of beauty, with which painters generally draw Hebe; open, sprightly, and commanding. Sophia's features were not so striking at first; but often did more certain execution; for they

27

were soft, modest, and alluring. The one vanquished by a single blow, the other by efforts successfully repeated.

The temper of a woman is generally formed from the turn of her features, at least it was so with my daughters. Olivia wished for many lovers, Sophia to secure one. Olivia was often affected from too great a desire to please. Sophia even represt excellence from her fears to offend. The one entertained me with her vivacity when I was gay, the other with her sense when I was serious. But these qualities were never carried to excess in either, and I have often seen them exchange characters for a whole day together. A suit of mourning has transformed my coquet into a prude, and a new set of ribbands has given her younger sister more than natural vivacity. My eldest son George was bred at Oxford, as I intended him for one of the learned professions. My second boy Moses, whom I designed for business, received a sort of miscellaneous education at home. But it is needless to attempt describing the particular characters of young people that had seen but very little of the world. In short, a family likeness prevailed through all; and properly speaking, they had but one character, that of being all equally generous, credulous, simple, and inoffensive.

2

*Family misfortunes. The loss of fortune only serves to increase
the pride of the worthy.*

THE temporal concerns of our family were chiefly committed to my wife's management; as to the spiritual I
took them entirely under my own direction. The profits
of my living, which amounted to but thirty-five pounds a
year, I made over to the orphans and widows of the
clergy of our diocese; for having a fortune of my own, I
was careless of temporalities, and felt a secret pleasure in
doing my duty without reward. I also set a resolution of
keeping no curate, and of being acquainted with every
man in the parish, exhorting the married men to temperance, and the bachelors to matrimony; so that in a
few years it was a common saying, that there were three
strange wants at Wakefield, a parson wanting pride,
young men wanting wives, and ale-houses wanting
customers.

Matrimony was always one of my favourite topics, and
I wrote several sermons to prove its happiness; but there
was a peculiar tenet which I made a point of supporting:
for I maintained with Whiston, that it was unlawful for a
priest of the church of England, after the death of his
first wife, to take a second, or to express it in one word, I
valued myself upon being a strict monogamist.

I was early initiated into this important dispute, on
which so many laborious volumes have been written. I
published some tracts upon the subject myself, which, as
they never sold, I have the consolation of thinking were
read only by the happy *few*. Some of my friends called
this my weak side; but alas! they had not like me made
it the subject of long contemplation. The more I reflected
upon it, the more important it appeared. I even went a
step beyond Whiston in displaying my principles: as he

had engraven upon his wife's tomb that she was the *only* wife of William Whiston; so I wrote a similar epitaph for my wife, though still living, in which I extolled her prudence, economy, and obedience till death; and having got it copied fair, with an elegant frame, it was placed over the chimney-piece, where it answered several very useful purposes. It admonished my wife of her duty to me, and my fidelity to her; it inspired her with a passion for fame, and constantly put her in mind of her end.

It was thus, perhaps, from hearing marriage so often recommended, that my eldest son, just upon leaving college, fixed his affections upon the daughter of a neighbouring clergyman, who was a dignitary in the church, and in circumstances to give her a large fortune: but fortune was her smallest accomplishment. Miss Arabella Wilmot was allowed by all (except my two daughters) to be completely pretty. Her youth, health, and innocence, were still heightened by a complexion so transparent and such an happy sensibility of look, as even age could not gaze on with indifference. As Mr. Wilmot knew that I could make a very handsome settlement on my son, he was not averse to the match; so both families lived together in all that harmony which generally precedes an expected alliance. Being convinced by experience that the days of courtship are the most happy of our lives, I was willing enough to lengthen the period; and the various amusements which the young couple every day shared in each other's company, seemed to encrease their passion. We were generally awaked in the morning by music, and on fine days rode a hunting. The hours between breakfast and dinner the ladies devoted to dress and study: they usually read a page, and then gazed at themselves in the glass, which even philosophers might own often presented the page of greatest beauty. At dinner my wife took the lead; for as she always insisted upon carving everything herself, it being her mother's way, she gave us upon these occasions the history of every dish. When we had dined, to prevent the ladies leaving us, I generally ordered the table to be removed; and sometimes, with the music-master's assistance, the girls would give us a very agreeable concert. Walking out, drinking tea, country dances, and forfeits shortened the rest of the day, without the assistance of cards, as I hated all manner of gaming, except backgammon, at which my old friend and I sometimes took a two-penny hit. Nor can I here pass over an ominous circumstance that happened the last time we played together; I only wanted to fling a quatre, and yet I threw deuce ace five times running.

Some months were elapsed in this manner, till at last it was thought convenient to fix a day for the nuptials of the young people, who seemed earnestly to desire it. During the preparations for the wedding, I need not describe the busy importance of my wife, nor the sly looks of my daughters: in fact, my attention was fixed on another object, the completing a tract which I intended shortly to publish in defence of my favourite principle. As I looked upon this as a master-piece, both for argument and style, I could not in the pride of my heart avoid showing it to my old friend Mr. Wilmot, as I made no doubt of receiving his approbation; but not till too late I discovered that he was most violently attached to the contrary opinion, and with good reason; for he was at that time actually courting a fourth wife. This, as may be expected, produced a dispute attended with some acrimony, which threatened to interrupt our intended alliance: but on the day before that appointed for the ceremony, we agreed to discuss the subject at large.

It was managed with proper spirit on both sides: he asserted that I was heterodox, I retorted the charge: he replied, and I rejoined. In the meantime, while the controversy was hottest, I was called out by one of my relations, who, with a face of concern, advised me to give up the dispute, at least till my son's wedding was over. "How," cried I, "relinquish the cause of truth, and let him be a husband, already driven to the very verge of absurdity. You might as well advise me to give up my fortune, as my argument." "Your fortune," returned my friend, "I am now sorry to inform you, is almost nothing. The merchant in town, in whose hands your money was lodged, has gone off, to avoid a statute of bankruptcy, and is thought not to have left a shilling in the pound. I was unwilling to shock you or the family with the account till after the wedding: but now it may serve to moderate your warmth in the argument, for, I suppose, your own prudence will enforce the necessity of dissembling, at least till your son has the young lady's fortune secure."— "Well," returned I, "if what you tell me be true, and if I am to be a beggar, it shall never make me a rascal, or induce me to disavow my principles. I'll go this moment and inform the company of my circumstances: and as for the argument, I even here retract my former concessions in the old gentleman's favour, nor will I allow him now to be a husband in any sense of the expression."

It would be endless to describe the different sensations of both families when I divulged the news of our misfortune: but what others felt was slight to what the lovers appeared to endure. Mr. Wilmot, who seemed before sufficiently inclined to break off the match, was by this blow soon determined: one virtue he had in perfection, which was prudence; too often the only one that is left us at seventy-two.

3

A migration. The fortunate circumstances of our lives are generally found at last to be of our own procuring.

THE only hope of our family now was, that the report of our misfortune might be malicious or premature: but a letter from my agent in town soon came with a confirmation of every particular. The loss of fortune to myself alone would have been trifling; the only uneasiness I felt was for my family, who were to be humble without an education to render them callous to contempt.

Near a fortnight had passed before I attempted to restrain their affliction; for premature consolation is but the remembrancer of sorrow. During this interval, my thoughts were employed on some future means of supporting them; and at last a small Cure of fifteen pounds a year was offered me in a distant neighbourhood, where I could still enjoy my principles without molestation. With this proposal I joyfully closed, having determined to increase my salary by managing a little farm.

Having taken this resolution, my next care was to get together the wrecks of my fortune; and, all debts collected and paid, out of fourteen thousand pounds we had but four hundred remaining. My chief attention, therefore, was now to bring down the pride of my family to their circumstances; for I well knew that aspiring beggary is wretchedness itself. "You cannot be ignorant, my children," cried I, "that no prudence of ours could have prevented our late misfortune; but prudence may do much in disappointing its effects. We are now poor, my fondlings, and wisdom bids us conform to our humble situation. Let us then, without repining, give up those splendours with which numbers are wretched, and seek in humbler circumstances that peace with which all may be happy. The poor live pleasantly without our help, why then should not we learn to live without theirs? No, my children, let us from this moment give up all pretensions to gentility; we have still enough left for happiness if we are wise, and let us draw upon content for the deficiencies of fortune."

As my eldest son was bred a scholar, I determined to send him to town, where his abilities might contribute to our support and his own. The separation of friends and families is, perhaps, one of the most distressful circumstances attendant on penury. The day soon arrived on which we were to disperse for the first time. My son, after taking leave of his mother and the rest, who mingled their tears with their kisses, came to ask a blessing from me. This I gave him from my heart, and which, added to five guineas, was all the patrimony I had now to bestow. "You are going, my boy," cried I, "to London on foot in the manner Hooker, your great ancestor, travelled there before you. Take from me the same horse that was given him by the good bishop Jewel, this staff; and take this book too, it will be your comfort on the way: these two lines in it are worth a million, *I have been young, and now am old; yet never saw I the righteous man forsaken, or his seed begging their bread*. Let this be your consolation as you travel on. Go, my boy, whatever be thy fortune let me see thee once a year; still keep a good heart, and farewell." As he was possest of integrity and honour, I was under no apprehensions from throwing him naked into the amphitheatre of life; for I knew he would act a good part whether vanquished or victorious.

His departure only prepared the way for our own, which arrived a few days afterwards. The leaving a neighbourhood in which we had enjoyed so many hours of tranquillity, was not without a tear, which scarce fortitude itself could suppress. Besides, a journey of seventy miles to a family that had hitherto never been above ten from home, filled us with apprehension; and the cries of the poor, who followed us for some miles, contributed to increase it. The first day's journey brought us

34

in safety within thirty miles of our future retreat, and we put up for the night at an obscure inn in a village by the way. When we were shewn a room, I desired the landlord, in my usual way, to let us have his company, with which he complied, as what he drank would increase the bill next morning. He knew, however, the whole neighbourhood to which I was removing, particularly 'Squire Thornhill, who was to be my landlord, and who lived within a few miles of the place. This gentleman he described as one who desired to know little more of the world than its pleasures, being particularly remarkable for his attachment to the fair sex. He observed that no virtue was able to resist his arts and assiduity, and that scarce a farmer's daughter within ten miles round but what had found him successful and faithless. Though this account gave me some pain, it had a very different effect upon my daughters, whose features seemed to brighten with the expectation of an approaching triumph; nor was my wife less pleased and confident of their allurements and virtue. While our thoughts were thus employed, the hostess entered the room to inform her husband, that the strange gentleman, who had been two days in the house, wanted money, and could not satisfy them for his reckoning. "Want money!" replied the host, "that must be impossible; for it was no later than yesterday he paid three guineas to our beadle to spare an old broken soldier that was to be whipped through the town for dog-stealing." The hostess, however, still persisting in her first assertion, he was preparing to leave the room, swearing that he would be satisfied one way or another, when I begged the landlord would introduce me to a stranger of so much charity as he described. With this he complied, shewing in a gentleman who seemed to be about thirty, drest in clothes that once were laced. His person was well formed, and his face marked with the lines of thinking. He had something short and dry in his address, and seemed not to understand ceremony, or to despise it. Upon the landlord's

35

leaving the room, I could not avoid expressing my concern to the stranger at seeing a gentleman in such circumstances, and offered him my purse to satisfy the present demand. "I take it with all my heart, Sir," replied he, "and am glad that a late oversight in giving what money I had about me, has shewn me that there are still some men like you. I must, however, previously intreat being informed of the name and residence of my benefactor, in order to repay him as soon as possible." In this I satisfied him fully, not only mentioning my name and late misfortunes, but the place to which I was going to remove. "This," cried he, "happens still more luckily than I hoped for, as I am going the same way myself, having been detained here two days by the floods, which I hope by to-morrow will be found passable." I testified the pleasure I should have in his company, and my wife and daughters joining in intreaty, he was prevailed upon to stay supper. The stranger's conversation, which was at once pleasing and instructive, induced me to wish for a continuance of it; but it was now high time to retire and take refreshment against the fatigues of the following day.

The next morning we all set forward together: my family on horseback, while Mr. Burchell, our new companion, walked along the foot-path by the road-side, observing with a smile, that as we were ill mounted, he would be too generous to attempt leaving us behind. As the floods were not yet subsided, we were obliged to hire a guide, who trotted on before, Mr. Burchell and I bringing up the rear. We lightened the fatigues of the road with philosophical disputes, which he seemed to understand perfectly. But what surprised me most was, that though he was a money-borrower, he defended his opinions with as much obstinacy as if he had been my patron. He now and then also informed me to whom the different seats belonged that lay in our view as we travelled the road. "That," cried he, pointing to a very magnificent house which stood at some distance, "belongs to Mr. Thornhill, a young gentleman who enjoys a large fortune, though entirely dependent on the will of his uncle, Sir William Thornhill, a gentleman who, content with a little himself, permits his nephew to enjoy the rest, and chiefly resides in town." "What!" cried I, "is my young landlord then the nephew of a man whose virtues, generosity, and singularities are so universally known? I have heard Sir William Thornhill represented as one of the most generous, yet whimsical men in the kingdom; a man of consummate benevolence."—"Something, perhaps, too much so," replied Mr. Burchell, "at least he carried benevolence to an excess when young; for his passions were then strong, and as they were all upon the side of virtue, they led it up to a romantic extreme. He early began to aim at the qualifications of the soldier and scholar; was soon distinguished in the army, and had some reputation among men of learning. Adulation ever follows the ambitious; for such alone receive most pleasure from flattery. He was surrounded with crowds, who shewed him only one side of their character, so that he began to lose a regard for private interest in universal sympathy. He loved all mankind; for fortune prevented him from knowing that there were rascals. Physicians tell us of a disorder in which the whole body is so exquisitely sensible, that the slightest touch gives pain: what some have thus suffered in their persons, this gentleman felt in his mind. The slightest distress, whether real or fictitious, touched him to the quick, and his soul laboured under a sickly sensibility of the miseries of others. Thus disposed to relieve, it will be easily conjectured, he found numbers disposed to solicit: his profusions began to impair his fortune, but not his good-nature; that, indeed, was seen to increase as the other seemed to decay: he grew improvident as he grew poor: and though he talked like a man of sense, his actions were those of a fool. Still, however, being surrounded with importunity, and no longer able to satisfy every request that was made him, instead of *money* he gave *promises.* They were all he had to bestow, and he had not resolution enough to give any man pain by a denial. By this he drew round him crowds of dependents, whom he was sure to disappoint, yet wished to relieve. These hung upon him for a time, and left him with merited reproaches and contempt. But in proportion as he became contemptible to others, he became despicable to himself. His mind had leaned upon their adulation, and that support taken away, he could find no pleasure in the applause of his heart, which he had never learnt to reverence. The world now began to wear a different aspect; the flattery of his friends began to dwindle into simple approbation. Approbation soon took the more friendly form of advice, and advice when rejected produced their reproaches. He now therefore found that such friends as benefits had gathered round him, were little estimable; he now found that a man's own heart must be ever given to gain that of another. I now found, that—that—I forgot what I was going to observe: in short, Sir, he resolved to respect himself, and laid down a plan of restoring his falling fortune. For this purpose, in his own whimsical manner, he travelled through Europe on foot, and now, though he has scarce attained the age of thirty, his circumstances are more affluent than ever. At present, his bounties are more rational and moderate than before; but still he preserves the character of an humorist, and finds most pleasure in eccentric virtues."

My attention was so much taken up by Mr. Burchell's account, that I scarce looked forward as he went along, till we were alarmed by the cries of my family; when turning, I perceived my youngest daughter in the midst of a rapid stream, thrown from her horse, and struggling with the torrent. She had sunk twice, nor was it in my power to disengage myself in time to bring her relief. My sensations were even too violent to permit my attempting her rescue: she must have certainly perished had not my companion, perceiving her danger, instantly plunged in to her relief, and, with some difficulty, brought her in

38

safety to the opposite shore. By taking the current a little farther up, the rest of the family got safely over, where we had an opportunity of joining our acknowledgments to hers. Her gratitude may be more readily imagined than described: she thanked her deliverer more with looks than words, and continued to lean upon his arm, as if still willing to receive assistance. My wife also hoped one day to have the pleasure of returning his kindness at her own house. Thus, after we were refreshed at the next inn, and had dined together, as Mr. Burchell was going to a different part of the country, he took leave; and we pursued our journey: my wife observing as he went, that she liked him extremely, and protesting, that if he had birth and fortune to entitle him to match into such a family as ours, she knew no man she would sooner fix upon. I could not but smile to hear her talk in this lofty strain; but I was never much displeased with those harmless delusions that tend to make us more happy.

4

A proof that even the humblest fortune may grant happiness,
which depends not on circumstances but constitution.

THE place of our retreat was in a little neighbourhood,
consisting of farmers, who tilled their own grounds, and
were equal strangers to opulence and poverty. As they
had almost all the conveniences of life within themselves,
they seldom visited towns or cities, in search of superfluity. Remote from the polite, they still retained the
primaeval simplicity of manners; and frugal by habit,
they scarce knew that temperance was a virtue. They
wrought with cheerfulness on days of labour; but
observed festivals as intervals of idleness and pleasure.
They kept up the Christmas carol, sent true love-knots on
Valentine morning, ate pancakes on Shrove-tide, shewed
their wit on the first of April, and religiously cracked
nuts on Michaelmas eve. Being apprized of our approach,
the whole neighbourhood came out to meet their
minister, drest in their finest clothes, and preceded by a
pipe and tabor. A feast also was provided for our reception, at which we sate chearfully down; and what the
conversation wanted in wit, was made up in laughter.

Our little habitation was situated at the foot of a
sloping hill, sheltered with a beautiful underwood
behind, and a prattling river before: on one side a
meadow, on the other a green. My farm consisted of
about twenty acres of excellent land, having given an
hundred pound for my predecessor's good-will. Nothing
could exceed the neatness of my little enclosures: the
elms and hedge-rows appearing with inexpressible
beauty. My house consisted of but one story, and was
covered with thatch, which gave it an air of great snug-
ness; the walls on the inside were nicely white-washed,
and my daughters undertook to adorn them with pictures

of their own designing. Though the same room served us for parlour and kitchen, that only made it the warmer. Besides, as it was kept with the utmost neatness, the dishes, plates, and coppers being well scoured, and all disposed in bright rows on the shelves, the eye was agreeably relieved, and did not want richer furniture. There were three other apartments, one for my wife and me, another for our two daughters, within our own, and the third, with two beds, for the rest of the children.

The little republic to which I gave laws, was regulated in the following manner: by sun-rise we all assembled in our common apartment; the fire being previously kindled by the servant. After we had saluted each other with proper ceremony, for I always thought fit to keep up some mechanical forms of good breeding, without which freedom ever destroys friendship, we all bent in gratitude to that Being who gave us another day. This duty being performed, my son and I went to pursue our usual industry abroad, while my wife and daughters employed themselves in providing breakfast, which was always ready at a certain time. I allowed half an hour for this meal, and an hour for dinner; which time was taken up in innocent mirth between my wife and daughters, and in philosophical arguments between my son and me.

As we rose with the sun, so we never pursued our labours after it was gone down, but returned home to the expecting family; where smiling looks, a neat hearth, and pleasant fire were prepared for our reception. Nor were we without guests: sometimes farmer Flamborough, our talkative neighbour, and often the blind piper, would pay us a visit, and taste our gooseberry-wine; for the making of which we had lost neither the receipt nor the reputation. These harmless people had several ways of being good company; while one played, the other would sing some soothing ballad, "Johnny Armstrong's Last Good Night," or "The Cruelty of Barbara Allen." The night was concluded in the manner we began the morning, my youngest boys being appointed to read the lessons of the day, and he that read loudest, distinctest, and best, was to have an halfpenny on Sunday to put in the poor's box.

When Sunday came, it was indeed a day of finery, which all my sumptuary edicts could not restrain. How well soever I fancied my lectures against pride had conquered the vanity of my daughters; yet I still found them secretly attached to all their former finery: they still loved laces, ribbands, bugles and catgut; my wife herself retained a passion for her crimson paduasoy, because I formerly happened to say it became her.

The first Sunday in particular their behaviour served to mortify me: I had desired my girls the preceding night to be drest early the next day; for I always loved to be at church a good while before the rest of the congregation. They punctually obeyed my directions; but when we were to assemble in the morning at breakfast, down came my wife and daughters, drest out in all their former splendour: their hair plastered up with pomatum, their faces patched to taste, their trains bundled up in an heap behind, and rustling at every motion. I could not help smiling at their vanity, particularly that of my wife, from whom I expected more discretion. In this exigence, therefore, my only resource was to order my son, with an important air, to call our coach. The girls were amazed at the command; but I repeated it with more solemnity than before.—"Surely, my dear, you jest," cried my wife, "we can walk it perfectly well: we want no coach to carry us now." "You mistake, child," returned I, "we do want a coach; for if we walk to church in this trim, the very children in the parish will hoot after us."— "Indeed," replied my wife, "I always imagined that my Charles was fond of seeing his children neat and handsome about him."—"You may be as neat as you please," interrupted I, "and I shall love you the better for it; but all this is not neatness, but frippery. These rufflings, and pinkings, and patchings will only make us hated by all the wives of our neighbours. No, my children," continued

. . . drest out in all their former splendour . . .

I, more gravely, "those gowns may be altered into something of a plainer cut; for finery is very unbecoming in us, who want the means of decency. I do not know whether such flouncing and shredding is becoming even in the rich, if we consider, upon a moderate calculation, that the nakedness of the indigent world may be clothed from the trimmings of the vain."

This remonstrance had the proper effect; they went with great composure, that very instant, to change their dress; and the next day I had the satisfaction of finding my daughters, at their own request, employed in cutting up their trains into Sunday waistcoats for Dick and Bill, the two little ones; and what was still more satisfactory, the gowns seemed improved by this curtailing.

5

A new and great acquaintance introduced. What we place most hopes upon, generally proves most fatal.

AT a small distance from the house, my predecessor had made a seat, overshaded by an hedge of hawthorn and honeysuckle. Here, when the weather was fine and our labour soon finished, we usually sat together, to enjoy an extensive landscape in the calm of the evening. Here too we drank tea, which was now become an occasional banquet; and as we had it but seldom, it diffused a new joy, the preparations for it being made with no small share of bustle and ceremony. On these occasions our two little ones always read for us, and they were regularly served after we had done. Sometimes, to give a variety to our amusements, the girls sang to the guitar; and while they thus formed a little concert, my wife and I would stroll down the sloping field, that was embellished with blue bells and centaury, talk of our children with rapture, and enjoy the breeze that wafted both health and harmony.

In this manner we began to find that every situation in life may bring its own peculiar pleasures: every morning waked us to a repetition of toil; but the evening repaid it with vacant hilarity.

It was about the beginning of autumn, on a holiday, for I kept such as intervals of relaxation from labour, that I had drawn out my family to our usual place of amusement, and our young musicians began their usual concert. As we were thus engaged, we saw a stag bound nimbly by, within about twenty paces of where we were sitting, and by its panting it seemed prest by the hunters. We had not much time to reflect upon the poor animal's distress, when we perceived the dogs and horsemen come sweeping along at some distance behind, and making the

very path it had taken. I was instantly for returning in
with my family; but either curiosity, or surprise, or some
more hidden motive, held my wife and daughters to their
seats. The huntsman, who rode foremost, passed us with
great swiftness, followed by four or five persons more, who
seemed in equal haste. At last, a young gentleman of
more genteel appearance than the rest, came forward,
and for a while regarding us, instead of pursuing the
chace, stopt short, and giving his horse to a servant, who
attended, approached us with a careless superior air. He
seemed to want no introduction, but was going to salute
my daughters, as one certain of a kind reception; but
they had early learnt the lesson of looking presumption
out of countenance. Upon which he let us know his
name was Thornhill, and that he was owner of the estate
that lay for some extent round us. He again therefore
offered to salute the female part of the family, and such
was the power of fortune and fine clothes, that he found
no second repulse. As his address, though confident, was
easy, we soon became more familiar; and perceiving
musical instruments lying near, he begged to be favoured
with a song. As I did not approve of such disproportioned
acquaintances, I winked upon my daughters in order to
prevent their compliance; but my hint was counteracted
by one from their mother; so that, with a cheerful air,
they gave us a favourite song of Dryden's. Mr. Thornhill
seemed highly delighted with their performance and
choice, and then took up the guitar himself. He played
but very indifferently; however, my eldest daughter
repaid his former applause with interest, and assured him
that his tones were louder than even those of her master.
At this compliment he bowed, which she returned with a
curtesy. He praised her taste, and she commended his
understanding: an age could not have made them better
acquainted; while the fond mother, too, equally happy,
insisted upon her landlord's stepping in, and tasting a
glass of her gooseberry. The whole family seemed earnest
to please him: my girls attempted to entertain him with

topics they thought most modern, while Moses, on the contrary, gave him a question or two from the ancients, for which he had the satisfaction of being laughed at: my little ones were no less busy, and fondly stuck close to the stranger. All my endeavours could scarce keep their dirty fingers from handling and tarnishing the lace on his clothes, and lifting up the flaps of his pocket-holes, to see what was there. At the approach of evening he took leave; but not till he had requested permission to renew his visit, which as he was our landlord, we most readily agreed to.

As soon as he was gone, my wife called a council on the conduct of the day. She was of opinion, that it was a most fortunate hit; for that she had known even stranger things than that brought to bear. She hoped again to see the day in which we might hold up our heads with the best of them; and concluded, she protested she could see no reason why the two Miss Wrinklers should marry great fortunes, and her children get none. As this last argument was directed to me, I protested I could see no reason for it neither, nor why Mr. Simkins got the ten thousand pound prize in the lottery, and we sate down with a blank. "I protest, Charles," cried my wife, "this is the way you always damp my girls and me when we are in spirits. Tell me, Sophy, my dear, what do you think of our new visitor? Don't you think he seemed to be good-natured?"—"Immensely so indeed, Mamma," replied she. "I think he has a great deal to say upon every thing, and is never at a loss; and the more trifling the subject the more he has to say." "Yes," cried Olivia, "he is well enough for a man; but for my part, I don't much like him, he is so extremely impudent and familiar; but on the guitar he is shocking." These two last speeches I interpreted by contraries. I found by this, that Sophia internally despised, as much as Olivia secretly admired him.—"Whatever may be your opinions of him, my children," cried I, "to confess the truth, he has not pre-possest me in his favour. Disproportioned friendships ever terminate in disgust; and I thought, notwithstanding all his ease, that he seemed perfectly sensible of the distance between us. Let us keep to companions of our own rank. There is no character more contemptible than a man that is a fortune-hunter; and I can see no reason why fortune-hunting women should not be contemptible too. Thus, at best, we shall be contemptible if his views are honourable; but if they be otherwise! I should shudder but to think of that! It is true I have no apprehensions from the conduct of my children, but I think there are some from his character."—I would have proceeded, but for the interruption of a servant from the 'Squire, who, with his compliments, sent us a side of venison, and a promise to dine with us some days after. This well-timed present pleaded more powerfully in his favour than any thing I had to say could obviate. I therefore continued silent, satisfied with just having pointed out danger, and leaving it to their own discretion to avoid it. That virtue which requires to be ever guarded is scarce worth the centinel.

6

The happiness of a country fireside.

As we carried on the former dispute with some degree of
warmth, in order to accommodate matters it was universally agreed that we should have a part of the venison
for supper, and the girls undertook the task with alacrity.
"I am sorry," cried I, "that we have no neighbour or
stranger to take a part in this good chear: feasts of this
kind acquire a double relish from hospitality."—"Bless
me," cried my wife, "here comes our good friend Mr.
Burchell, that saved our Sophia, and that run you down
fairly in the argument." "Confute me in argument,
child!" cried I. "You mistake there, my dear, I believe
there are but few that can do that: I never dispute your
abilities at making a goose-pye, and I beg you'll leave
argument to me."—As I spoke, poor Mr. Burchell
entered the house, and was welcomed by the family, who
shook him heartily by the hand, while little Dick
officiously reached him a chair.

I was pleased with the poor man's friendship, for two
reasons: because I knew that he wanted mine, and I knew
him to be friendly as far as he was able. He was known in
our neighbourhood by the character of the poor Gentleman that would do no good when he was young, though
he was not yet thirty. He would at intervals talk with
great good sense; but in general he was fondest of the
company of children, whom he used to call harmless
little men. He was famous, I found, for singing them
ballads, and telling them stories; and seldom went out
without something in his pockets for them, a piece of
gingerbread, or an halfpenny whistle. He generally came
for a few days into our neighbourhood once a year, and
lived upon the neighbours' hospitality. He sat down to
supper among us, and my wife was not sparing of her

gooseberry-wine. The tale went round; he sang us old songs, and gave the children the story of the Buck of Beverland, with the history of Patient Grissel, the adventures of Catskin, and then Fair Rosamond's Bower. Our cock, which always crew at eleven, now told us it was time for repose; but an unforeseen difficulty started about lodging the stranger; all our beds were already taken up, and it was too late to send him to the next ale-house. In this dilemma, little Dick offered him his part of the bed, if his brother Moses would let him lie with him; "And I," cried Bill, "will give Mr. Burchell my part, if my sisters will take me to theirs."—"Well done, my good children," cried I, "hospitality is one of the first Christian duties. The beast retires to its shelter, and the bird flies to its nest; but helpless man can only find refuge from his fellow-creature. The greatest stranger in this world, was He that came to save it. He never had an house, as if willing to see what hospitality was left remaining amongst us. Deborah, my dear," cried I, to my wife, "give those boys a lump of sugar each, and let Dick's be the largest because he spoke first."

In the morning early I called out my whole family to help at saving an after-growth of hay, and our guest offering his assistance, he was accepted among the number. Our labours went on lightly; we turned the swath to the wind. I went foremost, and the rest followed in due succession. I could not avoid, however, observing the assiduity of Mr. Burchell in assisting my daughter Sophia in her part of the task. When he had finished his own, he would join in her's, and enter into a close conversation: but I had too good an opinion of Sophia's understanding, and was too well convinced of her ambition, to be under any uneasiness from a man of broken fortune. When we were finished for the day, Mr. Burchell was invited as on the night before; but he refused, as he was to lie that night at a neighbour's, to whose child he was carrying a whistle. When gone, our conversation at supper turned upon our late unfortunate guest. "What a strong instance," said I, "is that poor man of the miseries attending a youth of levity and extravagance. He by no means wants sense, which only serves to aggravate his former folly. Poor forlorn creature, where are now the revellers, the flatterers, that he could once inspire and command? Gone, perhaps, to attend the bagnio pander, grown rich by his extravagance. They once praised him, and now they applaud the pander: their former raptures at his wit are now converted into sarcasms at his folly: he is poor, and perhaps deserves poverty; for he has neither the ambition to be independent, nor the skill to be useful." Prompted perhaps by some secret reasons, I delivered this observation with too much acrimony, which my Sophia gently reproved. "Whatsoever his former conduct may have been, Papa, his circumstances should exempt him from censure now. His present indigence is a sufficient punishment for former folly, and I have heard my Papa himself say, that we should never strike one unnecessary blow at a victim over whom Providence holds the scourge of its resentment."—"You are right, Sophy," cried my son Moses, "and one of the ancients finely represents so malicious a conduct, by the attempts of a rustic to flay Marsyas whose skin, the fable tells us, had been wholly stript off by another. Besides, I don't know if this poor man's situation be so bad as my father would represent it. We are not to judge of the feelings of others by what we might feel if in their place. However dark the habitation of the mole to our eyes, yet the animal itself finds the apartment sufficiently lightsome. And to confess a truth, this man's mind seems fitted to his station; for I never heard any one more sprightly than he was to-day, when he conversed with you." This was said without the least design; however, it excited a blush, which she strove to cover by an affected laugh, assuring him, that she scarce took any notice of what he said to her; but that she believed he might once have been a very fine gentleman. The readiness with which she undertook to vindicate herself, and her blushing, were symptoms I did not internally approve; but I represt my suspicions.

As we expected our landlord the next day, my wife went to make the venison pasty. Moses sate reading, while I taught the little ones: my daughters seemed equally busy with the rest; and I observed them for a good while cooking something over the fire. I at first supposed they were assisting their mother; but little Dick informed me in a whisper, that they were making a *wash* for the face. Washes of all kinds I had a natural antipathy to; for I knew that instead of mending the complexion they spoiled it. I therefore approached my chair by sly degrees to the fire, and grasping the poker, as if it wanted mending, seemingly by accident, overturned the whole composition, and it was too late to begin another.

7

A town wit described. The dullest fellows may learn to be comical for a night or two.

WHEN the morning arrived on which we were to entertain our young landlord, it may be easily supposed what provisions were exhausted to make an appearance. It may also be conjectured that my wife and daughters expanded their gayest plumage upon this occasion. Mr. Thornhill came with a couple of friends, his chaplain and feeder. The servants, who were numerous, he politely ordered to the next alehouse, but my wife, in the triumph of her heart, insisted on entertaining them all; for which, by the by, our family was pinched for three weeks after. As Mr. Burchell had hinted to us the day before, that he was making some proposals of marriage to Miss Wilmot, my son George's former mistress, this a good deal damped the heartiness of his reception: but accident, in some measure, relieved our embarrassment; for one of the company happening to mention her name, Mr. Thornhill observed with an oath, that he never knew any thing more absurd than calling such a fright a beauty: "For strike me ugly," continued he, "if I should not find as much pleasure in choosing my mistress by the information of a lamp under the clock at St. Dunstan's." At this he laughed, and so did we:—the jests of the rich are ever successful. Olivia too could not avoid whispering loud enough to be heard, that he had an infinite fund of humour.

After dinner, I began with my usual toast, the Church; for this I was thanked by the chaplain, as he said the Church was the only mistress of his affections.—"Come, tell us honestly, Frank," said the 'Squire, with his usual archness, "suppose the Church, your present mistress, drest in lawn sleeves, on one hand, and Miss Sophia, with no lawn about her, on the other, which would you be for?" "For both, to be sure," cried the chaplain.— "Right, Frank," cried the 'Squire, "for may this glass suffocate me but a fine girl is worth all the priestcraft in the Creation. For what are tithes and tricks but an imposition, all a confounded imposture, and I can prove it."—"I wish you would," cried my son Moses, "and I think," continued he, "that I should be able to answer you."—"Very well, Sir," cried the 'Squire, who immediately smoked him, and winking on the rest of the company, to prepare us for the sport, "if you are for a cool argument upon that subject, I am ready to accept the challenge. And first, whether are you for managing it analogically or dialogically?" "I am for managing it rationally," cried Moses, quite happy at being permitted to dispute. "Good again," cried the 'Squire, "and firstly, of the first. I hope you'll not deny that whatever is, is. If you don't grant me that I can go no further."—"Why," returned Moses, "I think I may grant that, and make the best of it."—"I hope too," returned the other, "you'll grant that a part is less than the whole." "I grant that too," cried Moses, "it is but just and reasonable."—"I hope," cried the 'Squire, "you will not deny, that the two angles of a triangle are equal to two right ones."— "Nothing can be plainer," returned t'other, and looked round with his usual importance.—"Very well," cried the 'Squire, speaking very quick, "the premises being thus settled, I proceed to observe, that the concatenation of self-existence, proceeding in a reciprocal duplicate ratio, naturally produces a problematical dialogism, which in some measure proves that the essence of spirituality may be referred to the second predicable."—"Hold, hold," cried the other, "I deny that: Do you think I can thus tamely submit to such heterodox doctrines?"—"What," replied the 'Squire, as if in a passion, "not submit! Answer me one plain question: Do you think Aristotle right when he says, that relatives are related?" "Undoubtedly," replied the other. "If so then," cried the

'Squire, "answer me directly to what I propose: Whether do you judge the analytical investigation of the first part of my enthymem deficient secundum quoad, or quoad minus, and give me your reasons, give me your reasons, I say, directly."—"I protest," cried Moses, "I don't rightly comprehend the force of your reasoning; but if it be reduced to one simple proposition, I fancy it may then have an answer."—"Oh, Sir," cried the 'Squire, "I am your most humble servant, I find you want me to furnish you with argument and intellects too. No, Sir, there I protest you are too hard for me." This effectually raised the laugh against poor Moses, who sate the only dismal figure in a group of merry faces: nor did he offer a single syllable more during the whole entertainment.

But though all this gave me no pleasure, it had a very different effect upon Olivia, who mistook it for humour, though but a mere act of the memory. She thought him therefore a very fine gentleman; and such as consider what powerful ingredients a good figure, fine clothes, and fortune are in that character, will easily forgive her. Mr. Thornhill, notwithstanding his real ignorance, talked with ease, and could expatiate upon the common topics of conversation with fluency. It is not surprising then that such talents should win the affections of a girl, who by education was taught to value an appearance in herself, and consequently to set a value upon it in another.

Upon his departure, we again entered into a debate upon the merits of our young landlord. As he directed his looks and conversation to Olivia, it was no longer doubted but that she was the object that induced him to be our visitor. Nor did she seem to be much displeased at the innocent raillery of her brother and sister upon this occasion. Even Deborah herself seemed to share the glory of the day, and exulted in her daughter's victory as if it were her own. "And now, my dear," cried she to me, "I'll fairly own, that it was I that instructed my girls to encourage our landlord's addresses. I had always some ambition, and you now see that I was right; for who knows how this may end?" "Aye, who knows that, indeed," answered I, with a groan: "for my part I don't much like it; and I could have been better pleased with one that was poor and honest, than this fine gentleman with his fortune and infidelity; for depend on't, if he be what I suspect him, no free-thinker shall ever have a child of mine."

"Sure, father," cried Moses, "you are too severe in this; for Heaven will never arraign him for what he thinks, but for what he does. Every man has a thousand vicious thoughts, which arise without his power to suppress. Thinking freely of religion may be involuntary with this gentleman: so that allowing his sentiments to be wrong, yet as he is purely passive in his assent, he is no more to be blamed for his errors, than the governor of a city without walls for the shelter he is obliged to afford an invading enemy."

"True, my son," cried I; "but, if the governor invites the enemy there, he is justly culpable. And such is always the case with those who embrace error. The vice does not lie in assenting to the proofs they see; but in being blind to many of the proofs that offer. So that, though our erroneous opinions be involuntary when formed, yet as we have been wilfully corrupt, or very negligent in forming them, we deserve punishment for our vice, or contempt for our folly."

My wife now kept up the conversation, though not the argument: she observed, that several very prudent men of our acquaintance were free-thinkers, and made very good husbands; and she knew some sensible girls that had skill enough to make converts of their spouses: "And who knows, my dear," continued she, "what Olivia may be able to do. The girl has a great deal to say upon every subject, and to my knowledge is very well skilled in controversy."

"Why, my dear, what controversy can she have read?" cried I. "It does not occur to me that I ever put such books into her hands: you certainly over-rate her merit."

"Indeed, Papa," replied Olivia, "she does not: I have read a great deal of controversy. I have read the disputes between Thwackum and Square; the controversy between Robinson Crusoe and Friday the savage, and I am now employed in reading the controversy in Religious Courtship." "Very well," cried I, "that's a good girl, I find you are perfectly qualified for making converts, and so go help your mother to make the gooseberry-pye."

An amour, which promises little good fortune, yet may be productive of much.

THE next morning we were again visited by Mr. Burchell, though I began, for certain reasons, to be displeased with the frequency of his return; but I could not refuse him my company and fire-side. It is true his labour more than requited his entertainment; for he wrought among us with vigour, and either in the meadow or at the hay-rick put himself foremost. Besides, he had always something amusing to say that lessened our toil, and was at once so out of the way, and yet so sensible, that I loved, laughed at, and pitied him. My only dislike arose from an attachment he discovered to my daughter: he would in a jesting manner, call her his little mistress, and when he bought each of the girls a set of ribbands, her's was the finest. I knew not how, but he every day seemed to become more amiable, his wit to improve, and his simplicity to assume the superior airs of wisdom.

Our family dined in the field, and we sate, or rather reclined, round a temperate repast, our cloth spread upon the hay, while Mr. Burchell gave cheerfulness to the feast. To heighten our satisfaction, two blackbirds answered each other from opposite hedges, the familiar red-breast came and pecked the crumbs from our hands, and every sound seemed but the echo of tranquillity. "I never sit thus," says Sophia, "but I think of the two lovers so sweetly described by Mr. Gay, who were struck dead in each other's arms. There is something so pathetic in the description, that I have read it an hundred times with new rapture."—"In my opinion," cried my son, "the finest strokes in that description are much below those in the Acis and Galatea of Ovid. The Roman poet understands the use of *contrast* better, and upon that figure artfully managed, all strength in the pathetic depends."—"It is remarkable," cried Mr. Burchell, "that both the poets you mention have equally contributed to introduce a false taste into their respective countries, by loading all their lines with epithet. Men of little genius found them most easily imitated in their defects; and English poetry, like that in the latter empire of Rome, is nothing at present but a combination of luxuriant images, without plot or connexion; a string of epithets that improve the sound, without carrying on the sense. But perhaps, madam, while I thus reprehend others, you'll think it just that I should give them an opportunity to retaliate, and indeed, I have made this remark only to have an opportunity of introducing to the company a ballad, which, whatever be its other defects, is I think at least free from those I have mentioned."

A BALLAD

I

"TURN, gentle Hermit of the dale,
    And guide my lonely way,
To where yon taper cheers the vale
    With hospitable ray.

2

"For here forlorn and lost I tread,
    With fainting steps and slow;
Where wilds, immeasurably spread,
    Seem length'ning as I go."

3

"Forbear, my son," the Hermit cries,
    "To tempt the dangerous gloom;
For yonder faithless phantom flies
    To lure thee to thy doom.

4

"Here to the houseless child of want
  My door is open still;
And though my portion is but scant,
  I give it with good will.

5

"Then turn to-night, and freely share
  Whate'er my cell bestows;
My rushy couch and frugal fare,
  My blessing and respose.

6

"No flocks that range the valley free,
  To slaughter I condemn;
Taught by that power that pities me,
  I learn to pity them:

7

"But from the mountain's grassy side
  A guiltless feast I bring;
A scrip with herbs and fruit supply'd,
  And water from the spring.

8

"Then, pilgrim, turn, thy cares forego:
  All earth-born cares are wrong;
Man wants but little here below,
  Nor wants that little long."

9

Soft as the dew from Heav'n descends,
  His gentle accents fell:
The modest stranger lowly bends,
  And follows to the cell.

10

Far in a wilderness obscure
  The lonely mansion lay;
A refuge to the neighb'ring poor
  And strangers led astray.

11

No stores beneath its humble thatch
　Requir'd a master's care;
The wicket, op'ning with a latch,
　Receiv'd the harmless pair.

12

And now, when busy crowds retire
　To take their ev'ning rest,
The Hermit trimm'd his little fire,
　And cheer'd his pensive guest:

13

And spread his vegetable store,
　And gayly prest, and smil'd;
And skill'd in legendary lore
　The ling'ring hours beguil'd.

14

Around in sympathetic mirth
　Its tricks the kitten tries,
The cricket chirrups in the hearth,
　The crackling faggot flies.

15

But nothing could a charm impart
　To soothe the stranger's woe;
For grief was heavy at his heart,
　And tears began to flow.

16

His rising cares the Hermit spied,
　With answ'ring care opprest:
"And whence, unhappy youth," he cried,
　"The sorrows of thy breast?

17

"From better habitations spurn'd,
　Reluctant dost thou rove?
Or grieve for friendship unreturn'd,
　Or unregarded love?

18

"Alas! the joys that fortune brings,
　　Are trifling and decay;
And those who prize the paltry things,
　　More trifling still than they.

19

"And what is friendship but a name,
　　A charm that lulls to sleep:
A shade that follows wealth or fame,
　　But leaves the wretch to weep?

20

"And love is still an emptier sound,
　　The modern fair one's jest
On earth unseen, or only found
　　To warm the turtle's nest.

21

"For shame, fond youth, thy sorrows hush,
　　And spurn the sex," he said:
But while he spoke, a rising blush
　　His love-lorn guest betray'd.

22

Surpris'd he sees new beauties rise,
　　Swift mantling to the view;
Like colours o'er the morning skies,
　　As bright, as transient too.

23

The bashful look, the rising breast,
　　Alternate spread alarms:
The lovely stranger stands confest
　　A maid in all her charms.

24

"And ah! forgive a stranger rude,
　　A wretch forlorn," she cried;
"Whose feet unhallow'd thus intrude
　　Where Heav'n and you reside.

25

"But let a maid thy pity share,
  Whom love has taught to stray:
Who seeks for rest, but finds despair
  Companion of her way.

26

"My father liv'd beside the Tyne,
  A wealthy Lord was he:
And all his wealth was mark'd as mine,
  He had but only me.

27

"To win me from his tender arms,
  Unnumber'd suitors came;
Who praised me for imputed charms
  And felt or feign'd a flame.

28

"Each hour a mercenary crowd
  With richest proffers strove:
Among the rest young Edwin bow'd,
  But never talk'd of love.

29

"In humble, simplest habit clad,
  No wealth nor power had he;
Wisdom and worth were all he had,
  But these were all to me.

30

"And when, beside me in the dale,
  He carol'd lays of love,
His breath lent fragrance to the gale,
  And music to the grove.

31

"The blossom opening to the day,
  The dews of Heav'n refin'd,
Could nought of purity display
  To emulate his mind.

32

"The dew, the blossom on the tree,
  With charms inconstant shine;
Their charms were his, but woe to me,
  Their constancy was mine.

33

"For still I try'd each fickle art,
  Importunate and vain;
And while his passion touch'd my heart,
  I triumph'd in his pain.

34

"Till quite dejected with my scorn,
  He left me to my pride;
And sought a solitude forlorn,
  In secret where he died.

35

"But mine the sorrow, mine the fault,
  And well my life shall pay;
I'll seek the solitude he sought,
  And stretch me where he lay.

36

"And there forlorn, despairing, hid,
  I'll lay me down and die;
'Twas so for me that Edwin did,
  And so for him will I."

37

"Forbid it Heav'n!" the Hermit cried,
  And clasp'd her to his breast:
The wond'ring fair one turn'd to chide,—
  'Twas Edwin's self that prest.

38

"Turn, Angelina, ever dear,
  My charmer turn to see
Thy own, thy long-lost Edwin here,
  Restor'd to love and thee.

39

"Thus let me hold thee to my heart,
    And ev'ry care resign:
And shall we never, never part,
    My life,—my all that's mine?

40

"No, never from this hour to part,
    We'll live and love so true;
The sigh that rends thy constant heart,
    Shall break thy Edwin's too."

While this ballad was reading, Sophia seemed to mix
an air of tenderness with her approbation. But our
tranquillity was soon disturbed by the report of a gun
just by us, and immediately after a man was seen bursting
through the hedge, to take up the game he had killed.
This sportsman was the 'Squire's chaplain, who had shot
one of the blackbirds that so agreeably entertained us. So
loud a report, and so near, startled my daughters: and I
could perceive that Sophia in the fright had thrown herself into Mr. Burchell's arms for protection. The gentleman came up, and asked pardon for having disturbed us,
affirming that he was ignorant of our being so near. He
therefore sat down by my youngest daughter, and sports-
man-like, offered her what he had killed that morning.
She was going to refuse, but a private look from her
mother soon induced her to correct the mistake, and
accept his present, though with some reluctance. My
wife, as usual, discovered her pride in a whisper, observing, that Sophy had made a conquest of the
chaplain, as well as her sister had of the 'Squire. I
suspected, however, with more probability, that her
affections were placed upon a different object. The
chaplain's errand was to inform us, that Mr. Thornhill
had provided music and refreshments, and intended that
night giving the young ladies a ball by moonlight, on the
grass-plot before our door. "Nor can I deny," continued he, "but I have an interest in being first to deliver

this message, as I expect for my reward to be honoured with Miss Sophy's hand as a partner." To this my girl replied, that she should have no objection, if she could do it with honour; "But here," continued she, "is a gentleman," looking at Mr. Burchell, "who has been my companion in the task for the day, and it is fit he should share in its amusements." Mr. Burchell returned her a compliment for her intentions; but resigned her up to the chaplain, adding that he was to go that night five miles, being invited to an harvest supper. His refusal appeared to me a little extraordinary, nor could I conceive how so sensible a girl as my youngest, could thus prefer a man of broken fortune to one whose expectations were much greater. But as men are most capable of distinguishing merit in women, so the ladies often form the truest judgments of us. The two sexes seem placed as spies upon each other, and are furnished with different abilities, adapted for mutual inspection.

Two ladies of great distinction introduced. Superior finery ever seems to confer superior breeding.

MR. BURCHELL had scarce taken leave, and Sophia consented to dance with the chaplain, when my little ones came running out to tell us that the 'Squire was come with a crowd of company. Upon our return, we found our landlord, with a couple of under gentlemen and two young ladies richly drest, whom he introduced as women of very great distinction and fashion from town. We happened not to have chairs enough for the whole company: but Mr. Thornhill immediately proposed that every gentleman should sit in a lady's lap. This I positively objected to, notwithstanding a look of disapprobation from my wife. Moses was therefore despatched to borrow a couple of chairs; and as we were in want of ladies to make up a set at country dances, the two gentlemen went with him in quest of a couple of partners. Chairs and partners were soon provided. The gentlemen returned with my neighbour Flamborough's rosy daughters, flaunting with red top-knots. But an unlucky circumstance was not adverted to; though the Miss Flamboroughs were reckoned the very best of dancers in the parish, and understood the jig and the round-about to perfection, yet they were totally unacquainted with country dances. This at first discomposed us: however, after a little shoving and dragging, they at last went merrily on. Our music consisted of two fiddles, with a pipe and tabor. The moon shone bright, Mr. Thornhill and my eldest daughter led up the ball, to the great delight of the spectators; for the neighbours, hearing what was going forward, came flocking about us. My girl moved with so much grace and vivacity, that my wife could not avoid discovering the pride of her heart, by assuring me, that though the little chit did it so cleverly, all the steps were stolen from herself. The ladies of the town strove hard to be equally easy, but without success. They swam, sprawled, languished, and frisked; but all would not do: the gazers indeed owned that it was fine; but neighbour Flamborough observed, that Miss Livy's feet seemed as pat to the music as its echo. After the dance had continued about an hour, the two ladies, who were apprehensive of catching cold, moved to break up the ball. One of them, I thought, expressed her sentiments upon this occasion in a very coarse manner, when she observed, that by the *living jingo, she was all of a muck of sweat*. Upon our return to the house, we found a very elegant cold supper, which Mr. Thornhill had ordered to be brought with him. The conversation at this time was more reserved than before. The two ladies threw my girls quite into the shade; for they would talk of nothing but high life, and high-lived company; with other fashionable topics, such as pictures, taste, Shakespear, and the musical glasses. 'Tis true they once or twice mortified us sensibly by slipping out an oath; but that appeared to me as the surest symptom of their distinction, (though I am since informed that swearing is perfectly unfashionable). Their finery, however, threw a veil over any grossness in their conversation. My daughters seemed to regard their superior accomplishments with envy; and what appeared amiss was ascribed to tip-top quality breeding. But the condescension of the ladies was still superior to their other accomplishments. One of them observed that had Miss Olivia seen a little more of the world, it would greatly improve her. To which the other added, that a single winter in town would make little Sophia quite another thing. My wife warmly assented to both, adding, that there was nothing she more ardently wished than to give her girls a single winter's polishing. To this I could not help replying, that their breeding was already superior to their fortune; and that greater refinement would only serve to make their poverty ridiculous, and give them a taste for pleasures they had no right to possess.—"And what pleasures," cried Mr. Thornhill, "do they not deserve to possess, who have so much in their power to bestow? As for my part," continued he, "my fortune is pretty large, love, liberty and pleasure are my maxims; but curse me if a settlement of half my estate could give my charming Olivia pleasure, it should be hers; and the only favour I would ask in return would be to add myself to the benefit." I was not such a stranger to the world as to be ignorant that this was the fashionable cant to disguise the insolence of the basest proposal; but I made an effort to suppress my resentment. "Sir," cried I, "the family which you now condescend to favour with your company, has been bred with as nice a sense of honour as you. Any attempts to injure that, may be attended with very dangerous consequences. Honour, Sir, is our only possession at present, and of that last treasure we must be particularly careful."—I was soon sorry for the warmth with which I had spoken this, when the young gentleman, grasping my hand, swore he commended my spirit, though he disapproved my suspicions. "As to your present hint," continued he, "I protest nothing was farther from my heart than such a thought. No, by all that's tempting, the virtue that will stand a regular siege was never to my taste; for all my amours are carried by a coup de main."

The two ladies, who affected to be ignorant of the rest, seemed highly displeased with this last stroke of freedom, and began a very discreet and serious dialogue upon virtue; in this my wife, the chaplain, and I soon joined; and the 'Squire himself was at last brought to confess a sense of sorrow for his former excesses. We talked of the pleasures of temperance, and of the sunshine in the mind unpolluted with guilt. I was so well pleased, that my little ones were kept up beyond the usual time to be edified by so much good conversation. Mr. Thornhill even went beyond me, and demanded if I had any objection to giving prayers. I joyfully embraced the proposal, and in this manner the night was passed in a most comfortable way, till at last the company began to think of returning. The ladies seemed very unwilling to part with my daughters; for whom they had conceived a particular affection, and joined in a request to have the pleasure of their company home. The 'Squire seconded the proposal, and my wife added her entreaties; the girls too looked upon me as if they wished to go. In this perplexity I made two or three excuses, which my daughters as readily removed; so that at last I was obliged to give a peremptory refusal; for which we had nothing but sullen looks and short answers the whole day ensuing.

10

The family endeavours to cope with their betters. The miseries of the poor when they attempt to appear above their circumstances.

I NOW begin to find that all my long and painful lectures upon temperance, simplicity, and contentment, were entirely disregarded. The distinctions lately paid us by our betters awaked that pride which I had laid asleep, but not removed. Our windows again, as formerly, were filled with washes for the neck and face. The sun was dreaded as an enemy to the skin without doors, and the fire as a spoiler of the complexion within. My wife observed, that rising too early would hurt her daughters' eyes, that working after dinner would redden their noses, and she convinced me that the hands never looked so white as when they did nothing. Instead, therefore, of finishing George's shirts, we now had them new modelling their old gauzes, or flourishing upon cat-gut. The poor Miss Flamboroughs, their former gay companions, were cast off as mean acquaintance, and the whole conversation ran upon high life, and high-lived company, with pictures, taste, Shakespear, and the musical glasses.

But we could have borne all this, had not a fortune-telling gipsey come to raise us into perfect sublimity. The tawny sibyl no sooner appeared, than my girls came running to me for a shilling a piece to cross her hand with silver. To say the truth, I was tired of being always wise, and could not help gratifying their request, because I loved to see them happy. I gave each of them a shilling; though, for the honour of the family, it must be observed that they never went without money themselves, as my wife always generously let them have a guinea each, to keep in their pockets; but with strict injunctions never to change it. After they had been closeted up with the fortune-telling for some time, I knew by their looks, upon their returning, that they had been promised something great.—"Well, my girls, how have you sped? Tell me, Livy, has the fortune-teller given thee a pennyworth?"— "I protest, Papa," says the girl, "I believe she deals with somebody that's not right; for she positively declared, that I am to be married to a 'Squire in less than a twelve-month!"—"Well, now, Sophy, my child," said I, "and what sort of a husband are you to have?" "Sir," replied she, "I am to have a Lord soon after my sister has married the 'Squire."—"How," cried I, "is that all you are to have for your two shillings! Only a Lord and a 'Squire for two shillings! You fools, I could have promised you a Prince and a Nabob for half the money."

This curiosity of theirs, however, was attended with very serious effects: we now began to think ourselves designed by the stars to something exalted, and already anticipated our future grandeur.

It has been a thousand times observed, and I must observe it once more, that the hours we pass with happy prospects in view, are more pleasing than those crowned with fruition. In the first case, we cook the dish to our own appetite; in the latter, nature cooks it for us. It is impossible to repeat the train of agreeable reveries we called up for our entertainment. We looked upon our fortunes as once more rising; and as the whole parish asserted that the 'Squire was in love with my daughter, she was actually so with him; for they persuaded her into the passion. In this agreeable interval, my wife had the most lucky dreams in the world, which she took care to tell us every morning, with great solemnity and exactness. It was one night a coffin and cross bones, the sign of an approaching wedding; at another time she imagined her daughters' pockets filled with farthings, a certain sign they would shortly be stuffed with gold. The girls themselves had their omens. They felt strange kisses on their lips;

they saw rings in the candle, purses bounced from the fire, and true love-knots lurked in the bottom of every tea-cup.

Towards the end of the week we received a card from the town ladies; in which, with their compliments, they hoped to see all our family at church the Sunday following. All Saturday morning I could perceive, in consequence of this, my wife and daughters in close conference together, and now and then glancing at me with looks that betrayed a latent plot. To be sincere, I had strong suspicions that some absurd proposal was preparing for appearing with splendour the next day. In the evening they began their operations in a very regular manner, and my wife undertook to conduct the siege. After tea, when I seemed in spirits, she began thus—"I fancy, Charles, my dear, we shall have a great deal of good company at our church to-morrow."—"Perhaps we may, my dear," returned I, "though you need be under no uneasiness about that, you shall have a sermon whether there be or not."—"That is what I expect," returned she; "but I think, my dear, we ought to appear there as decently as possible, for who knows what may happen?" "Your precautions," replied I, "are highly commend-able. A decent behaviour and appearance in church is what charms me. We should be devout and humble, cheerful and serene."—"Yes," cried she, "I know that; but I mean we should go there in as proper a manner as possible; not altogether like the scrubs about us." "You are quite right, my dear," returned I, "and I was going to make the very same proposal. The proper manner of going is, to go there as early as possible to have time for meditation before the service begins."—"Phoo, Charles," interrupted she, "all that is very true; but not what I would be at. I mean we should go there genteelly. You know the church is two miles off, and I protest I don't like to see my daughters trudging up to their pew all blowzed and red with walking, and looking for all the world as if they had been winners at a smock race. Now, my dear, my proposal is this: there are our two plow horses, the Colt that has been in our family these nine years, and his companion Blackberry, that has scarce done an earthly thing for this month past. They are both grown fat and lazy. Why should not they do something as well as we? And let me tell you, when Moses has trimmed them a little, they will cut a very tolerable figure."

To this proposal I objected, that walking would be twenty times more genteel than such a paltry conveyance, as Blackberry was wall-eyed, and the Colt wanted a tail: that they had never been broke to the rein; but had an hundred vicious tricks; and that we had but one saddle and pillion in the whole house. All these objections, however, were over-ruled; so that I was obliged to comply. The next morning I perceived them not a little busy in collecting such materials as might be necessary for the expedition; but as I found it would be a business of time, I walked on to the church before, and they promised speedily to follow. I waited near an hour in the reading desk for their arrival; but not finding them come as expected, I was obliged to begin, and went through the service, not without some uneasiness at finding them absent. This was increased when all was finished, and no appearance of the family. I therefore walked back by the horse-way, which was five miles round, though the foot-way was but two, and when got about half-way home, perceived the procession marching slowly forward towards the church; my son, my wife, and the two little ones exalted on one horse, and my two daughters upon the other. I demanded the cause of their delay; but I soon found by their looks they had met with a thousand misfortunes on the road. The horses had at first refused to move from the door, till Mr. Burchell was kind enough to beat them forward for about two hundred yards with his cudgel. Next, the straps of my wife's pillion broke down, and they were obliged to stop to repair them before they could proceed. After that, one of the horses took it into his head to stand still, and neither blows nor entreaties could prevail with him to proceed. He was just recovering from this dismal situation when I found them; but perceiving every thing safe, I own their present mortification did not much displease me, as it would give me many opportunities of future triumph, and teach my daughters more humility.

11

The family still resolve to hold up their heads.

MICHAELMAS eve happening on the next day, we were invited to burn nuts and play tricks at neighbour Flamborough's. Our late mortifications had humbled us a little, or it is probable we might have rejected such an invitation with contempt: however, we suffered ourselves to be happy. Our honest neighbour's goose and dumplings were fine, and the lamb's-wool, even in the opinion of my wife, who was a connoisseur, was excellent. It is true, his manner of telling stories was not quite so well. They were very long, and very dull, and all about himself, and we had laughed at them ten times before: however, we were kind enough to laugh at them once more.

Mr. Burchell who was of the party, was always fond of seeing some innocent amusement going forward, and set the boys and girls to blind man's buff. My wife too was persuaded to join in the diversion, and it gave me pleasure to think she was not yet too old. In the mean time, my neighbour and I looked on, laughed at every feat, and praised our own dexterity when we were young. Hot cockles succeeded next, questions and commands followed that, and last of all, they sat down to hunt the slipper. As every person may not be acquainted with this primaeval pastime, it may be necessary to observe, that the company at this play plant themselves in a ring upon the ground all except one who stands in the middle, whose business it is to catch a shoe, which the company shove about under their hams from one to another, something like a weaver's shuttle. As it is impossible, in this case, for the lady who is up to face all the company at once, the great beauty of the play lies in hitting her a thump with the heel of the shoe on that side least capable of making a defence. It was in this manner that my eldest daughter was hemmed in, and thumped about, all blowzed, in spirits, and bawling for fair play, fair play, with a voice that might deafen a ballad singer, when, confusion on confusion who should enter the room but our two great acquaintances from town, Lady Blarney and Miss Carolina Wilhelmina Amelia Skeggs! Description would but beggar, therefore it is unnecessary to describe this new mortification. Death! To be seen by ladies of such high breeding in such vulgar attitudes! Nothing better could ensue from such a vulgar play of Mr. Flamborough's proposing. We seemed stuck to the ground for some time, as if actually petrified with amazement.

The two ladies had been at our house to see us, and finding us from home, came after us hither, as they were uneasy to know what accident could have kept us from church the day before. Olivia undertook to be our pro-locutor, and delivered the whole in a summary way, only saying, "We were thrown from our horses." At which account the ladies were greatly concerned; but being told the family received no hurt, they were extremely glad: but being informed that we were almost killed by the fright, they were vastly sorry; but hearing that we had a very good night, they were extremely glad again. Nothing could exceed their complaisance to my daughters; their professions the last evening were warm, but now they were ardent. They protested a desire of having a more lasting acquaintance. Lady Blarney was particularly attached to Olivia; Miss Carolina Wilhelmina Amelia Skeggs (I love to give the whole name) took a greater fancy to her sister. They supported the conversation between themselves, while my daughters sate silent, admiring their exalted breeding. But as every reader, however beggarly himself, is fond of high-lived dialogues, with anecdotes of Lords, Ladies, and Knights of the Garter, I must beg leave to give him the concluding part of the present conversation.

"All that I know of the matter," cried Miss Skeggs,

76

"is this, that it may be true, or it may not be true: but this I can assure your Ladyship, that the whole rout was in amaze; his Lordship turned all manner of colours, my Lady fell into a sound, but Sir Tomkyn, drawing his sword, swore he was her's to the last drop of his blood."

"Well," replied our Peeress, "this I can say, that the Duchess never told me a syllable of the matter, and I believe her Grace would keep nothing a secret from me. This you may depend on as fact, that the next morning my Lord Duke cried out three times to his valet de chambre, 'Jernigan, Jernigan, Jernigan, bring me my garters.'"

But previously I should have mentioned the very impolite behaviour of Mr. Burchell, who during this discourse, sate with his face turned to the fire, and at the conclusion of every sentence would cry out *fudge*, an expression which displeased us all, and in some measure damped the rising spirit of the conversation.

"Besides, my dear Skeggs," continued our Peeress, "there is nothing of this in the copy of verses that Dr. Burdock made upon the occasion." *Fudge!*

"I am surprized at that," cried Miss Skeggs; "for he seldom leaves any thing out, as he writes only for his own ᷍musement. But can your Ladyship favour me with a ᷍ight of them?" *Fudge!*

"My dea᷍ creature," replied our Peeress, "do you think I carry such things about me? Though they are very fine to be sure, and I think myself something of a judge; at least I know what pleases myself. Indeed, I was ever an admirer of all Doctor Burdock's little pieces; for except what he does, and our dear Countess at Hanover-Square, there's nothing comes out but the most lowest stuff in nature; not a bit of high life among them." *Fudge!*

"Your Ladyship should except," says t'other, "your own things in the Lady's Magazine. I hope you'll say there's nothing low-lived there? But I suppose we are to have no more from that quarter?" *Fudge!*

"Why, my dear," says the Lady, "you know my

reader and companion has left me, to be married to Captain Roach, and as my poor eyes won't suffer me to write myself, I have been for some time looking out for another. A proper person is no easy matter to find, and to be sure thirty pounds a year is a small stipend for a well-bred girl of character, that can read, write, and behave in company; as for the chits about town, there is no bearing them about one." *Fudge!*

"That I know," cried Miss Skeggs, "by experience. For of the three companions I had this last half year, one of them refused to do plain-work an hour in the day, another thought twenty-five guineas a year too small a salary, and I was obliged to send away the third, because I suspected an intrigue with the chaplain. Virtue, my dear Lady Blarney, virtue is worth any price; but where is that to be found?" *Fudge!*

My wife had been for a long time all attention to this discourse; but was particularly struck with the latter part of it. Thirty pounds and twenty-five guineas a year made fifty-six pounds five shillings English money, all which was in a manner going a-begging, and might easily be secured in the family. She for a moment studied my looks for approbation; and, to own a truth, I was of opinion, that two such places would fit our two daughters exactly. Besides, if the 'Squire had any real affection for my eldest daughter, this would be the way to make her every way qualified for her fortune. My wife therefore was resolved that we should not be deprived of such advantages for want of assurance, and undertook to harangue for the family. "I hope," cried she, "your Ladyships will pardon my present presumption. It is true, we have no right to pretend to such favours; but yet it is natural for me to wish putting my children forward in the world. And I will be bold to say my two girls have had a pretty good education, and capacity, at least the country can't shew better. They can read, write, and cast accompts; they understand their needle, breadstitch, cross and change, and all manner of plain-work; they can pink, point, and frill; and know something of music; they can do up small clothes, work upon catgut; my eldest can cut paper, and my youngest has a very pretty manner of telling fortunes upon the cards." *Fudge!*

When she had delivered this pretty piece of eloquence, the two ladies looked at each other a few minutes in silence, with an air of doubt and importance. At last, Miss Carolina Wilhelmina Amelia Skeggs condescended to observe, that the young ladies, from the opinion she could form of them from so slight an acquaintance, seemed very fit for such employments: "But a thing of this kind, Madam," cried she, addressing my spouse, "requires a thorough examination into characters, and a more perfect knowledge of each other. Not, madam," continued she, "that I in the least suspect the young ladies' virtue, prudence, and discretion; but there is a form in these things, Madam, there is a form."

My wife approved her suspicions very much, observing, that she was very apt to be suspicious herself; but referred her to all the neighbours for a character: but this our Peeress declined as unnecessary, alleging that her cousin Thornhill's recommendation would be sufficient, and upon this we rested our petition.

12

*Fortune seems resolved to humble the family of Wakefield.
Mortifications are often more painful than real calamities.*

WHEN we were returned home, the night was dedicated
to schemes of future conquest. Deborah exerted much
sagacity in conjecturing which of the two girls was likely
to have the best place, and most opportunities of seeing
good company. The only obstacle to our preferment was
in obtaining the 'Squire's recommendation; but he had
already shewn us too many instances of his friendship to
doubt of it now. Even in bed my wife kept up the usual
theme: "Well, faith, my dear Charles, between ourselves, I think we have made an excellent day's work of
it."—"Pretty well," cried I, not knowing what to say.—
"What, only pretty well!" returned she. "I think it is
very well. Suppose the girls should come to make
acquaintances of taste in town! This I am assured of, that
London is the only place in the world for all manner of
husbands. Besides, my dear, stranger things happen every
day: and as ladies of quality are so taken with my
daughters, what will not men of quality be! *Entre nous*, I
protest I like my Lady Blarney vastly, so very obliging.
However, Miss Carolina Wilhelmina Amelia Skeggs has
my warm heart. But yet, when they came to talk of
places in town, you saw at once how I nailed them. Tell
me, my dear, don't you think I did for my children
there?"—"Aye," returned I, not knowing well what to
think of the matter, "Heaven grant they may be both the
better for it this day three months!" This was one of
those observations I usually made to impress my wife
with an opinion of my sagacity: for if the girls succeeded,
then it was a pious wish fulfilled; but if any thing
unfortunate ensued, then it might be looked upon as
a prophecy. All this conversation, however, was only

preparatory to another scheme, and indeed I dreaded as much. This was nothing less than, that as we were now to hold up our heads a little higher in the world, it would be proper to sell the Colt, which was grown old, at a neighbouring fair, and buy us a horse that would carry single or double upon an occasion, and make a pretty appearance at church or upon a visit. This at first I opposed stoutly; but it was as stoutly defended. However, as I weakened, my antagonists gained strength, till at last it was resolved to part with him.

As the fair happened on the following day, I had intentions of going myself; but my wife persuaded me that I had got a cold, and nothing could prevail upon her to permit me from home. "No, my dear," said she, "our son Moses is a discreet boy, and can buy and sell to very good advantage; you know all our great bargains are of his purchasing. He always stands out and higgles, and actually tires them till he gets a bargain."

As I had some opinion of my son's prudence, I was willing enough to entrust him with this commission; and the next morning I perceived his sisters mighty busy in fitting out Moses for the fair; trimming his hair, brushing his buckles, and cocking his hat with pins. The business of the toilet being over, we had at last the satisfaction of seeing him mounted upon the Colt, with a deal box before him to bring home groceries in. He had on a coat made of that cloth they call thunder and lightning, which, though grown too short, was much too good to be thrown away. His waistcoat was of gosling green, and his sisters had tied his hair with a broad black ribband. We all followed him several paces from the door, bawling after him good luck, till we could see him no longer.

He was scarce gone, when Mr. Thornhill's butler came to congratulate us upon our good fortune, saying, that he overheard his young master mention our names with great commendation.

Good fortune seemed resolved not to come alone. Another footman from the same family followed, with a card for my daughters, importing, that the two ladies had received such pleasing accounts from Mr. Thornhill of us all, that, after a few previous enquiries, they hoped to be perfectly satisfied. "Ay," cried my wife, "I now see it is no easy matter to get into the families of the great; but when one once gets in, then, as Moses says, one may go to sleep." To this piece of humour, for she intended it for wit, my daughters assented with a loud laugh of pleasure. In short, such was her satisfaction at this message, that she actually put her hand in her pocket, and gave the messenger seven-pence halfpenny.

This was to be our visiting day. The next that came was Mr. Burchell, who had been at the fair. He brought my little ones a pennyworth of gingerbread each, which my wife undertook to keep for them, and give them by letters at a time. He brought my daughters also a couple of boxes, in which they might keep wafers, snuff, patches, or even money, when they got it. My wife was usually fond of a weasel-skin purse, as being the most lucky; but this by the by. We had still a regard for Mr. Burchell, though his late rude behaviour was in some measure displeasing; nor could we now avoid communicating our happiness to him, and asking his advice: although we seldom followed advice, we were all ready enough to ask it. When he read the note from the two ladies, he shook his head, and observed, that an affair of this sort demanded the utmost circumspection.—This air of diffidence highly displeased my wife. "I never doubted, Sir," cried she, "your readiness to be against my daughters and me. You have more circumspection than is wanted. However, I fancy when we come to ask advice, we will apply to persons who seem to have made use of it themselves."—"Whatever my own conduct may have been, Madam," replied he, "is not the present question; though as I have made no use of advice myself, I should in conscience give it to those that will."—As I was apprehensive this answer might draw on a repartee, making up by abuse what it wanted in wit, I changed the subject, by seeming to wonder what could keep our son so long at the fair, as it was now almost nightfall.— "Never mind our son," cried my wife, "depend upon it he knows what he is about. I'll warrant we'll never see him sell his hen of a rainy day. I have seen him buy such bargains as would amaze one. I'll tell you a good story about that, that will make you split your sides with laughing—But as I live, yonder comes Moses, without an horse, and the box at his back."

As she spoke, Moses came slowly on foot, and sweating under the deal box, which he had strapt round his shoulders like a pedlar.—"Welcome, welcome, Moses; well, my boy, what have you brought us from the fair?" —"I have brought you myself," cried Moses, with a sly look, and resting the box on the dresser.—"Ah, Moses," cried my wife, "that we know, but where is the horse?" "I have sold him," cried Moses, "for three pounds five shillings and two-pence."—"Well done, my good boy," returned she, "I knew you would touch them off. Between ourselves, three pounds five shillings and two-pence is no bad day's work. Come, let us have it then."— "I have brought back no money," cried Moses again, "I have laid it all out in a bargain, and here it is," pulling out a bundle from his breast: "here they are; a groce of green spectacles, with silver rims and shagreen cases."—"A groce of green spectacles!" repeated my wife in a faint voice. "And you have parted with the Colt, and brought us back nothing but a groce of green paltry spectacles!"—"Dear mother," cried the boy, "why won't you listen to reason? I had them a dead bargain, or I should not have bought them. The silver rims alone will sell for double the money."—"A fig for the silver rims," cried my wife in a passion: "I dare swear they won't sell for above half the money at the rate of broken silver, five shillings an ounce." "You need be under no uneasiness," cried I, "about selling the rims; for they are not worth sixpence, for I perceive they are only copper varnished over."—"What," cried my wife, "not silver, the rims not silver!" "No," cried I, "no more silver than your saucepan."—"And so," returned she, "we have parted with the Colt, and have only got a groce of green spectacles, with copper rims and shagreen cases! A murrain take such trumpery. The blockhead has been imposed upon, and should have known his company better."—"There, my dear," cried I, "you are wrong, he should not have known them at all."—"Marry, hang the idiot," returned she, "to bring me such stuff; if I had them I would throw them in the fire." "There again you are wrong, my dear," cried I; "for though they be copper, we will keep them by us, as copper spectacles, you know, are better than nothing."

By this time the unfortunate Moses was undeceived. He now saw that he had indeed been imposed upon by a prowling sharper, who, observing his figure, had marked him for an easy prey. I therefore asked the circumstances of his deception. He sold the horse, it seems, and walked the fair in search of another. A reverend looking man brought him to a tent, under pretence of having one to sell. "Here," continued Moses, "we met another man, very well drest, who desired to borrow twenty pounds upon these, saying, that he wanted money, and would dispose of them for a third of the value. The first gentleman, who pretended to be my friend, whispered me to buy them, and cautioned me not to let so good an offer pass. I sent for Mr. Flamborough, and they talked him up as finely as they did me, and so at last we were persuaded to buy the two groce between us."

13

Mr. Burchell is found to be an enemy; for he has the confidence to give disagreeable advice.

Our family had now made several attempts to be fine; but some unforeseen disaster demolished each as soon as projected. I endeavoured to take the advantage of every disappointment, to improve their good sense in proportion as they were frustrated in ambition. "You see, my children," cried I, "how little is to be got by attempts to impose upon the world, in coping with our betters. Such as are poor and will associate with none but the rich, are hated by those they avoid, and despised by those they follow. Unequal combinations are always disadvantageous to the weaker side: the rich having the pleasure, and the poor the inconveniences that result from them. But come, Dick, my boy, and repeat the fable that you were reading to-day, for the good of the company."

"Once upon a time," cried the child, "a Giant and a Dwarf were friends, and kept together. They made a bargain that they would never forsake each other, but go seek adventures. The first battle they fought was with two Saracens, and the Dwarf, who was very courageous, dealt one of the champions a most angry blow. It did the Saracen very little injury, who lifting up his sword, fairly struck off the poor Dwarf's arm. He was now in a woeful plight; but the Giant coming to his assistance, in a short time left the two Saracens dead on the plain, and the Dwarf cut off the dead man's head out of spite. They then travelled on to another adventure. This was against three bloody-minded Satyrs, who were carrying away a damsel in distress. The Dwarf was not quite so fierce now as before; but for all that, struck the first blow, which was returned by another, that knocked out his eye; but the Giant was soon up with them, and had they not fled, would certainly have killed them every one. They were all very joyful for this victory, and the damsel who was relieved fell in love with the Giant and married him. They now travelled far, and farther than I can tell, till they met with a company of robbers. The Giant, for the first time, was foremost now; but the Dwarf was not far behind. The battle was stout and long. Wherever the Giant came all fell before him; but the Dwarf had like to have been killed more than once. At last the victory declared for the two adventurers; but the Dwarf lost his leg. The Dwarf was now without an arm, a leg, and an eye, while the Giant was without a single wound. Upon which he cried out to his little companion, My little hero, this is glorious sport; let us get one victory more, and then we shall have honour for ever. No, cries the Dwarf, who was by this time grown wiser, no, I declare off; I'll fight no more: for I find in every battle that you get all the honour and rewards, but all the blows fall upon me."

I was going to moralize this fable, when our attention was called off to a warm dispute between my wife and Mr. Burchell, upon my daughters' intended expedition to town. My wife very strenuously insisted upon the advantages that would result from it; Mr. Burchell, on the contrary, dissuaded her with great ardour, and I stood neuter. His present dissuasions seemed but the second part of those which were received with so ill a grace in the morning. The dispute grew high, while poor Deborah, instead of reasoning stronger, talked louder, and at last was obliged to take shelter from a defeat in clamour. The conclusion of her harangue, however, was highly displeasing to us all: she knew, she said, of some who had their own secret reasons for what they advised; but, for her part, she wished such to stay away from her house for the future.—"Madam," cried Burchell, with looks of great composure, which tended to inflame her the more, "as for secret reasons, you are right: I have secret reasons, which I forbear to mention, because you are not able to answer those of which I make no secret:

86

I was going to moralize this fable . . .

but I find my visits here are become troublesome: I'll take my leave therefore now, and perhaps come once more to take a final farewell when I am quitting the country." Thus saying, he took up his hat, nor could the attempts of Sophia, whose looks seemed to upbraid his precipitancy, prevent his going.

When gone, we all regarded each other for some minutes with confusion. My wife, who knew herself to be the cause, strove to hide her concern with a forced smile, and an air of assurance, which I was willing to reprove: "How, woman," cried I to her, "is it thus we treat strangers? Is it thus we return their kindness? Be assured, my dear, that these were the harshest words, and to me the most unpleasing, that have escaped your lips!"— "Why would he provoke me then?" replied she; "but I know the motives of his advice perfectly well. He would prevent my girls from going to town, that he may have the pleasure of my youngest daughter's company here at home. But whatever happens, she shall chuse better company than such low-lived fellows as he."—"Low-lived, my dear, do you call him?" cried I; "it is very possible we may mistake this man's character, for he seems upon some occasions the most finished gentleman I ever knew.—Tell me, Sophia, my girl, has he ever given you any secret instances of his attachment!"—"His conversation with me, Sir," replied my daughter, "has ever been sensible, modest, and pleasing. As to aught else, no, never. Once, indeed, I remember to have heard him say he never knew a woman who could find merit in a man that seemed poor." "Such, my dear," cried I, "is the common cant of all the unfortunate or idle. But I hope you have been taught to judge properly of such men, and that it would be even madness to expect happiness from one who has been so very bad an economist of his own. Your mother and I have now better prospects for you. The next winter, which you will probably spend in town, will give you opportunities of making a more prudent choice."

What Sophia's reflections were upon this occasion I can't pretend to determine; but I was not displeased at the bottom, that we were rid of a guest from whom I had much to fear. Our breach of hospitality went to my conscience a little; but I quickly silenced that monitor by two or three specious reasons, which served to satisfy and reconcile me to myself. The pain which conscience gives the man who has already done wrong, is soon got over. Conscience is a coward, and those faults it has not strength enough to prevent, it seldom has justice enough to accuse.

14

*Fresh mortifications, or a demonstration that seeming calamities
may be real blessings.*

The journey of my daughters to town was now resolved
upon, Mr. Thornhill having kindly promised to inspect
their conduct himself, and inform us by letter of their
behaviour. But it was thought indispensably necessary
that their appearance should equal the greatness of their
expectations, which could not be done without expence.
We debated therefore in full council what were the
easiest methods of raising money, or more properly
speaking, what we could most conveniently sell. The
deliberation was soon finished; it was found that our
remaining horse was utterly useless for the plough, without his companion, and equally unfit for the road, as
wanting an eye; it was therefore determined that we
should dispose of him for the purpose above mentioned,
at the neighbouring fair, and, to prevent imposition, that
I should go with him myself. Though this was one of the
first mercantile transactions of my life, yet I had no doubt
about acquitting myself with reputation. The opinion a
man forms of his own prudence is measured by that of the
company he keeps; and as mine was mostly in the family
way, I had conceived no unfavourable sentiments of my
worldly wisdom. My wife, however, next morning, at
parting, after I had got some paces from the door, called
me back, to advise me, in a whisper, to have all my eyes
about me.

I had, in the usual forms, when I came to the fair, put
my horse through all his paces; but for some time had no
bidders. At last a chapman approached, and, after he had
for a good while examined the horse round, finding him
blind of one eye, he would have nothing to say to him: a
second came up; but observing he had a spavin, declared

he would not take him for the driving home: a third
perceived he had a windgall, and would bid no money: a
fourth knew by his eye that he had the botts: a fifth
wondered what a plague I could do at the fair with a
blind, spavined, galled hack, that was only fit to be cut up
for a dog-kennel. By this time I began to have a most
hearty contempt for the poor animal myself, and was
almost ashamed at the approach of every customer; for
though I did not entirely believe all the fellows told me,
yet I reflected that the number of witnesses was a strong
presumption they were right, and St. Gregory, upon
Good Works, professes himself to be of the same opinion.

I was in this mortifying situation, when a brother
clergyman, an old acquaintance, who had also business
at the fair, came up, and shaking me by the hand,
proposed adjoining to a public-house and taking a glass
of whatever we could get. I readily closed with the offer,
and entering an ale-house, we were shewn into a little
back room, where there was only a venerable old man,
who sat wholly intent over a large book, which he was
reading. I never in my life saw a figure that prepossessed
me more favourably. His locks of silver grey venerably
shaded his temples, and his green old age seemed to be
the result of health and benevolence. However, his
presence did not interrupt our conversation; my friend
and I discoursed on the various turns of fortune we had
met; the Whistonian controversy, my last pamphlet, the
archdeacon's reply, and the hard measure that was dealt
me. But our attention was in a short time taken off by the
appearance of a youth, who, entering the room, respectfully said something softly to the old stranger. "Make no
apologies, my child," said the old man, "to do good is a
duty we owe to all our fellow creatures: take this, I wish it
were more; but five pounds will relieve your distress, and
you are welcome." The modest youth shed tears of
gratitude, and yet his gratitude was scarce equal to mine.
I could have hugged the good old man in my arms, his
benevolence pleased me so. He continued to read, and we

resumed our conversation, until my companion, after some time, recollecting that he had business to transact in the fair, promised to be soon back: adding, that he always desired to have as much of Dr. Primrose's company as possible. The old gentleman hearing my name mentioned, seemed to look at me with attention for some time, and when my friend was gone, most respectfully demanded if I was in any way related to the great Primrose, that courageous Monogamist, who had been the bulwark of the Church. Never did my heart feel sincerer rapture than at that moment. "Sir," cried I, "the applause of so good a man, as I am sure you are, adds to that happiness in my breast which your benevolence has already excited. You behold before you, Sir, that Dr. Primrose, the Monogamist, whom you have been pleased to call great. You here see that unfortunate Divine, who has so long, and it would ill become me to say, successfully, fought against the Deuterogamy of the age." "Sir," cried the stranger, struck with awe, "I fear I have been too familiar; but you'll forgive my curiosity, Sir: I beg pardon." "Sir," cried I, grasping his hand, "you are so far from displeasing me by your familiarity, that I must beg you'll accept my friendship, as you already have my esteem."—"Then with gratitude I accept the offer," cried he, squeezing me by the hand, "thou glorious pillar of unshaken orthodoxy; and do I behold"—I here interrupted what he was going to say; for though, as an author, I could digest no small share of flattery, yet now my modesty would permit no more. However, no lovers in romance ever cemented a more instantaneous friendship. We talked upon several subjects: at first I thought he seemed rather devout than learned, and began to think he despised all human doctrines as dross. Yet this no way lessened him in my esteem; for I had for some time begun privately to harbour such an opinion myself. I therefore took occasion to observe, that the world in general began to be blameably indifferent as to doctrinal matters, and followed human speculations too much.—"Aye, Sir," replied he, as if he had reserved all his learning to that moment, "Ay, Sir, the world is in its dotage, and yet the cosmogony, or creation of the world has puzzled philosophers of all ages. What a medley of opinions have they not broached upon the creation of the world? Sanchoniathon, Manetho, Berosus, and Ocellus Lucanus have all attempted it in vain. The latter has these words, *Anarchon ara kai atelutaion to pan*, which imply that all things have neither beginning nor end. Manetho also, who lived about the time of Nebuchadon-Asser, Asser being a Syriac word usually applied as a surname to the kings of that country, as Teglat Phael-Asser, Nabon-Asser, he, I say, formed a conjecture equally absurd; for as we usually say, *ek to biblion kubernetes*, which implies that books will never teach the world; so he attempted to investigate—But, Sir, I ask pardon, I am straying from the question."—That he actually was; nor could I for my life see how the creation of the world had any thing to do with the business I was talking of; but it was sufficient to shew me that he was a man of letters, and I now reverenced him the more. I was resolved, therefore, to bring him to the touchstone; but he was too mild and too gentle to contend for victory. Whenever I made any observation that looked like a challenge to controversy, he would smile, shake his head, and say nothing; by which, I understood he could say much, if he thought proper. The subject therefore insensibly changed from the business of antiquity to that which brought us both to the fair; mine I told him was to sell an horse, and very luckily, indeed, his was to buy one for one of his tenants. My horse was soon produced, and in fine we struck a bargain. Nothing now remained but to pay me, and he accordingly pulled out a thirty pound note, and bid me change it. Not being in a capacity of complying with his demand, he ordered his footman to be called up, who made his appearance in a very genteel livery. "Here Abraham," cried he, "go and get gold for this; you'll do it at neighbour Jackson's or any where." While the fellow was gone, he entertained me with a pathetic harangue on the great scarcity of silver, which I undertook to improve, by deploring also the great scarcity of gold; so that by the time Abraham returned, we had both agreed that money was never so hard to be come at as now. Abraham returned to inform us, that he had been over the whole fair, and could not get change, though he had offered half a crown for doing it. This was a very great disappointment to us all; but the old gentleman, having paused a little, asked me if I knew one Solomon Flamborough, in my part of the country; upon replying that he was my next door neighbour; "If that be the case then," returned he, "I believe we shall deal. You shall have a draught upon him, payable at sight; and let me tell you he is as warm a man as any within five miles round him. Honest Solomon and I have been acquainted for many years together. I remember I always beat him at three jumps; but he could hop upon one leg farther than I." A draught upon my neighbour was to me the same as money; for I was sufficiently convinced of his ability. The draught was signed, and put into my hands, and Mr. Jenkinson, the old gentleman, his man Abraham, and my horse, old Blackberry, trotted off very well pleased with each other.

After a short interval, being left to reflection, I began to recollect that I had done wrong in taking a draught from a stranger, and so prudently resolved upon following the purchaser, and having back my horse. But this was now too late; I therefore made directly homewards, resolving to get the draught changed into money at my friend's as fast as possible. I found my honest neighbour smoking his pipe at his own door, and informing him that I had a small bill upon him, he read it twice over. "You can read the name, I suppose," cried I, "Ephraim Jenkinson." "Yes," returned he, "the name is written plain enough, and I know the gentleman too, the greatest rascal under the canopy of heaven. This is the very same rogue who sold us the spectacles. Was he not a venerable

93

looking man, with grey hair, and no flaps to his pocket-holes? And did he not talk a long string of learning about Greek and cosmogony, and the world?" To this I replied with a groan. "Ay," continued he, "he has but that one piece of learning in the world, and he always talks it away whenever he finds a scholar in company; but I know the rogue, and will catch him yet."

Though I was already sufficiently mortified, my greatest struggle was to come, in facing my wife and daughters. No truant was ever more afraid of returning to school, there to behold the master's visage, than I was of going home. I was determined, however, to anticipate their fury, by first falling into a passion myself.

But, alas! upon entering, I found the family no way disposed for battle. My wife and girls were all in tears, Mr. Thornhill having been there that day to inform them, that their journey to town was entirely over. The two ladies having heard reports of us from some malicious person about us, were that day set out for London. He could neither discover the tendency, nor the author of these: but whatever they might be, or whoever might have broached them, he continued to assure our family of his friendship and protection. I found, therefore, that they bore my disappointment with great resignation, as it was eclipsed in the greatness of their own. But what perplexed us most was to think who could be so base as to asperse the character of a family so harmless as ours, too humble to excite envy, and too inoffensive to create disgust.

All Mr. Burchell's villainy at once detected. The folly of being over-wise.

THAT evening and a part of the following day was employed in fruitless attempts to discover our enemies: scarcely a family in the neighbourhood but incurred our suspicions, and each of us had reasons for our opinion best known to ourselves. As we were in this perplexity, one of our little boys, who had been playing abroad, brought in a letter-case, which he found on the Green. It was quickly known to belong to Mr. Burchell, with whom it had been seen, and, upon examination, contained some hints upon different subjects; but what particularly engaged our attention was a sealed note, superscribed, *the copy of a letter to be sent to the ladies at Thornhill-castle.* It instantly occurred that he was the base informer, and we deliberated whether the note should not be broke open. I was against it; but Sophia, who said she was sure that of all men he would be the last to be guilty of so much baseness, insisted upon its being read. In this she was seconded by the rest of the family, and at their joint solicitation, I read as follows:

"LADIES,

The bearer will sufficiently satisfy you as to the person from whom this comes: one at least the friend of innocence, and ready to prevent its being seduced. I am informed for a truth, that you have some intention of bringing two young ladies to town whom I have some knowledge of, under the character of companions. As I would neither have simplicity imposed upon, nor virtue contaminated, I must offer it as my opinion, that the impropriety of such a step will be attended with dangerous consequences. It has never been my way to treat the infamous or the lewd with severity; nor should I now have taken this method of explaining myself, or reproving folly, did it not aim at guilt. Take therefore the admonition of a friend, and seriously reflect on the consequences of introducing infamy and vice into retreats where peace and innocence have hitherto resided."

Our doubts were now at an end. There seemed indeed something applicable to both sides in this letter, and its censures might as well be referred to those to whom it was written, as to us; but the malicious meaning was obvious, and we went no farther. My wife had scarce patience to hear me to the end, but railed at the writer with unrestrained resentment. Olivia was equally severe, and Sophia seemed perfectly amazed at his baseness. As for my part, it appeared to me one of the vilest instances of unprovoked ingratitude I had met with. Nor could I account for it in any other manner than by imputing it to his desire of detaining my youngest daughter in the country, to have the more frequent opportunities of an interview. In this manner we all sate ruminating upon schemes of vengeance, when our other little boy came running in to tell us that Mr. Burchell was approaching at the other end of the field. It is easier to conceive than describe the complicated sensations which are felt from the pain of a recent injury, and the pleasure of approaching vengeance. Though our intentions were only to upbraid him with his ingratitude, yet it was resolved to do it in a manner that would be perfectly cutting. For this purpose we agreed to meet him with our usual smiles, to chat in the beginning with more than ordinary kindness, to amuse him a little; and then in the midst of the flattering calm to burst upon him like an earthquake, and overwhelm him with the sense of his own baseness. This being resolved upon, my wife undertook to manage the business herself, as she really had some talents for such an undertaking. We saw him approach, he entered, drew a chair, and sat down.—"A fine day, Mr. Burchell."— "A very fine day, Doctor; though I fancy we shall have some rain by the shooting of my corns."—"The shooting of your horns," cried my wife in a loud fit of laughter, and then asked pardon for being fond of a joke.—"Dear madam," replied he, "I pardon you with all my heart, for I protest I should not have thought it a joke had you not told me."—"Perhaps not, Sir," cried my wife, winking at us, "and yet I dare say you can tell us how many jokes go to an ounce."—"I fancy, madam," returned Burchell, "you have been reading a jest book this morning, that ounce of jokes is so very good a conceit; and yet, madam, I had rather see half an ounce of under-standing." "I believe you might," cried my wife, still smiling at us, though the laugh was against her; "and yet I have seen some men pretend to understanding that have very little." "And no doubt," replied her antagonist, "you have known ladies set up for wit that had none."—I quickly began to find that my wife was likely to gain but little at this business; so I resolved to treat him in a style of more severity myself. "Both wit and understanding," cried I, "are trifles without integrity; it is that which gives value to every character. The ignorant peasant without fault, is greater than the philosopher with many; for what is genius or courage without an heart? *An honest man is the noblest work of God.*"

"I always held that hackney'd maxim of Pope," returned Mr. Burchell, "as very unworthy a man of genius, and a base desertion of his own superiority. As the reputation of books is raised not by their freedom from defect, but the greatness of their beauties; so should that of men be prized, not for their exemption from fault, but the size of those virtues they are possessed of. The scholar may want prudence, the statesman may have pride, and the champion ferocity; but shall we prefer to these the low mechanic, who laboriously plods through life without censure or applause? We might as well prefer the tame correct paintings of the Flemish school to the erroneous, but sublime animations of the Roman pencil."

"Sir," replied I, "your present observation is just, when there are shining virtues and minute defects; but when it appears that great vices are opposed in the same mind to as extraordinary virtues, such a character deserves contempt."

"Perhaps," cried he, "there may be some such monsters as you describe, of great vices joined to great virtues; yet in my progress through life, I never yet found one instance of their existence: on the contrary, I have ever perceived, that where the mind was capacious, the affections were good. And indeed Providence seems kindly our friend in this particular, thus to debilitate the understanding where the heart is corrupt, and diminish the power, where there is the will to do mischief. This rule seems to extend even to other animals: the little vermin race are ever treacherous, cruel, and cowardly, whilst those endowed with strength and power are generous, brave, and gentle."

"These observations sound well," returned I, "and yet it would be easy this moment to point out a man," and I fixed my eye steadfastly upon him, "whose head and heart form a most detestable contrast. Ay, Sir," continued I, raising my voice, "and I am glad to have this opportunity of detecting him in the midst of his fancied security. Do you know this, Sir, this pocket-book?"— "Yes, Sir," returned he, with a face of impenetrable assurance, "that pocket-book is mine, and I am glad you have found it."—"And do you know," cried I, "this letter? Nay, never falter, man; but look me full in the face: I say, do you know this letter?"—"That letter,"— returned he, "yes, it was I that wrote that letter."— "And how could you," said I, "so basely, so ungratefully presume to write this letter?"—"And how came you," replied he, with looks of unparalleled effrontery, "so basely to presume to break open this letter? Don't you know, now, I could hang you all for this? All that I have to do is to swear at the next justice's, that you have been guilty of breaking open the lock of my pocket-book, and so hang you all up at his door." This piece of unexpected insolence raised me to such a pitch, that I could scarcely govern my passion. "Ungrateful wretch, begone, and no longer pollute my dwelling with thy baseness: begone, and never let me see thee again: go from my door, and the only punishment I wish thee is an alarmed conscience, which will be a sufficient tormentor!" So saying, I threw him his pocket-book, which he took up with a smile, and shutting the clasps with the utmost composure, left us, quite astonished at the serenity of his assurance. My wife was particularly enraged that nothing could make him angry, or make him seem ashamed of his villainies. "My dear," cried I, willing to calm those passions that had been raised too high among us, "we are not to be surprised that bad men want shame; they only blush at being detected in doing good, but glory in their vices.

"Guilt and Shame, says the allegory, were at first companions, and in the beginning of their journey inseparably kept together. But their union was soon found to be disagreeable and inconvenient to both; Guilt gave Shame frequent uneasiness, and Shame often betrayed the secret conspiracies of Guilt. After long disagreement, therefore, they at length consented to part for ever. Guilt boldly walked forward alone, to overtake Fate, that went before in the shape of an executioner: but Shame being naturally timorous, returned back to keep company with Virtue, which, in the beginning of their journey, they had left behind. Thus my children, after men have travelled through a few stages in vice, Shame forsakes them, and returns back to wait upon the few virtues they have still remaining."

16

The family use art, which is opposed with still greater.

WHATEVER might have been Sophia's sensations, the rest of the family was easily consoled for Mr. Burchell's absence by the company of our landlord, whose visits now became more frequent and longer. Though he had been disappointed in procuring my daughters the amusements of the town as he designed, he took every opportunity of supplying them with those little recreations which our retirement would admit of. He usually came in the morning, and while my son and I followed our occupations abroad, he sat with the family at home, and amused them by describing the town, with every part of which he was particularly acquainted. He could repeat all the observations that were retailed in the atmosphere of the play-houses, and had all the good things of the high wits by rote long before they made way into the jest-books. The intervals between conversation were employed in teaching my daughters piquet, or sometimes in setting my two little ones to box to make them *sharp*, as he called it: but the hopes of having him for a son-in-law, in some measure blinded us to all his imperfections. It must be owned that my wife laid a thousand schemes to entrap him; or, to speak it more tenderly, used every art to magnify the merit of her daughter. If the cakes at tea eat short and crisp, they were made by Olivia; if the gooseberry wine was well knit, the gooseberries were of her gathering; it was her fingers which gave the pickles their peculiar green; and in the composition of a pudding, it was her judgment that mixed the ingredients. Then the poor woman would sometimes tell the 'Squire, that she thought him and Olivia extremely of a size, and would bid both stand up to see which was tallest. These instances of cunning, which she thought impenetrable, yet

which every body saw through, were very pleasing to our
benefactor, who gave every day some new proofs of his
passion, which, though they had not arisen to proposals
of marriage, yet we thought fell but little short of it; and
his slowness was attributed sometimes to native bashfulness and sometimes to his fear of offending his uncle. An
occurrence, however, which happened soon after, put it
beyond a doubt that he designed to become one of our
family; my wife even regarded it as an absolute promise.

My wife and daughters happening to return a visit to
neighbour Flamborough's, found that family had lately
got their pictures drawn by a limner, who travelled the
country, and took likenesses for fifteen shillings a head.
As this family and ours had long a sort of rivalry in point
of taste, our spirit took the alarm at this stolen march
upon us, and notwithstanding all I could say, and I said
much, it was resolved that we should have our pictures
done too. Having, therefore, engaged the limner, for
what could I do? our next deliberation was to shew the
superiority of our taste in the attitudes. As for our neighbour's family, there were seven of them, and they were
drawn with seven oranges, a thing quite out of taste, no
variety in life, no composition in the world. We desired to
have something in a brighter style, and, after many
debates, at length came to an unanimous resolution of
being drawn together in one large historical family piece.
This would be cheaper, since one frame would serve for
all, and it would be infinitely more genteel; for all
families of any taste were now drawn in the same manner.
As we did not immediately recollect an historical subject
to hit us, we were contented each with being drawn as
independent historical figures. My wife desired to be
represented as Venus, and the painter was desired not to
be too frugal of his diamonds in her stomacher and hair.
Her two little ones were to be as Cupids by her side, while
I, in my gown and band, was to present her with my
books on the Whistonian controversy. Olivia would be
drawn as an Amazon, sitting upon a bank of flowers,

drest in a green joseph, richly laced with gold, and a whip
in her hand; Sophia was to be a shepherdess, with as
many sheep as the painter could put in for nothing; and
Moses was to be drest out with an hat and white feather.
Our taste so much pleased the 'Squire, that he insisted on
being put in as one of the family in the character of
Alexander the Great, at Olivia's feet. This was considered by us all as an indication of his desire to be introduced into the family, nor could we refuse his request.
The painter was therefore set to work, and as he wrought
with assiduity and expedition, in less than four days the
whole was completed. The piece was large, and it must
be owned he did not spare his colours; for which my wife
gave him great encomiums. We were all perfectly satisfied with his performance; but an unfortunate circumstance had not occurred till the picture was finished,
which now struck us with dismay. It was so very large
that we had no place in the house to fix it. How we all
came to disregard so material a point is inconceivable;
but certain it is, we had been all greatly overseen. The
picture, therefore, instead of gratifying our vanity, as we
hoped, leaned, in a most mortifying manner, against the
kitchen wall, where the canvas was stretched and painted,
much too large to be got through any of the doors, and
the jest of all our neighbours. One compared it to Robinson Crusoe's long-boat, too large to be removed; another
thought it more resembled a reel in a bottle; some
wondered how it could be got out, but still more were
amazed how it ever got in.

But though it excited the ridicule of some, it effectually raised more malicious suggestions in many. The
'Squire's portrait being found united with ours, was an
honour too great to escape envy. Scandalous whispers
began to circulate at our expence, and our tranquillity
was continually disturbed by persons who came as friends
to tell us what was said of us by enemies. These reports we
always resented with becoming spirit; but scandal ever
improves by opposition.

We once again therefore entered into a consultation upon obviating the malice of our enemies, and at last came to a resolution which had too much cunning to give me entire satisfaction. It was this: as our principal object was to discover the honour of Mr. Thornhill's addresses, my wife undertook to sound him, by pretending to ask his advice in the choice of a husband for her eldest daughter. If this was not found sufficient to induce him to a declaration, it was then resolved to terrify him with a rival. To this last step, however, I would by no means give my consent, till Olivia gave me the most solemn assurances that she would marry the person provided to rival him upon this occasion, if he did not prevent it, by taking her himself. Such was the scheme laid, which, though I did not strenuously oppose, I did not entirely approve.

The next time, therefore, that Mr. Thornhill came to see us, my girls took care to be out of the way, in order to give their mamma an opportunity of putting her scheme in execution; but they only retired to the next room, from whence they could overhear the whole conversation: my wife artfully introduced it, by observing, that one of the Miss Flamboroughs was like to have a very good match of it in Mr. Spanker. To this the 'Squire assenting, she proceeded to remark, that they who had warm fortunes were always sure of getting good husbands: "But heaven help," continued she, "the girls that have none. What signifies beauty, Mr. Thornhill? or what signifies all the virtue, and all the qualifications in the world, in this age of self-interest? It is not, what is she? but what has she? is all the cry."

"Madam," returned he, "I highly approve the justice, as well as the novelty of your remarks, and if I were a king, it should be otherwise. It should then, indeed, be fine times with the girls without fortunes: our too young ladies should be the first for whom I would provide."

"Ah, Sir," returned my wife, "you are pleased to be facetious: but I wish I were a queen, and then I know where my eldest daughter should look for an husband. But now, that you have put it into my head, seriously, Mr. Thornhill, can't you recommend me a proper husband for her? she is now nineteen years old, well grown and well educated, and in my humble opinion, does not want for parts."

"Madam," replied he, "if I were to choose, I would find out a person possessed of every accomplishment that can make an angel happy. One with prudence, fortune, taste, and sincerity; such, madam, would be, in my opinion, the proper husband." "Ay, Sir," said she, "but do you know of any such person?"—"No, madam," returned he, "it is impossible to know any person that deserves to be her husband: she's too great a treasure for one man's possession: she's a goddess. Upon my soul, I speak what I think, she's an angel."—"Ah, Mr. Thornhill, you only flatter my poor girl: but we have been thinking of marrying her to one of your tenants, whose mother is lately dead, and who wants a manager: you know whom I mean, farmer Williams; a warm man, Mr. Thornhill, able to give her good bread; and who has several times made her proposals:" (which was actually the case) "but, Sir," concluded she, "I should be glad to have your approbation of our choice."—"How, Madam," replied he, "my approbation! My approbation of such a choice! Never. What! Sacrifice so much beauty, and sense, and goodness, to a creature insensible of the blessing! Excuse me, I can never approve of such a piece of injustice! And I have my reasons"!—"Indeed, Sir," cried Deborah, "if you have your reasons, that's another affair; but I should be glad to know those reasons."—"Excuse me, Madam," returned he, "they lie too deep for discovery:" (laying his hand upon his bosom) "they remain buried, riveted here."

After he was gone, upon general consultation, we could not tell what to make of these fine sentiments. Olivia considered them as instances of the most exalted passion; but I was not quite so sanguine: it seemed to me pretty plain, that they had more of love than matrimony in them: yet whatever they might portend, it was resolved to prosecute the scheme of farmer Williams, who, from my daughter's first appearance in the country, had paid her his addresses.

17

Scarcely any virtue found to resist the power of long and pleasing temptation.

As I only studied my child's real happiness, the assiduity of Mr. Williams pleased me, as he was in easy circumstances, prudent, and sincere. It required but very little encouragement to revive his former passion; so that in an evening or two he and Mr. Thornhill met at our house, and surveyed each other for some time with looks of anger, but Williams owed his landlord no rent, and little regarded his indignation. Olivia, on her side, acted the coquet to perfection, if that might be called acting which was her real character, pretending to lavish all her tenderness on her new lover. Mr. Thornhill appeared quite dejected at this preference, and with a pensive air took leave, though I own it puzzled me to find him so much in pain as he appeared to be, when he had it in his power so easily to remove the cause, by declaring an honourable passion. But whatever uneasiness he seemed to endure, it could easily be perceived that Olivia's anguish was still greater. After any of these interviews between her lovers, of which there were several, she usually retired to solitude, and there indulged her grief. It was in such a situation I found her one evening, after she had been for some time supporting a fictitious gaiety. —"You now see, my child," said I, "that your confidence in Mr. Thornhill's passion was all a dream: he permits the rivalry of another, every way his inferior, though he knows it lies in his power to secure you to himself by a candid declaration."—"Yes, papa," returned she, "but he has his reasons for this delay: I know he has. The sincerity of his looks and words convinces me of his real esteem. A short time, I hope, will discover the generosity of his sentiments, and convince you that my opinion of him has been more just than yours."—

"Olivia, my darling," returned I, "every scheme that has been hitherto pursued to compel him to a declaration, has been proposed and planned by yourself, nor can you in the least say that I have constrained you. But you must not suppose, my dear, that I will ever be instrumental in suffering his honest rival to be the dupe of your ill-placed passion. Whatever time you require to bring your fancied admirer to an explanation shall be granted; but at the expiration of that term, if he is still regardless, I must absolutely insist that honest Mr. Williams shall be rewarded for his fidelity. The character which I have hitherto supported in life demands this from me, and my tenderness, as a parent, shall never influence my integrity as a man. Name then your day, let it be as distant as you think proper, and in the mean time take care to let Mr. Thornhill know the exact time on which I design delivering you up to another. If he really loves you, his own good sense will readily suggest that there is but one method alone to prevent his losing you for ever."—This proposal, which she could not avoid considering as perfectly just, was readily agreed to. She again renewed her most positive promise of marrying Mr. Williams, in case of the other's insensibility; and at the next opportunity, in Mr. Thornhill's presence, that day month was fixed upon for her nuptials with his rival.

Such vigorous proceedings seemed to redouble Mr. Thornhill's anxiety: but what Olivia really felt gave me some uneasiness. In this struggle between prudence and passion, her vivacity quite forsook her, and every opportunity of solitude was sought, and spent in tears. One week passed away; but Mr. Thornhill made no efforts to restrain her nuptials. The succeeding week he was still assiduous; but not more open. On the third he discontinued his visits entirely, and instead of my daughter testifying any impatience, as I expected, she seemed to retain a pensive tranquillity, which I looked upon as resignation. For my own part, I was now sincerely pleased with thinking that my child was going to be secured in a continuance of competence and peace, and frequently applauded her resolution, in preferring happiness to ostentation.

It was within about four days of her intended nuptials, that my little family at night were gathered round a charming fire, telling stories of the past, and laying schemes for the future. Busied in forming a thousand projects, and laughing at whatever folly came uppermost. "Well, Moses," cried I, "we shall soon, my boy, have a wedding in the family; what is your opinion of matters and things in general?"—"My opinion, father, is, that all things go on very well; and I was just now thinking, that when sister Livy is married to farmer Williams, we shall then have the loan of his cyder-press and brewing-tubs for nothing."—"That we shall, Moses," cried I, "and he will sing us 'Death and the Lady,' to raise our spirits, into the bargain."—"He has taught that song to our Dick," cried Moses, "and I think he goes through it very prettily." "Does he so?" cried I, "then let us have it: where's little Dick? let him up with it boldly."—"My brother Dick," cried Bill my youngest, "is just gone out with sister Livy: but Mr. Williams has taught me two songs, and I'll sing them for you, papa. Which song do you choose, *the Dying Swan*, or *the Elegy on the Death of a Mad Dog?*" "The elegy, child, by all means," said I; "I never heard that yet; and Deborah, my love, grief you know is dry, let us have a bottle of the best gooseberry wine, to keep up our spirits. I have wept so much at all sorts of elegies of late, that without an enlivening glass, I am sure this will overcome me; and Sophy, love, take your guitar, and thrum in with the boy a little."

AN ELEGY ON THE DEATH OF A MAD DOG

Good people all, of every sort,
   Give ear unto my song;
And if you find it wond'rous short,
   It cannot hold you long.

In Islington there was a man,
    Of whom the world might say,
That still a godly race he ran,
    Whene'er he went to pray.

A kind and gentle heart he had,
    To comfort friends and foes;
The naked every day he clad,
    When he put on his cloaths.

And in that town a dog was found,
    As many dogs there be,
Both mungrel, puppy, whelp, and hound,
    And curs of low degree.

This dog and man at first were friends;
    But when a pique began,
The dog, to gain some private ends,
    Went mad and bit the man.

Around from all the neighbouring streets,
    The wondering neighbours ran,
And swore the dog had lost his wits,
    To bite so good a man.

The wound it seem'd both sore and sad,
    To every christian eye;
And while they swore the dog was mad,
    They swore the man would die.

But soon a wonder came to light,
    That shew'd the rogues they lied,
The man recover'd of the bite,
    The dog it was that died.*

"A very good boy, Bill, upon my word, and an elegy that may truly be called tragical. Come, my children, here's Bill's health, and may he one day be a bishop."

"With all my heart," cried my wife; "and if he but preaches as well as he sings, I make no doubt of him. The

* Goldsmith had already inserted this *Elegy* in *The Bee*.

most of his family, by the mother's side, could sing a good song: it was a common saying in our country, that the family of the Blenkinsops could never look straight before them, nor the Hugginsons blow out a candle; that there were none of the Grograms but could sing a song, or of the Marjorams but could tell a story."—"However that be," cried I, "the most vulgar ballad of them all generally pleases me better than the fine modern odes, and things that petrify us in a single stanza; productions that we at once detest and praise. Put the glass to your brother, Moses. The great fault of these elegiasts is, that they are in despair for griefs that give the sensible part of mankind very little pain. A lady loses her muff, her fan, or her lap-dog, and so the silly poet runs home to versify the disaster."

"That may be the mode," cried Moses, "in sublimer compositions; but the Ranelagh songs that come down to us are perfectly familiar, and all cast in the same mould: Colin meets Dolly, and they hold a dialogue together; he gives her a fairing to put in her hair, and she presents him with a nosegay; and then they go together to church, where they give good advice to young nymphs and swains to get married as fast as they can."

"And very good advice too," cried I, "and I am told there is not a place in the world where advice can be given with so much propriety as there; for as it persuades us to marry, it also furnishes us with a wife; and surely that must be an excellent market my boy, where we are told what we want, and supplied with it when wanting."

"Yes, Sir," returned Moses, "and I know but of two such markets for wives in Europe, Ranelagh in England, and Fontarabia in Spain. The Spanish market is open once a year. But our English wives are saleable every night."

"You are right, my boy," cried his mother, "Old England is the only place in the world for husbands to get wives."—"And for wives to manage their husbands," interrupted I. "It is a proverb abroad, that if a bridge were built across the sea, all the ladies of the continent would come over to take pattern from ours; for there are no such wives in Europe as our own. But let us have one bottle more, Deborah, my life, and Moses give us a good song. What thanks do we not owe to heaven for thus bestowing tranquillity, health and competence? I think myself happier now than the greatest monarch upon earth. He has no such fire-side, nor such pleasant faces about it. Yes, Deborah, we are now growing old; but the evening of our life is likely to be happy. We are descended from ancestors that knew no stain, and we shall leave a good and virtuous race of children behind us. While we live they will be our support and our pleasure here, and when we die they will transmit our honour untainted to posterity. Come, my son, we wait for a song; let us have a chorus. But where is my darling Olivia? That little cherub's voice is always sweetest in the concert."—Just as I spoke Dick came running in, "O pappa, pappa, she is gone from us, she is gone from us, my sister Livy is gone from us for ever."—"Gone, child!" "Yes, she is gone off with two gentlemen in a post-chaise, and one of them kissed her, and said he would die for her: and she cried very much, and was for coming back; but he persuaded her again, and she went into the chaise, and said, "O what will my poor papa do when he knows I am undone!"'"—"Now then," cried I, "my children, go and be miserable; for we shall never enjoy one hour more. And O may heaven's everlasting fury light upon him and his! Thus to rob me of my child! And sure it will, for taking back my sweet innocent that I was leading up to heaven. Such sincerity as my child was possessed of! But all our earthly happiness is now over! Go, my children, go and be miserable and infamous; for my heart is broken within me!"—"Father," cried my son, "is this your fortitude?" "Fortitude, child! Yes, he shall see I have fortitude! Bring me my pistols. I'll pursue the traitor. While he is on earth I'll pursue him. Old as I am, he shall find I can sting him yet. The villain! The perfidious villain!" I had by this time reached down my pistols, when my poor wife, whose passions were not so strong as mine, caught me in her arms. "My dearest, dearest husband," cried she, "the Bible is the only weapon that is fit for your old hands now. Open that, my love, and read our anguish into patience, for she has vilely deceived us." "Indeed, Sir," resumed my son, after a pause, "your rage is too violent and unbecoming. You should be my mother's comforter, and you encrease her pain. It ill suited you and your reverend character, thus to curse your greatest enemy: you should not have curst him, villain as he is."—"I did not curse him, child, did I?"—"Indeed, Sir, you did; you curst him twice."—"Then may heaven forgive me and him if I did. And now, my son, I see it was more than human benevolence that first taught us to bless our enemies! Blest be his holy name for all the good he hath given, and for all that he hath taken away. But it is not, it is not, a small distress that can wring tears from these old eyes, that have not wept for so many years. My child!—To undo my darling! May confusion seize!—Heaven forgive me, what am I about to say! You may remember, my love, how good she was, and how charming; till this vile moment all her care was to make us happy. Had she but died! But she is gone, the honour of our family contaminated, and I must look out for happiness in other worlds than here. But my child, you saw them go off: perhaps he forced her away? If he forced her, she may yet be innocent."—"Ah, no, Sir," cried the child; "he only kissed her, and called her his angel, and she wept very much, and leaned upon his arm, and they drove off very fast."—"She's an ungrateful creature," cried my wife, who could scarce speak for weeping, "to use us thus. She never had the least constraint put upon her affections. The vile strumpet has basely deserted her parents without any provocation, thus to bring your grey hairs to the grave, and I must shortly follow."

In this manner that night, the first of our real

misfortunes, was spent in the bitterness of complaint, and ill-supported sallies of enthusiasm. I determined, however, to find out our betrayer, wherever he was, and reproach his baseness. The next morning we missed our wretched child at breakfast, where she used to give life and cheerfulness to us all. My wife, as before, attempted to ease her heart by reproaches. "Never," cried she, "shall that vilest stain of our family again darken these harmless doors. I will never call her daughter more. No, let the strumpet live with her vile seducer: she may bring us to shame, but she shall never more deceive us."

"Wife," said I, "do not talk thus hardly: my detestation of her guilt is as great as yours; but ever shall this house and this heart be open to a poor returning repentant sinner. The sooner she returns from her transgression, the more welcome shall she be to me. For the first time the very best may err; art may persuade, and novelty spread out its charm. The first fault is the child of simplicity; but every other the offspring of guilt. Yes, the wretched creature shall be welcome to this heart and this house, though stained with ten thousand vices. I will again hearken to the music of her voice, again will I hang fondly on her bosom, if I find but repentance there. My son, bring hither my Bible and my staff; I will pursue her, wherever she is, and though I cannot save her from shame, I may prevent the continuance of iniquity."

18

The pursuit of a father to reclaim a lost child to virtue.

THOUGH the child could not describe the gentleman's person who handed his sister into the post-chaise, yet my suspicions fell entirely upon our young landlord, whose character for such intrigues was but too well known. I therefore directed my steps towards Thornhill-castle, resolving to upbraid him, and, if possible, to bring back my daughter: but before I had reached his seat, I was met by one of my parishioners, who said he saw a young lady resembling my daughter, in a post-chaise with a gentleman whom, by the description, I could only guess to be Mr. Burchell, and that they drove very fast. This information, however, did by no means satisfy me. I therefore went to the young 'Squire's, and though it was yet early, insisted upon seeing him immediately; he soon appeared with the most open familiar air, and seemed perfectly amazed at my daughter's elopement, protesting upon his honour that he was quite a stranger to it. I now therefore condemned my former suspicions, and could turn them only on Mr. Burchell, who I recollected had of late several private conferences with her: but the appearance of another witness left me no room to doubt his villainy, who averred, that he and my daughter were actually gone towards the Wells, about thirty miles off, where there was a great deal of company. Being driven to that state of mind in which we are more ready to act precipitately than to reason right, I never debated with myself, whether these accounts might not have been given by persons purposely placed in my way to mislead me, but resolved to pursue my daughter and her fancied deluder thither. I walked along with earnestness, and inquired of several by the way; but received no accounts,

till entering the town, I was met by a person on horseback, whom I remembered to have seen at the 'Squire's,
and he assured me, that if I followed them to the races,
which were but thirty miles farther, I might depend upon
overtaking them; for he had seen them dance there the
night before, and the whole assembly seemed charmed
with my daughter's performance. Early the next day I
walked forward to the races, and about four in the afternoon I came upon the course. The company made a very
brilliant appearance, all earnestly employed in one pursuit, that of pleasure; how different from mine, that of
reclaiming a lost child to virtue! I thought I perceived
Mr. Burchell at some distance from me; but, as if he
dreaded an interview, upon my approaching him, he
mixed among a crowd, and I saw him no more. I now
reflected that it would be to no purpose to continue my
pursuit farther, and resolved to return home to an
innocent family, who wanted my assistance. But the
agitations of my mind, and the fatigues I had undergone,
threw me into a fever, the symptoms of which I perceived
before I came off the course. This was another unexpected
stroke, as I was more than seventy miles distant from
home: however, I retired to a little ale-house by the
roadside, and in this place, the usual retreat of indigence
and frugality, I laid me down patiently to wait the issue
of my disorder. I languished here for near three weeks;
but at last my constitution prevailed, though I was
unprovided with money to defray the expences of my
entertainment. It is possible the anxiety from this last
circumstance alone might have brought on a relapse, had
I not been supplied by a traveller, who stopt to take a
cursory refreshment. This person was no other than the
philanthropic bookseller in St. Paul's church-yard, who
has written so many little books for children: he called
himself their friend; but he was the friend of all mankind.
He was no sooner alighted, but he was in haste to be
gone; for he was ever on business of the utmost importance, and was at that time actually compiling materials

for the history of one Mr. Thomas Trip. I immediately recollected this good-natured man's red pimpled face; for he had published for me against the Deuterogamists of the age, and from him I had borrowed a few pieces, to be paid at my return. Leaving the inn, therefore, as I was yet but weak, I resolved to return home by easy journies of ten miles a day. My health and usual tranquillity were almost restored, and I now condemned that pride which had made me refractory to the hand of correction. Man little knows what calamities are beyond his patience to bear till he tries them; as in ascending the heights of ambition, which look bright from below, every step we rise shews us some new and gloomy prospect of hidden disappointment; so in our descent from the summits of pleasure, though the vale of misery below may appear at first dark and gloomy, yet the busy mind, still attentive to its own amusement, finds as we descend something to flatter and to please. Still, as we approach, the darkest objects appear to brighten, and the mental eye becomes adapted to its gloomy situation.

I now proceeded forwards, and had walked about two hours, when I perceived what appeared at a distance like a waggon, which I was resolved to overtake; but when I came up with it, found it to be a strolling company's cart, that was carrying their scenes and other theatrical furniture to the next village, where they were to exhibit. The cart was attended only by the person who drove it, and one of the company, as the rest of the players were to follow the ensuing day. Good company upon the road, says the proverb, is the shortest cut, I therefore entered into conversation with the poor player; and as I once had some theatrical powers myself, I disserted on such topics with my usual freedom: but as I was pretty much unacquainted with the present state of the stage, I demanded who were the present theatrical writers in vogue, who the Drydens and Otways of the day.—— "I fancy, Sir," cried the player, "few of our modern dramatists would think themselves much honoured by being compared to the writers you mention. Dryden and Rowe's manner, Sir, are quite out of fashion; our taste has gone back a whole century; Fletcher, Ben Jonson, and all the plays of Shakespear are the only things that go down."—"How," cried I, "is it possible the present age can be pleased with that antiquated dialect, that obsolete humour, those over-charged characters, which abound in the works you mention?"—"Sir," returned my companion, "the public think nothing about dialect, or humour, or character: for that is none of their business, they only go to be amused, and find themselves happy when they can enjoy a pantomime, under the sanction of Jonson's or Shakespear's name."—"So then, I suppose," cried I, "that our modern dramatists are rather imitators of Shakespear than of nature."—"To say the truth," returned my companion, "I don't know that they imitate any thing at all; nor indeed does the public require it of them: it is not the composition of the piece, but the number of starts and attitudes, that may be introduced into it, that elicits applause. I have known a piece, with not one jest in the whole, shrugged into popularity, and another saved by the poet's throwing in a fit of the gripes. No, Sir, the works of Congreve and Farquhar have too much wit in them for the present taste; our modern dialect is much more natural."

By this time the equipage of the strolling company was arrived at the village, which, it seems, had been apprized of our approach, and was come out to gaze at us: for my companion observed, that strollers always have more spectators without doors than within. I did not consider the impropriety of my being in such company, till I saw a mob gather about me. I therefore took shelter, as fast as possible, in the first ale-house that offered, and being shewn into the common room, was accosted by a very well-drest gentleman, who demanded whether I was the real chaplain of the company, or whether it was only to be my masquerade character in the play. Upon informing him of the truth, and that I did not belong in any sort to the company, he was condescending enough to desire me and the player to partake in a bowl of punch, over which he discussed modern politics with great earnestness and interest. I set him down in my own mind for nothing less than a parliament-man at least; but was almost confirmed in my conjectures, when upon asking what there was in the house for supper, he insisted that the player and I should sup with him at his house, with which request, after some entreaties, we were prevailed on to comply.

19

*The description of a person discontented with the present
government, and apprehensive of the loss of our liberties.*

THE house where we were to be entertained lying at a
small distance from the village, our inviter observed, that
as the coach was not ready, he would conduct us on foot
and we soon arrived at one of the most magnificent
mansions I had seen in that part of the country. The
apartment into which we were shewn was perfectly
elegant and modern; he went to give orders for supper,
while the player, with a wink, observed that we were
perfectly in luck. Our entertainer soon returned, an
elegant supper was brought in, two or three ladies, in an
easy dishabille, were introduced, and the conversation
began with some sprightliness. Politics, however, were
the subject on which our entertainer chiefly expatiated :
for he asserted that liberty was at once his boast and his
terror. After the cloth was removed, he asked me if I had
seen the last Monitor, to which replying in the negative,
"What, nor the Auditor, I suppose?" cried he. "Neither,
Sir," returned I. "That's strange, very strange," replied
my entertainer. "Now I read all the politics that come
out. The Daily, the Public Ledger, the Chronicle, the
London Evening, the Whitehall Evening Post, the seventeen magazines and the two reviews; and though they
hate each other, I love them all. Liberty, Sir, liberty is the
Briton's boast, and by all my coal mines in Cornwall, I
reverence its guardians." "Then it is to be hoped," cried
I, "you reverence the king." "Yes," returned my
entertainer, "when he does what we would have him;
but if he goes on as he has done of late, I'll never trouble
myself more with his matters. I say nothing. I think only.
I could have directed some things better. I don't think
there has been a sufficient number of advisers : he should

advise with every person willing to give him advice, and then we should have things done in anotherguess manner."

"I wish," cried I, "that such intruding advisers were fixed in the pillory. It should be the duty of honest men to assist the weaker side of our Constitution, that sacred power that has for some years been every day declining, and losing its due share of influence in the State. But these ignorants still continue the cry of liberty, and if they have any weight, basely throw it into the subsiding scale."

"How," cried one of the ladies; "do I live to see one so base, so sordid, as to be an enemy to liberty, and a defender of tyrants? Liberty, that sacred gift of heaven, that glorious privilege of Britons!"

"Can it be possible," cried our entertainer, "that there should be any found at present advocates for slavery? Any who are for meanly giving up the privileges of Britons? Can any, Sir, be so abject?"

"No, Sir," replied I, "I am for liberty, that attribute of Gods! Glorious liberty! that theme of modern declamation. I would have all men kings. I would be a king myself. We have all naturally an equal right to the throne: we are all originally equal. This is my opinion, and was once the opinion of a set of honest men who were called Levellers. They tried to erect themselves into a community, where all should be equally free. But, alas! it would never answer; for there were some among them stronger, and some more cunning than others, and these became masters of the rest; for as sure as your groom rides your horses, because he is a cunninger animal than they, so surely will the animal that is cunninger or stronger than he, sit upon his shoulders in turn. Since then it is entailed upon humanity to submit, and some are born to command, and others to obey, the question is, as there must be tyrants, whether it is better to have them in the same house with us, or in the same village, or still farther off, in the metropolis. Now, Sir, for my own part, as I naturally hate the face of a tyrant, the farther off he

Can any, Sir, be so abject?

is removed from me, the better pleased am I. The generality of mankind also are of my way of thinking, and have unanimously created one king, whose election at once diminishes the number of tyrants, and puts tyranny at the greatest distance from the greatest number of people. Now the great who were tyrants themselves before the election of one tyrant, are naturally averse to a power raised over them, and whose weight must ever lean heaviest on the subordinate orders. It is the interest of the great, therefore, to diminish kingly power as much as possible; because whatever they take from that is naturally restored to themselves; and all they have to do in the state is to undermine the single tyrant, by which they resume their primaeval authority. Now the state may be so circumstanced, or its laws may be so disposed, or its men of opulence so minded, as all to conspire in carrying on this business of undermining monarchy. For, in the first place, if the circumstances of our state be such, as to favour the accumulation of wealth, and make the opulent still more rich, this will increase their ambition. An accumulation of wealth, however, must necessarily be the consequence, when, as at present, more riches flow in from external commerce than arise from internal industry; for external commerce can only be managed to advantage by the rich, and they have also at the same time all the emoluments arising from internal industry; so that the rich, with us, have two sources of wealth, whereas the poor have but one. For this reason, wealth, in all commercial states, is found to accumulate, and all such have hitherto in time become aristocratical. Again, the very laws also of this country may contribute to the accumulation of wealth; as when by their means the natural ties that bind the rich and poor together are broken, and it is ordained, that the rich shall only marry with the rich; or when the learned are held unqualified to serve their country as councillors merely from a defect of opulence, and wealth is thus made the object of a wise man's ambition; by these means, I say, and such means as these, riches will accumulate. Now the possessor of accumulated wealth, when furnished with the necessaries and pleasures of life, has no other method to employ the superfluity of his fortune but in purchasing power. That is, differently speaking, in making dependants, by purchasing the liberty of the needy or the venal, of men who are willing to bear the mortification of contiguous tyranny for bread. Thus each very opulent man generally gathers round him a circle of the poorest of the people; and the polity abounding in accumulated wealth, may be compared to a Cartesian system, each orb with a vortex of its own. Those, however, who are willing to move in a great man's vortex are only such as must be slaves, the rabble of mankind, whose souls and whose education are adapted to servitude, and who know nothing of liberty except the name. But there must still be a large number of the people without the sphere of the opulent man's influence, namely, that order of men which subsists between the very rich and the very rabble; those men who are possest of too large fortunes to submit to the neighbouring man in power, and yet are too poor to set up for tyranny themselves. In this middle order of mankind are generally to be found all the arts, wisdom, and virtues of society. This order alone is known to be the true preserver of freedom, and may be called the People. Now it may happen that this middle order of mankind may lose all its influence in a state, and its voice be in a manner drowned in that of the rabble: for if the fortune sufficient for qualifying a person at present to give his voice in state affairs be ten times less than was judged sufficient upon forming the constitution, it is evident that great numbers of the rabble will thus be introduced into the political system, and they, ever moving in the vortex of the great, will follow where greatness shall direct. In such a state, therefore, all that the middle order has left, is to preserve the prerogative and privileges of the one principal governor with the most sacred circumspection. For he divides the power of the rich, and calls off the great from falling with tenfold weight on the middle order placed beneath them. The middle order may be compared to a town of which the opulent are forming the siege, and which the governor from without is hastening the relief. While the besiegers are in dread of an enemy over them, it is but natural to offer the townsmen the most specious terms; to flatter them with sounds, and amuse them with privileges; but if they once defeat the governor from behind, the walls of the town will be but a small defence to its inhabitants. What they may then expect, may be seen by turning our eyes to Holland, Genoa, or Venice, where the laws govern the poor, and the rich govern the law. I am then for, and would die for, monarchy, sacred monarchy; for if there be any thing sacred amongst men, it must be the anointed Sovereign of his people, and every diminution of his power in war, or in peace, is an infringement upon the real liberties of the subject. The sounds of liberty, patriotism, and Britons have already done *much*, it is to be hoped that the true sons of freedom will prevent their ever doing *more*. I have known many of those pretended champions for liberty in my time, yet do I not remember one that was not in his heart and in his family a tyrant."

My warmth I found had lengthened this harangue beyond the rules of good breeding: but the impatience of my entertainer, who often strove to interrupt it, could be restrained no longer. "What," cried he, "then I have been all this while entertaining a Jesuit in parson's cloaths; but by all the coal mines of Cornwall, out he shall pack, if my name be Wilkinson." I now found I had gone too far, and asked pardon for the warmth with which I had spoken. "Pardon," returned he in a fury: "I think such principles demand ten thousand pardons. What, give up liberty, property, and, as the Gazetteer says, lie down to be saddled with wooden shoes! Sir, I insist upon your marching out of this house immediately, to prevent worse consequences; Sir, I insist upon it." I was going to repeat my remonstrances; but just then we heard a footman's rap at the door, and the two ladies cried out, "As sure as death there is our master and mistress come home." It seems my entertainer was all this while only the butler, who in his master's absence, had a mind to cut a figure, and be for a while the gentleman himself; and, to say the truth, he talked politics as well as most country gentlemen do. But nothing could now exceed my confusion upon seeing the gentleman and his lady enter, nor was their surprise at finding such company and good chear, less than ours. "Gentlemen," cried the real master of the house to me and my companion, "my wife and I are your most humble servants; but I protest this is so unexpected a favour, that we almost sink under the obligation." However unexpected our company might be to them, theirs, I am sure, was still more so to us, and I was struck dumb with the apprehensions of my own absurdity, when whom should I next see enter the room but my dear Miss Arabella Wilmot, who was formally designed to be married to my son George; but whose match was broken off as already related. As soon as she saw me, she flew to my arms with the utmost joy.—"My dear sir," cried she, "to what happy accident is it that we owe so unexpected a visit? I am sure my uncle and aunt will be in raptures when they find they have the good Dr. Primrose for their guest." Upon hearing my name, the old gentleman and lady very politely stept up, and welcomed me with most cordial hospitality. Nor could they forbear smiling upon being informed of the nature of my present visit: but the unfortunate butler, whom they at first seemed disposed to turn away, was at my intercession forgiven.

Mr. Arnold and his lady, to whom the house belonged, now insisted upon having the pleasure of my stay for some days, and as their niece, my charming pupil, whose mind, in some measure, had been formed under my own instructions, joined in their entreaties, I complied. That night I was shewn to a magnificent chamber, and the next morning early Miss Wilmot desired to walk with me in the garden, which was decorated in the modern manner. After some time spent in pointing out the beauties of the place, she enquired with seeming unconcern, when last I had heard from my son George. "Alas! Madam," cried I, "he has now been near three years absent, without ever writing to his friends or me. Where he is I know not; perhaps I shall never see him or happiness more. No, my dear Madam, we shall never more see such pleasing hours as were once spent by our fire-side at Wakefield. My little family are now dispersing very fast, and poverty has brought not only want, but infamy upon us." The good-natured girl let fall a tear at this account; but as I saw her possessed of too much sensibility, I forebore a more minute detail of our sufferings. It was, however, some consolation to me to find that time had made no alteration in her affections, and that she had rejected several matches that had been made her since our leaving her part of the country. She led me round all the extensive improvements of the place, pointing to the several walks and arbours, and at the same time catching from every object a hint for some new question relative to my son.

In this manner we spent the forenoon, till the bell summoned us in to dinner, where we found the manager of the strolling company that I mentioned before, who was come to dispose of tickets for the *Fair Penitent*, which was to be acted that evening, the part of Horatio by a young gentleman who had never appeared on any stage. He seemed to be very warm in the praises of the new performer, and averred that he never saw any who bid so fair for excellence. Acting, he observed, was not learned in a day; "But this gentleman," continued he, "seems born to tread the stage. His voice, his figure, and attitudes are all admirable. We caught him up accidentally in our journey down." This account, in some measure, excited our curiosity, and, at the entreaty of the ladies, I was prevailed upon to accompany them to the play-house, which was no other than a barn. As the company with which I went was incontestably the chief of the place, we were received with the greatest respect, and placed in the front seat of the theatre; where we sate for some time with no small impatience to see Horatio make his appearance. The new performer advanced at last, and let parents think of my sensations by their own, when I found it was my unfortunate son. He was going to begin, when turning his eyes upon the audience, he perceived Miss Wilmot and me, and stood at once speechless and immoveable. The actors behind the scene, who ascribed this pause to his natural timidity, attempted to encourage him; but instead of going on, he burst into a flood of tears, and retired off the stage. I don't know what were my feelings on this occasion; for they succeeded with too much rapidity for description; but I was soon awaked from this disagreeable reverie by Miss Wilmot, who pale and with a trembling voice desired me to conduct her back to her uncle's. When got home, Mr. Arnold, who was as yet a stranger to our extraordinary behaviour, being informed that the new performer was my son, sent his coach, and an invitation, for him; and as he persisted in his refusal to appear again upon the stage, the players put another in his place, and we soon had him with us. Mr. Arnold gave him the kindest reception, and I received him with my usual transport; for I could never counterfeit false resentment. Miss Wilmot's reception was mixed with seeming neglect, and yet I could perceive she acted a studied part. The tumult in her mind seemed not yet abated: she said twenty giddy things that looked like joy, and then laughed loud at her own want of meaning. At intervals she would take a sly peep at the glass, as if happy in the consciousness of unresisted beauty, and often would ask questions without giving any manner of attention to the answers.

20

*The history of a philosophic vagabond, pursuing novelty, but
losing content.*

AFTER we had supped, Mrs. Arnold politely offered to
send a couple of her footmen for my son's baggage, which
he at first seemed to decline; but upon her pressing the
request, he was obliged to inform her, that a stick and a
wallet were all the moveable things upon this earth that
he could boast of. "Why, ay, my son," cried I, "you left
me but poor, and poor I find you are come back; and yet
I make no doubt you have seen a great deal of the world."
—"Yes, Sir," replied my son, "but travelling after fortune is not the way to secure her; and indeed, of late I
have desisted from the pursuit."—"I fancy, Sir," cried
Mrs. Arnold, "that the account of your adventures would
be amusing: the first part of them I have often heard
from my niece; but could the company prevail for the
rest, it would be an additional obligation."—"Madam,"
replied my son, "I promise you the pleasure you have in
hearing, will not be half so great as my vanity in repeating them; and yet in the whole narrative I can scarce
promise you one adventure, as my account is rather of
what I saw than what I did. The first misfortune of my
life, which you all know, was great; but though it distressed, it could not sink me. No person ever had a better
knack at hoping than I. The less kind I found fortune at
one time, the more I expected from her another, and
being now at the bottom of her wheel, every new revolu-
tion might lift, but could not depress me. I proceeded,
therefore, towards London in a fine morning, no way
uneasy about to-morrow, but cheerful as the birds that
carolled by the road, and comforted myself with reflect-
ing, that London was the mart where abilities of every
kind were sure of meeting distinction and reward.

"Upon my arrival in town, Sir, my first care was to deliver your letter of recommendation to our cousin, who was himself in little better circumstances than I. My first scheme, you know, Sir, was to be usher at an academy, and I asked his advice on the affair. Our cousin received the proposal with a true sardonic grin. Ay, cried he, this is indeed a very pretty career, that has been chalked out for you. I have been an usher at a boarding school myself; and may I die by an anodyne necklace, but I had rather be an under-turnkey in Newgate. I was up early and late: I was brow-beat by the master, hated for my ugly face by the mistress, worried by the boys within, and never permitted to stir out to meet civility abroad. But are you sure you are fit for a school? Let me examine you a little. Have you been bred apprentice to the business? No. Then you won't do for a school. Can you dress the boy's hair? No. Then you won't do for a school. Have you had the small-pox? No. Then you won't do for a school. Can you lie three in a bed? No. Then you will never do for a school. Have you got a good stomach? Yes. Then you will by no means do for a school. No, Sir, if you are for a genteel, easy profession, bind yourself seven years as an apprentice to turn a cutler's wheel; but avoid a school by any means. Yet come, continued he, I see you are a lad of spirit and some learning, what do you think of commencing author, like me? You have read in books, no doubt, of men of genius starving at the trade: At present I'll shew you forty very dull fellows about town that live by it in opulence. All honest jogg-trot men, who go on smoothly and dully, and write history and politics, and are praised: men, Sir, who, had they been bred cobblers, would all their lives have only mended shoes, but never made them.

"Finding that there was no great degree of gentility affixed to the character of an usher, I resolved to accept his proposal; and having the highest respect for literature, hailed the *antiqua Mater* of Grub-street with reverence. I thought it my glory to pursue a track which Dryden and Otway trod before me. I considered the goddess of this

128

region as the parent of excellence; and however an intercourse with the world might give us good sense, the poverty she granted I supposed to be the nurse of genius! Big with these reflections, I sate down, and finding that the best things remained to be said on the wrong side, I resolved to write a book that should be wholly new. I therefore drest up some paradoxes with ingenuity. They were false, indeed, but they were new. The jewels of truth have been so often imported by others, that nothing was left for me to import but some splendid things that, at a distance, looked every bit as well. Witness, you powers, what fancied importance sate perched upon my quill while I was writing. The whole learned world, I made no doubt, would rise to oppose my systems; but then I was prepared to oppose the whole learned world. Like the porcupine I sate self-collected, with a quill pointed against every opposer."

"Well said, my boy," cried I, "and what subject did you treat upon? I hope you did not pass over the importance of monogamy. But I interrupt, go on; you published your paradoxes; well, and what did the learned world say to your paradoxes?"

"Sir," replied my son, "the learned world said nothing to my paradoxes; nothing at all, Sir. Every man of them was employed in praising his friends and himself, or condemning his enemies; and unfortunately, as I had neither, I suffered the cruellest mortification, neglect.

"As I was meditating one day in a coffee-house on the fate of my paradoxes, a little man happening to enter the room, placed himself in the box before me, and after some preliminary discourse, finding me to be a scholar, drew out a bundle of proposals, begging me to subscribe to a new edition he was going to give to the world of Propertius, with notes. This demand necessarily produced a reply that I had no money; and that concession led him to inquire into the nature of my expectations. Finding that my expectations were just as great as my purse, I see, cried he, you are unacquainted with the town, I'll teach you a part of it. Look at these proposals; upon these very proposals I have subsisted very comfortably for twelve years. The moment a noble man returns from his travels, a Creolian arrives from Jamaica, or dowager from her country seat, I strike for a subscription. I first besiege their hearts with flattery, and then pour in my proposals at the breach. If they subscribe readily the first time, I renew my request to beg a dedication fee. If they let me have that, I smite them once more for engraving their coat of arms at the top. Thus, continued he, I live by vanity, and laugh at it. But between ourselves, I am now too well known. I should be glad to borrow your face a bit: a nobleman of distinction has just returned from Italy; my face is familiar to his porter; but if you bring this copy of verses, my life for it you succeed, and we divide the spoil."

"Bless us, George," cried I, "and is this the employment of poets now! Do men of their exalted talents thus stoop to beggary? Can they so far disgrace their calling, as to make a vile traffic of praise for bread?"

"O no, Sir," returned he, "a true poet can never be so base; for wherever there is genius there is pride. The creatures I now describe are only beggars in rhyme. The real poet, as he braves every hardship for fame, so he is equally a coward to contempt, and none but those who are unworthy protection condescend to solicit it.

"Having a mind too proud to stoop to such indignities, and yet a fortune too humble to hazard a second attempt for fame, I was now obliged to take a middle course, and write for bread. But I was unqualified for a profession where mere industry alone was to ensure success. I could not suppress my lurking passion for applause; but usually consumed that time in efforts after excellence which takes up but little room, when it should have been more advantageously employed in the diffusive productions of fruitful mediocrity. My little piece would therefore come forth in the midst of periodical publications, unnoticed and unknown. The public were more importantly employed, than to observe the easy simplicity of my style, or the harmony of my periods. Sheet after sheet was thrown off to oblivion. My essays were buried among the essays upon liberty, eastern tales, and cures for the bite of a mad dog; while Philautos, Philalethes, Philelutheros, and Philanthropos all wrote better, because they wrote faster, than I.

"Now, therefore, I began to associate with none but disappointed authors, like myself, who praised, deplored, and despised each other. The satisfaction we found in every celebrated writer's attempts, was inversely as their merits. I found that no genius in another could please me. My unfortunate paradoxes had entirely dried up that source of comfort. I could neither read nor write with satisfaction; for excellence in another was my aversion, and writing was my trade.

"In the midst of these gloomy reflections, as I was one day sitting on a bench in St. James's park, a young gentleman of distinction, who had been my intimate acquaintance at the university, approached me. We saluted each other with some hesitation, he almost ashamed of being known to one who made so shabby an appearance, and I afraid of a repulse. But my suspicions soon vanished; for Ned Thornhill was at the bottom a very good-natured fellow."

"What did you say, George?" interrupted I.— "Thornhill, was not that his name? It can certainly be no other than my landlord."—"Bless me," cried Mrs. Arnold, "is Mr. Thornhill so near a neighbour of yours? He has long been a friend in our family, and we expect a visit from him shortly."

"My friend's first care," continued my son, "was to alter my appearance by a very fine suit of his own clothes, and then I was admitted to his table, upon the footing of half-friend, half-underling. My business was to attend him at auctions, to put him in spirits when he sate for his picture, to take the left hand in his chariot when not filled by another, and to assist at tattering a kip, as the phrase was, when we had a mind for a frolic. Besides this, I had twenty other little employments in the family. I was to do many small things without bidding; to carry the cork-screw; to stand god father to all the butler's children; to sing when I was bid; to be never out of humour; always to be humble, and, if I could, to be very happy.

"In this honourable post, however, I was not without a rival. A captain of marines, who was formed for the place by nature, opposed me in my patron's affections. His mother had been laundress to a man of quality, and thus he early acquired a taste for pimping and pedigree. As this gentleman made it the study of his life to be acquainted with lords, though he was dismissed from several for his stupidity; yet he found many of them who were as dull as himself that permitted his assiduities. As flattery was his trade, he practised it with the easiest address imaginable: but it came awkward and stiff from me; and as every day my patron's desire of flattery increased, so every hour being better acquainted with his defects, I became more unwilling to give it. Thus I was once more fairly going to give up the field to the captain, when my friend found occasion for my assistance. This was nothing less than to fight a duel for him, with a gentleman whose sister it was pretended he had used ill. I readily complied with his request, and though I see you are displeased at my conduct, yet as it was a debt indispensably due to friendship, I could not refuse. I undertook the affair, disarmed my antagonist, and soon after had the pleasure of finding that the lady was only a woman of the town, and the fellow her bully and a sharper. This piece of service was repaid with the warmest professions of gratitude; but as my friend was to leave town in a few days he knew no other method of serving me, but by recommending me to his uncle Sir William Thornhill, and another nobleman of great distinction who enjoyed a post under the government. When he was gone, my first care was to carry his recom-

mendatory letter to his uncle, a man whose character for
every virtue was universal, yet just. I was received by his
servants with the most hospitable smiles; for the looks of
the domestics ever transmit their master's benevolence.
Being shewn into a grand apartment, where Sir William
soon came to me, I delivered my message and letter,
which he read, and after pausing some minutes, Pray,
Sir, cried he, inform me what you have done for my
kinsman to deserve this warm recommendation? But I
suppose, Sir, I guess your merits, you have fought for
him; and so you would expect a reward from me for
being the instrument of his vices. I wish, sincerely wish,
that my present refusal may be some punishment for your
guilt; but still more, that it may be some inducement to
your repentance.—The severity of this rebuke I bore
patiently, because I knew it was just. My whole expectations now, therefore, lay in my letter to the great man.
As the doors of the nobility are almost ever beset with
beggars, all ready to thrust in some sly petition, I found
it no easy matter to gain admittance. However, after
bribing the servants with half my worldly fortune, I was
at last shewn into a spacious apartment, my letter being
previously sent up for his lordship's inspection. During
this anxious interval I had full time to look round me.
Every thing was grand, and of happy contrivance: the
paintings, the furniture, the gildings petrified me with
awe, and raised my idea of the owner. Ah, thought I to
myself, how very great must the possessor of all these
things be, who carries in his head the business of the
state, and whose house displays half the wealth of a kingdom: sure his genius must be unfathomable! During
these awful reflections, I heard a step come heavily
forward. Ah, this is the great man himself! No, it was
only a chambermaid. Another foot was heard soon after.
This must be He! No, it was only the great man's valet de
chambre. At last his lordship actually made his appearance. Are you, cried he, the bearer of this here letter? I
answered with a bow. I learn by this, continued he, as

how that—But just at that instant a servant delivered him a card, and without taking farther notice, he went out of the room, and left me to digest my own happiness at leisure. I saw no more of him, till told by a footman that his lordship was going to his coach at the door. Down I immediately followed, and joined my voice to that of three or four more, who came like me, to petition for favours. His lordship, however, went too fast for us, and was gaining his chariot door with large strides, when I hallooed out to know if I was to have any reply. He was by this time got in, and muttered an answer, half of which I only heard, the other half was lost in the rattling of his chariot wheels. I stood for some time with my neck stretched out, in the posture of one that was listening to catch the glorious sounds, till looking round me, I found myself alone at his lordship's gate.

"My patience," continued my son, "was now quite exhausted: stung with the thousand indignities I had met with, I was willing to cast myself away, and only wanted the gulph to receive me. I regarded myself as one of those vile beings that nature designed should be thrown by into her lumber room, there to perish in obscurity. I had still however, half a guinea left, and of that I thought nature herself should not deprive me; but in order to be sure of this, I was resolved to go instantly and spend it while I had it, and then trust to occurrences for the rest. As I was going along with this resolution, it happened that Mr. Crispe's office seemed invitingly open to give me a welcome reception. In this office Mr. Crispe kindly offers all his majesty's subjects a generous promise of £30 a year, for which promise all they give in return is their liberty for life, and permission to let him transport them to America as slaves. I was happy at finding a place where I could lose my fears in desperation, and entered this cell, for it had the appearance of one, with the devotion of a monastic. Here I found a number of poor creatures, all in circumstances like myself, expecting the arrival of Mr. Crispe, presenting a true epitome of English impatience.

Each untractable soul at variance with fortune, wreaked her injuries on their own hearts: but Mr. Crispe at last came down and all our murmurs were hushed. He deigned to regard me with an air of peculiar approbation, and indeed he was the first man who for a month past talked to me with smiles. After a few questions, he found I was fit for every thing in the world. He paused a while upon the properest means of providing for me, and slapping his forehead as if he had found it, assured me, that there was at that time an embassy talked of from the synod of Pennsylvania to the Chickasaw Indians, and that he would use his interest to get me made secretary. I knew in my own heart that the fellow lied, and yet his promise gave me pleasure, there was something so magnificent in the sound. I fairly therefore divided my half guinea, one half of which went to be added to his thirty thousand pound, and with the other half I resolved to go to the next tavern to be there more happy than he.

"As I was going out with that resolution I was met at the door by the captain of a ship, with whom I had formerly some little acquaintance, and he agreed to be my companion over a bowl of punch. As I never chose to make a secret of my circumstances, he assured me that I was upon the very point of ruin, in listening to the office-keeper's promises; for that he only designed to sell me to the plantations. But, continued he, I fancy you might, by a much shorter voyage, be very easily put into a genteel way of bread. Take my advice. My ship sails to-morrow for Amsterdam. What if you go in her as a passenger? The moment you land all you have to do is to teach the Dutchmen English, and I'll warrant you'll get pupils and money enough. I suppose you understand English, added he, by this time, or the deuce is in it. I confidently assured him of that; but expressed a doubt whether the Dutch would be willing to learn English. He affirmed with an oath that they were fond of it to distraction; and upon that affirmation I agreed with his proposal, and embarked the next day to teach the Dutch English in

Holland. The wind was fair, our voyage short, and after having paid my passage with half my moveables, I found myself fallen as from the skies a stranger in one of the principal streets of Amsterdam. In this situation I was unwilling to let any time pass unemployed in teaching. I addressed myself therefore to two or three of those I met, whose appearance seemed most promising; but it was impossible to make ourselves mutually understood. It was not till this very moment I recollected, that in order to teach Dutchmen English, it was necessary that they should first teach me Dutch. How I came to overlook so obvious an objection is to me amazing; but certain it is I overlooked it.

"This scheme thus blown up, I had some thoughts of fairly shipping back to England again; but falling into company with an Irish student who was returning from Louvain, our conversation turning upon topics of literature (for by the way it may be observed that I always forgot the meanness of my circumstances when I could converse upon such subjects), from him I learned that there were not two men in his whole university who understood Greek. This amazed me. I instantly resolved to travel to Louvain, and there live by teaching Greek; and in this design I was heartened by my brother student, who threw out some hints that a fortune might be got by it.

"I set boldly forward the next morning. Every day lessened the burthen of my moveables, like Æsop and his basket of bread; for I paid them for my lodgings to the Dutch as I travelled on. When I came to Louvain, I was resolved not to go sneaking to the lower professors, but openly tendered my talents to the principal himself. I went, had admittance, and offered him my service as a master of the Greek language, which I had been told was a desideratum in this university. The principal seemed at first to doubt of my abilities; but of these I offered to convince him by turning a part of any Greek author he should fix upon into Latin. Finding me perfectly earnest

136

in my proposal, he addressed me thus: You see me, young man, continued he, I never learned Greek, and I don't find that I have ever missed it. I have had a doctor's cap and gown without Greek; I have ten thousand florins a year without Greek; I eat heartily without Greek, and in short, continued he, as I don't know Greek, I do not believe there is any good in it.

"I was now too far from home to think of returning; so I resolved to go forward. I had some knowledge of music, with a tolerable voice; now turned what was once my amusement into a present means of subsistence. I passed among the harmless peasants of Flanders, and among such of the French as were poor enough to be very merry; for I ever found them sprightly in proportion to their wants. Whenever I approached a peasant's house towards night-fall, I played one of my most merry tunes, and that procured me not only a lodging, but subsistence for the next day. I once or twice attempted to play for people of fashion; but they always thought my performance odious, and never rewarded me even with a trifle. This was to me the more extraordinary, as whenever I used in better days to play for company, when playing was my amusement, my music never failed to throw them into raptures, and the ladies especially; but as it was now my only means, it was received with contempt; a proof how ready the world is to underrate those talents by which a man is supported.

"In this manner I proceeded to Paris, with no design but just to look about me, and then to go forward. The people of Paris are much fonder of strangers that have money than of those that have wit. As I could not boast much of either, I was no great favourite. After walking about the town four or five days, and seeing the outsides of the best houses, I was preparing to leave this retreat of venal hospitality, when passing through one of the principal streets, whom should I meet but our cousin to whom you first recommended me. This meeting was very agreeable to me, and I believe not displeasing to him. He inquired into the nature of my journey to Paris, and informed me of his own business there, which was to collect pictures, medals, intaglios, and antiques of all kinds for a gentleman in London, who had just stept into taste and a large fortune. I was the more surprised at seeing our cousin pitched upon for this office, as he himself had often assured me he knew nothing of the matter. Upon asking how he had been taught the art of a cognoscento so very suddenly, he assured me that nothing was more easy. The whole secret consisted in a strict adherence to two rules: the one always to observe that the picture might have been better if the painter had taken more pains; and the other, to praise the works of Pietro Perugino. But, says he, as I once taught you how to be an author in London, I'll now undertake to instruct you in the art of picture buying at Paris.

"With this proposal I very readily closed, as it was living, and now all my ambition was to live. I went therefore to his lodgings, improved my dress by his assistance, and after some time accompanied him to auctions of pictures, where the English gentry were expected to be purchasers. I was not a little surprised at his intimacy with people of the best fashion, who referred themselves to his judgment upon every picture or medal, as an unerring standard of taste. He made very good use of my assistance upon these occasions; for when asked his opinion, he would gravely take me aside and ask mine, shrug, look wise, return, and assure the company that he could give no opinion upon an affair of so much importance. Yet there was sometimes an occasion for a more supported assurance. I remember to have seen him, after giving his opinion that the colouring of a picture was not mellow enough, very deliberately take a brush with brown varnish, that was accidentally lying by, and rub it over the piece with great composure before all the company, and then ask if he had not improved the tints.

"When he had finished his commission in Paris, he left me strongly recommended to several men of distinction, as a person very proper for a travelling tutor; and after some time I was employed in that capacity by a gentleman who brought his ward to Paris, in order to set him forward on his tour through Europe. I was to be the young gentleman's governor, but with a proviso that he should always be permitted to govern himself. My pupil in fact understood the art of guiding in money concerns much better than I. He was heir to a fortune of about two hundred thousand pounds, left him by an uncle in the West Indies; and his guardians, to qualify him for the management of it, had bound him apprentice to an attorney. Thus avarice was his prevailing passion: all his questions on the road were how money might be saved; which was the least expensive course of travel; whether any thing could be bought that would turn to account when disposed of again in London. Such curiosities on the way as could be seen for nothing he was ready enough to look at; but if the sight of them was to be paid for, he usually asserted that he had been told they were not worth seeing. He never paid a bill that he would not observe how amazingly expensive travelling was; and all this though he was not yet twenty-one. When arrived at Leghorn, as we took a walk to look at the port and shipping, he inquired the expence of the passage by sea home to England. This he was informed was but a trifle compared to his returning by land; he was therefore unable to withstand the temptation; so paying me the small part of my salary that was due, he took leave, and embarked with only one attendant for London.

"I now therefore was left once more upon the world at large; but then it was a thing I was used to. However, my skill in music could avail me nothing in a country where every peasant was a better musician than I; but by this time I had acquired another talent which answered my purpose as well, and this was a skill in disputation. In all the foreign universities and convents, there are upon certain days philosophical theses maintained against every adventitious disputant; for which, if the champion opposes with any dexterity, he can claim a gratuity in money, a dinner, and a bed for one night. In this manner therefore I fought my way towards England, walked along from city to city, examined mankind more nearly, and, if I may so express it, saw both sides of the picture. My remarks, however, are but few : I found that monarchy was the best government for the poor to live in, and commonwealths for the rich. I found that riches in general were in every country another name for freedom; and that no man is so fond of liberty himself as not to be desirous of subjecting the will of some individuals in society to his own.

"Upon my arrival in England I resolved to pay my respects first to you, and then to enlist as a volunteer in the first expedition that was going forward; but on my journey down my resolutions were changed, by meeting an old acquaintance, who I found belonged to a company of comedians that were going to make a summer campaign in the country. The company seemed not much to disapprove of me for an associate. They all, however, apprized me of the importance of the task at which I aimed ; that the public was a many-headed monster, and that only such as had very good heads could please it : that acting was not to be learnt in a day, and that without some traditional shrugs which had been on the stage, and only on the stage, these hundred years, I could never pretend to please. The next difficulty was in fitting me with parts, as almost every character was in keeping. I was driven for some time from one character to another, till at last Horatio was fixed upon, which the presence of the present company has happily hindered me from acting."

21

*The short continuance of friendship amongst the vicious, which
is coeval only with mutual satisfaction.*

MY son's account was too long to be delivered at once,
the first part of it was begun that night, and he was concluding the rest after dinner the next day, when the
appearance of Mr. Thornhill's equipage at the door
seemed to make a pause in the general satisfaction. The
butler, who was now become my friend in the family,
informed me with a whisper that the 'Squire had already
made some overtures to Miss Wilmot, and that her aunt
and uncle seemed highly to approve the match. Upon
Mr. Thornhill's entering, he seemed at seeing my son and
me to start back; but I readily imputed that to surprise
and not displeasure. However, upon our advancing to
salute him, he returned our greeting with the most
apparent candour; and after a short time his presence
served only to increase the general good humour.

After tea he called me aside to enquire after my
daughter; but upon my informing him that my enquiry
was unsuccessful, he seemed greatly surprised; adding,
that he had been since frequently at my house in order to
comfort the rest of my family, whom he left perfectly well.
He then asked if I had communicated her misfortune to
Miss Wilmot or my son; and upon my replying that I had
not told them as yet, he greatly approved my prudence
and precaution, desiring me by all means to keep it a
secret: "For at best," cried he, "it is but divulging one's
own infamy; and perhaps Miss Livy may not be so guilty
as we all imagine." We were here interrupted by a
servant who came to ask the 'Squire in to stand up at
country dances; so that he left me quite pleased with the
interest he seemed to take in my concerns. His addresses,
however, to Miss Wilmot were too obvious to be mis-

taken: and yet she seemed not perfectly pleased, but bore them rather in compliance to the will of her aunt than from real inclination. I had even the satisfaction to see her lavish some kind looks upon my unfortunate son, which the other could neither extort by his fortune nor assiduity. Mr. Thornhill's seeming composure however not a little surprised me: we had now continued here a week at the pressing instances of Mr. Arnold; but each day the more tenderness Miss Wilmot shewed my son, Mr. Thornhill's friendship seemed proportionably to increase for him.

He had formerly made us the most kind assurances of using his interest to serve the family; but now his generosity was not confined to promises alone: the morning I designed for my departure, Mr. Thornhill came to me with looks of real pleasure to inform me of a piece of service he had done for his friend George. This was nothing less than his having procured him an ensign's commission in one of the regiments that were going to the West Indies, for which he had promised but one hundred pounds, his interest having been sufficient to get an abatement of the other two. "As for this trifling piece of service," continued the young gentleman, "I desire no other reward but the pleasure of having served my friend; and as for the hundred pounds to be paid, if you are unable to raise it yourselves, I will advance it, and you shall repay me at your leisure." This was a favour we wanted words to express our sense of; I readily therefore gave my bond for the money, and testified as much gratitude as if I never intended to pay.

George was to depart for town the next day to secure his commission, in pursuance of his generous patron's directions, who judged it highly expedient to use despatch, lest in the mean time another should step in with more advantageous proposals. The next morning therefore our young soldier was early prepared for his departure, and seemed the only person among us that was not affected by it. Neither the fatigues and dangers he was going to encounter, nor the friends and mistress, for Miss Wilmot actually loved him, he was leaving behind, any way damped his spirits. After he had taken leave of the rest of the company, I gave him all I had, my blessing. "And now, my boy," cried I, "thou art going to fight for thy country, remember how thy brave grandfather fought for his sacred King, when loyalty among Britons was a virtue. Go, my boy, and imitate him in all but his misfortunes, if it was a misfortune to die with Lord Falkland. Go, my boy, and if you fall, though distant, exposed, and unwept by those that love you, the most precious tears are those with which heaven bedews the unburied head of a soldier."

The next morning I took leave of the good family that had been kind enough to entertain me so long, not without several expressions of gratitude to Mr. Thornhill for his late bounty. I left them in the enjoyment of all that happiness which affluence and good breeding procure, and returned towards home, despairing of ever finding my daughter more, but sending a sigh to heaven to spare and forgive her. I was now come within about twenty miles of home, having hired an horse to carry me, as I was yet but weak, and comforted myself with the hopes of soon seeing all I held dearest upon earth. But the night coming on, I put up at a little public-house by the roadside, and asked for the landlord's company over a pint of wine. We sate beside his kitchen fire, which was the best room in the house, and chatted on politics and the news of the country. We happened, among other topics, to talk of young 'Squire Thornhill, who the host assured me was hated as much as his uncle Sir William, who sometimes came down to the country, was loved. He went on to observe, that he made it his whole study to betray the daughters of such as received him to their houses, and after a fortnight or three weeks possession, turned them out unrewarded and abandoned to the world. As we continued our discourse in this manner, his wife, who had been out to get change, returned, and perceiving that her husband was enjoying a pleasure in which she was not a sharer, she asked him in an angry tone, what he did there, to which he only replied in an ironical way, by drinking her health. "Mr. Symmonds," cried she, "you use me very ill, and I'll bear it no longer. Here three parts of the business is left for me to do, and the fourth left unfinished: while you do nothing but soak with the guests all day long, whereas if a spoonful of liquor were to cure me of a fever I never touch a drop." I now found what she would be at, and immediately poured her out a glass, which she received with a curtsey, and drinking towards my good health, "Sir," resumed she, "it is not so much for the value of the liquor I am angry, but one cannot help it when the house is going out of the windows. If the customers or guests are to be dunned, all the burthen lies upon my back, he'd as lief eat that glass as budge after them himself. There now above stairs, we have a young woman who has come to take up her lodgings here, and I don't believe she has got any money by her over-civility. I am certain she is very slow of payment, and I wish she were put in mind of it."—"What signifies minding her?" cried the host; "if she be slow she is sure." —"I don't know that," replied the wife; "but I know that I am sure she has been here a fortnight and we have not yet seen the cross of her money."—"I suppose, my dear," cried he, "we shall have it all in a lump."—"In a lump!" cried the other, "I hope we may get it any way; and that I am resolved we will this very night, or out she tramps, bag and baggage."—"Consider, my dear," cried the husband, "she is a gentlewoman, and deserves more respect."—"As for the matter of that," returned the hostess, "gentle or simple, out she will pack with a sussarara. Gentry may be good things where they take; but for my part I never saw much good of them at the sign of the Harrow."—Thus saying, she ran up a narrow flight of stairs that went from the kitchen to a room over head, and I soon perceived by the loudness of her voice, and the bitterness of her reproaches, that no money was to be had from her lodger. I could hear her remonstrances very distinctly: "Out I say, pack out this moment, tramp thou infamous strumpet, or I'll give thee a mark thou won't be the better for these three months. What! you trumpery, to come and take up an honest house without cross or coin to bless yourself with; come along I say."—"O dear madam," cried the stranger, "pity me, pity a poor abandoned creature for one night, and death will soon do the rest."—I instantly knew the voice of my poor ruin'd child Olivia. I flew to her rescue, while the woman was dragging her along by her hair, and I caught the dear forlorn wretch in my arms.—"Welcome, any way welcome, my dearest lost one, my treasure, to your poor old father's bosom. Though the vicious forsake thee, there is yet one in the world that will never forsake thee; though thou hadst ten thousand crimes to answer for, he will forget them all."—"O my own dear,"—for minutes she could no more—"my own dearest good papa! Could angels be kinder! How do I deserve so much! The villain, I hate him and myself, to be a reproach to such goodness. You can't forgive me, I know you cannot."—"Yes, my child, from my heart I do forgive thee! Only repent, and we both shall yet be happy. We shall see many pleasant days yet, my Olivia!"—"Ah! never, Sir, never. The rest of my wretched life must be infamy abroad and shame at home. But, alas! papa, you look much paler than you used to do. Could such a thing as I am, give you so much uneasiness? Surely you have too much wisdom to take the miseries of my guilt upon yourself."—"Our wisdom, young woman," replied I—"Ah, why so cold a name, papa?" cried she. "This is the first time you ever called me by so cold a name."—"I ask pardon, my darling," returned I; "but I was going to observe, that wisdom makes but a slow defence against trouble, though at last a sure one." The landlady now returned to know if we did not choose a more genteel apartment, to which assenting, we were shewn a room where we cc ld converse more freely. After we had talked ourselves into some degree of tranquillity, I could not avoid desiring some account of the gradations that led to her present wretched situation. "That villain, Sir," said she, "from the first day of our meeting made me honourable though private proposals."

"Villain, indeed," cried I; "and yet it in some measure surprises me, how a person of Mr. Burchell's good sense and seeming honour could be guilty of such deliberate baseness, and thus step into a family to undo it."

"My dear papa," returned my daughter, "you labour under a strange mistake, Mr. Burchell never attempted to deceive me; instead of that he took every opportunity of privately admonishing me against the artifices of Mr. Thornhill, who I now find was even worse than he represented him."—"Mr. Thornhill," interrupted I, "can it be?" "Yes, Sir," returned she, "it was Mr. Thornhill who seduced me, who employed the two ladies as he called them, but who in fact were abandoned women of the town, without breeding or pity, to decoy us up to London. Their artifices, you may remember, would have certainly succeeded, but for Mr. Burchell's letter, who directed those reproaches at them, which we all applied to ourselves. How he came to have so much influence as to defeat their intentions still remains a secret to me; but I am convinced he was ever our warmest sincerest friend."

"You amaze me, my dear," cried I; "but now I find my first suspicions of Mr. Thornhill's baseness were too well grounded: but he can triumph in security; for he is rich and we are poor. But tell me, my child, sure it was no small temptation that could thus obliterate all the impressions of such an education, and so virtuous a disposition as thine?"

"Indeed, Sir," replied she, "he owes all his triumph to the desire I had of making him, and not myself, happy. I knew that the ceremony of our marriage, which was privately performed by a popish priest, was no way binding, and that I had nothing to trust to but his honour." "What," interrupted I, "and were you indeed married by a priest, and in orders?"—"Indeed, Sir, we were," replied she, "though we were both sworn to conceal his name."—"Why, then, my child, come to my arms again, and now you are a thousand times more welcome than before; for you are now his wife to all intents and purposes; nor can all the laws of man, though written upon tables of adamant, lessen the force of that sacred connection."

"Alas, papa," replied she, "you are but little acquainted with his villainies; he has been married already by the same priest to six or eight wives more, whom, like me, he has deceived and abandoned."

"Has he so?" cried I, "then we must hang the priest, and you shall inform against him to-morrow."—"But, Sir," returned she, "will that be right, when I am sworn to secrecy?"—"My dear," I replied, "if you have made such a promise, I cannot, nor will I tempt you to break it. Even though it may benefit the public, you must not inform against him. In all human institutions a smaller evil is allowed to procure a greater good; as in politics, a province may be given away to secure a kingdom; in medicine, a limb may be lopt off to preserve the body. But in religion the law is written, and inflexible, *never* to do evil. And this law, my child, is right: for otherwise, if we commit a smaller evil to procure a greater good, certain guilt would be thus incurred, in expectation of contingent advantage. And though the advantage should certainly follow, yet the interval between commission and advantage, which is allowed to be guilty, may be that in which we are called away to answer for the things we have done, and the volume of human actions is closed for ever. But I interrupt you, my dear; go on."

"The very next morning," continued she, "I found what little expectations I was to have from his sincerity. That very morning he introduced me to two unhappy women more, whom, like me, he had deceived, but who lived in contented prostitution. I loved him too tenderly to bear such rivals in his affections, and strove to forget my infamy in a tumult of pleasures. With this view I danced, dressed, and talked; but still was unhappy. The gentlemen who visited there told me every moment of the power of my charms, and this only contributed to increase my melancholy, as I had thrown all their power quite away. Thus each day I grew more pensive, and he more insolent, till at last the monster had the assurance to offer me to a young Baronet of his acquaintance. Need I describe, Sir, how his ingratitude stung me. My answer to this proposal was almost madness. I desired to part. As I was going, he offered me a purse; but I flung it at him with indignation, and burst from him in a rage, that for a while kept me insensible of the miseries of my situation. But I soon looked round me, and saw myself a vile, abject, guilty thing, without one friend in the world to apply to.

"Just in that interval a stage-coach happening to pass by, I took a place, it being my only aim to be driven at a distance from a wretch I despised and detested. I was set down here, where, since my arrival, my own anxiety and this woman's unkindness have been my only companions. The hours of pleasure that I have passed with my mamma and sister now grow painful to me. Their sorrows are much; but mine is greater than theirs; for mine are mixed with guilt and infamy."

"Have patience, my child," cried I, "and I hope things will yet be better. Take some repose to-night, and to-morrow I'll carry you home to your mother and the rest of the family, from whom you will receive a kind reception. Poor woman, this has gone to her heart: but she loves you still, Olivia, and will forget it."

22

Offences are easily pardoned where there is love at bottom.

THE next morning I took my daughter behind me, and
set out on my return home. As we travelled along, I
strove, by every persuasion, to calm her sorrows and
fears, and to arm her with resolution to bear the presence
of her offended mother. I took every opportunity, from
the prospect of a fine country through which we passed,
to observe how much kinder heaven was to us than we to
each other, and that the misfortunes of nature's making
were very few. I assured her that she should never perceive any change in my affections, and that during my
life, which yet might be long, she might depend upon a
guardian and an instructor. I armed her against the
censure of the world, shewed her that books were sweet
unreproaching companions to the miserable, and that if
they could not bring us to enjoy life, they would at least
teach us to endure it.

The hired horse that we rode was to be put up that
night at an inn by the way, within about five miles from
my house; and as I was willing to prepare my family for
my daughter's reception, I determined to leave her that
night at the inn, and to return for her, accompanied by my
daughter Sophia, early the next morning. It was night
before we reached our appointed stage: however, after
seeing her provided with a decent apartment, and having
ordered the hostess to prepare proper refreshments, I
kissed her, and proceeded towards home. And now my
heart caught new sensations of pleasure the nearer I
approached that peaceful mansion. As a bird that had
been frighted from its nest, my affections outwent my
haste, and hovered round my little fireside with all the
rapture of expectation. I called up the many fond things
I had to say, and anticipated the welcome I was to

receive. I already felt my wife's tender embrace, and smiled at the joy of my little ones. As I walked but slowly, the night waned apace. The labourers of the day were all retired to rest; the lights were out in every cottage; no sounds were heard but of the shrilling cock, and the deep-mouthed watch-dog at hollow distance. I approached my abode of pleasure, and before I was within a furlong of the place, our honest mastiff came running to welcome me.

It was now near midnight that I came to knock at my door: all was still and silent: my heart dilated with unutterable happiness, when, to my amazement, I saw the house bursting out in a blaze of fire, and every aperture red with conflagration! I gave a loud convulsive outcry, and fell upon the pavement insensible. This alarmed my son, who had till this been asleep, and he, perceiving the flames, instantly waked my wife and daughter, and all running out naked and wild with apprehension, recalled me to life with their anguish. But it was only to objects of new terror; for the flames had by this time caught the roof of our dwelling, part after part continuing to fall in, while the family stood with silent agony looking on as if they enjoyed the blaze. I gazed upon them and upon it by turns, and then looked round me for my two little ones; but they were not to be seen. O misery! "Where," cried I, "where are my little ones?" —"They are burnt to death in the flames," says my wife calmly, "and I will die with them."—That moment I heard the cry of the babes within, who were just awaked by the fire, and nothing could have stopped me. "Where, where, are my children?" cried I, rushing through the flames, and bursting the door of the chamber in which they were confined; "Where are my little ones?"— "Here, dear papa, here we are," cried they together, while the flames were just catching the bed where they lay. I caught them both in my arms, and snatching them through the fire as fast as possible, while just as I was got out, the roof sank in. "Now," cried I, holding up my children, "now let the flames burn on, and all my possessions perish. Here they are, I have saved my treasures. Here, my dearest, here are our treasures, and we shall yet be happy." We kissed our little darlings a thousand times; they clasped us round the neck, and seemed to share our transports, while their mother laughed and wept by turns.

I now stood a calm spectator of the flames, and after some time began to perceive that my arm to the shoulder was scorched in a terrible manner. It was therefore out of my power to give my son any assistance, either in attempting to save our goods, or preventing the flames spreading to our corn. By this time the neighbours were alarmed, and came running to our assistance; but all they could do was to stand, like us, spectators of the calamity. My goods, among which were the notes I had reserved for my daughters' fortunes, were entirely consumed, except a box with some papers that stood in the kitchen, and two or three things more of little consequence, which my son brought away in the beginning. The neighbours contributed, however, what they could to lighten our distress. They brought us clothes, and furnished one of our out-houses with kitchen utensils; so that by daylight we had another, though a wretched dwelling, to retire to. My honest next neighbour and his children were not the least assiduous in providing us with every thing necessary, and offering whatever consolation untutored benevolence could suggest.

When the fears of my family had subsided, curiosity to know the cause of my long stay began to take place; having therefore informed them of every particular, I proceeded to prepare them for the reception of our lost one, and though we had nothing but wretchedness now to impart, I was willing to procure her a welcome to what we had. This task would have been more difficult but for our recent calamity, which had humbled my wife's pride and blunted it by more poignant afflictions. Being unable to go for my poor child myself, as my arm grew very painful, I sent my son and daughter, who soon returned, supporting the wretched delinquent, who had not the courage to look up at her mother, whom no instructions of mine could persuade to a perfect reconciliation; for women have a much stronger sense of female error than men. "Ah Madam," cried her mother, "this is but a poor place you are come to after so much finery. My daughter Sophy and I can afford but little entertainment to persons who have kept company only with people of distinction. Yes, Miss Livy, your poor father and I have suffered very much of late; but I hope heaven will forgive you."— During this reception the unhappy victim stood pale and trembling, unable to weep or to reply; but I could not continue a silent spectator of her distress, wherefore assuming a degree of severity in my voice and manner, which was ever followed with instant submission, "I entreat, woman, that my words may be now marked once for all: I have here brought you back a poor deluded wanderer; her return to duty demands the revival of our tenderness. The real hardships of life are now coming fast upon us; let us not therefore increase them by dissension among each other. If we live harmoniously together, we may yet be contented, as there are enough of us to shut out the censuring world, and keep each other in countenance. The kindness of heaven is promised to the penitent, and let ours be directed by the example. Heaven, we are assured, is much more pleased to view a repentant sinner than ninety-nine persons who have supported a course of undeviating rectitude. And this is right; for that single effort by which we stop short in the down-hill path to perdition, is itself a greater exertion of virtue than an hundred acts of justice."

23

None but the guilty can be long and completely miserable.

Some assiduity was now required to make our present abode as convenient as possible, and we were soon again qualified to enjoy our former serenity. Being disabled myself from assisting my son in our usual occupations, I read to my family from the few books that were saved, and particularly from such as by amusing the imagination contributed to ease the heart. Our good neighbours, too, came every day with the kindest condolence, and fixed a time in which they were all to assist at repairing my former dwelling. Honest farmer Williams was not last among these visitors; but heartily offered his friendship. He would even have renewed his addresses to my daughter; but she rejected him in such a manner as totally represt his future solicitations.—Her grief seemed formed for continuing, and she was the only person of our little society that a week did not restore to cheerfulness. She now lost that unblushing innocence which had once taught her to respect herself, and to seek pleasure by pleasing. Anxiety now had taken strong possession of her mind, her beauty began to be impaired with her constitution, and neglect still more contributed to diminish it. Every tender epithet bestowed on her sister brought a pang to her heart and a tear to her eye; and as one vice, though cured, ever plants others where it has been, so her former guilt, though driven out by repentance, left jealousy and envy behind. I strove a thousand ways to lessen her care, and even forgot my own pain in a concern for hers, collecting such amusing passages of history as a strong memory and some reading could suggest.—"Our happiness, my dear," I would say, "is in the power of One who can bring it about a thousand unforeseen ways that mock our foresight. If example be necessary to prove this, I'll give you a story, my child, told us by a grave, though sometimes a romancing, historian.

"Matilda was married very young to a Neapolitan nobleman of the first quality, and found herself a widow and a mother at the age of fifteen. As she stood one day caressing her infant son in the open window of an apartment which hung over the river Volturna, the child with a sudden spring leaped from her arms into the flood below, and disappeared in a moment. The mother, struck with instant surprise, and making an effort to save him, plunged in after; but far from being able to assist the infant, she herself with great difficulty escaped to the opposite shore, just when some French soldiers were plundering the country on that side, who immediately made her their prisoner.

"As the war was then carried on between the French and Italians with the utmost inhumanity, they were going at once to perpetrate those two extremes suggested by appetite and cruelty. This base resolution, however, was opposed by a young officer, who, though their retreat required the utmost expedition, placed her behind him, and brought her in safety to his native city. Her beauty at first caught his eye, her merit soon after his heart. They were married: he rose to the highest posts; they lived long together, and were happy. But the felicity of a soldier can never be called permanent: after an interval of several years, the troops which he commanded having met with a repulse, he was obliged to take shelter in the city where he had lived with his wife. Here they suffered a siege, and the city at length was taken. Few histories can produce more various instances of cruelty, than those which the French and Italians at that time exercised upon each other. It was resolved by the victors upon this occasion, to put all the French prisoners to death; but particularly the husband of the unfortunate Matilda, as he was principally instrumental in protracting the siege. Their determinations were in general executed almost as soon as resolved upon. The captive soldier was led forth,

154

and the executioner with his sword stood ready, while the spectators in gloomy silence awaited the fatal blow, which was only suspended till the general, who presided as judge, should give the signal. It was in this interval of anguish and expectation, that Matilda came to take her last farewell of her husband and deliverer, deploring her wretched situation, and the cruelty of fate, that had saved her from perishing by a premature death in the river Volturna, to be the spectator of still greater calamities. The general, who was a young man, was struck with surprise at her beauty, and pity at her distress; but with still stronger emotions, when he heard her mention her former dangers. He was her son, the infant for whom she had encountered so much danger. He acknowledged her at once as his mother, and fell at her feet. The rest may be easily supposed; the captive was set free, and all the happiness that love, friendship, and duty could confer on each, were united."

In this manner I would attempt to amuse my daughter; but she listened with divided attention; for her own misfortunes engrossed all the pity she once had for those of another, and nothing gave her ease. In company she dreaded contempt; and in solitude she only found anxiety. Such was the colour of her wretchedness, when we received certain information, that Mr. Thornhill was going to be married to Miss Wilmot, for whom I always suspected he had a real passion, though he took every opportunity before me to express his contempt both of her person and fortune. This news only served to increase poor Olivia's affliction; such a flagrant breach of fidelity was more than her courage could support. I was resolved, however, to get more certain information, and to defeat, if possible, the completion of his designs, by sending my son to old Mr. Wilmot's with instructions to know the truth of the report, and to deliver Miss Wilmot a letter intimating Mr. Thornhill's conduct in my family. My son went, in pursuance of my directions, and in three days returned, assuring us of the truth of the account; but that he had found it impossible to deliver the letter, which he was therefore obliged to leave, as Mr. Thornhill and Miss Wilmot were visiting round the country. They were to be married, he said, in a few days, having appeared together at church the Sunday before he was there, in great splendour, the bride attended by six young ladies, and he by as many gentlemen. Their approaching nuptials filled the whole country with rejoicing, and they usually rode out together in the grandest equipage that had been seen in the country for many years. All the friends of both families, he said, were there, particularly the 'Squire's uncle, Sir William Thornhill, who bore so good a character. He added, that nothing but mirth and feasting were going forward; that all the country praised the young bride's beauty, and the bridegroom's fine person, and that they were immensely fond of each other; concluding that he could not help thinking Mr. Thornhill one of the most happy men in the world.

"Why let him if he can," returned I: "but, my son, observe this bed of straw and unsheltering roof; those mouldering walls and humid floor; my wretched body thus disabled by fire, and my children weeping round me for bread; you have come home, my child, to all this, yet here, even here, you see a man who would not for a thousand worlds exchange situations. O, my children, if you could but learn to commune with your own hearts, and know what noble company you can make them, you would little regard the elegance and splendour of the worthless. Almost all men have been taught to call life a passage, and themselves the travellers. The similitude still may be improved when we observe that the good are joyful and serene, like travellers that are going towards home; the wicked but by intervals happy, like travellers that are going into exile."

My compassion for my poor daughter, overpowered by this new disaster, interrupted what I had farther to observe. I bade her mother support her, and after a short time she recovered. She appeared from that time more calm, and I imagined had gained a new degree of resolution: but appearances deceived me; for her tranquillity was the languor of over-wrought resentment. A supply of provisions, charitably sent us by my kind parishioners, seemed to diffuse new cheerfulness amongst the rest of the family, nor was I displeased at seeing them once more sprightly and at ease. It would have been unjust to damp their satisfactions, merely to condole with resolute melancholy, or to burthen them with a sadness they did not feel. Thus once more the tale went round, and the song was demanded, and cheerfulness condescended to hover round our little habitation.

24

Fresh calamities.

THE next morning the sun arose with peculiar warmth for the season; so that we agreed to breakfast together on the honey-suckle bank: where while we sat, my youngest daughter at my request joined her voice to the concert on the trees about us. It was in this place my poor Olivia first met her seducer, and every object served to recall her sadness. But that melancholy which is excited by objects of pleasure, or inspired by sounds of harmony, soothes the heart instead of corroding it. Her mother too, upon this occasion, felt a pleasing distress, and wept, and loved her daughter as before. "Do, my pretty Olivia," cried she, "let us have that little melancholy air your pappa was so fond of; your sister Sophy has already obliged us. Do child, it will please your old father." She complied in a manner so exquisitely pathetic as moved me.

> When lovely woman stoops to folly
>   And finds too late that men betray
> What charm can soothe her melancholy,
>   What art can wash her guilt away?
>
> The only art her guilt to cover,
>   To hide her shame from every eye,
> To give repentance to her lover,
>   And wring his bosom—is to die.

As she was concluding the last stanza, to which an interruption in her voice from sorrow gave peculiar softness, the appearance of Mr. Thornhill's equipage at a distance alarmed us all, but particularly increased the uneasiness of my eldest daughter, who, desirous of shunning her betrayer, returned to the house with her sister. In a few minutes he was alighted from his chariot, and making up to the place where I was still sitting, inquired after my health with his usual air of familiarity. "Sir," replied I, "your present assurance only serves to aggravate the baseness of your character; and there was a time when I would have chastised your insolence for presuming thus to appear before me. But now you are safe; for age has cooled my passions, and my calling restrains them."

"I vow, my dear sir," returned he, "I am amazed at all this; nor can I understand what it means! I hope you don't think your daughter's late excursion with me had any thing criminal in it."

"Go," cried I, "thou art a wretch, a poor pitiful wretch, and every way a liar: but your meanness secures you from my anger! Yet, Sir, I am descended from a family that would not have borne this! And so, thou vile thing, to gratify a momentary passion, thou hast made one poor creature wretched for life, and polluted a family that had nothing but honour for their portion."

"If she or you," returned he, "are resolved to be miserable, I cannot help it. But you may still be happy: and whatever opinion you may have formed of me, you shall ever find me ready to contribute to it. We can marry her to another in a short time, and what is more, she may keep her lover beside; for I protest I shall ever continue to have a true regard for her."

I found all my passions alarmed at this new degrading proposal; for though the mind may often be calm under great injuries, little villainy can at any time get within the soul and sting it into rage.—"Avoid my sight, thou reptile," cried I, "nor continue to insult me with thy presence. Were my brave son at home he would not suffer this; but I am old and disabled, and every way undone."

"I find," cried he, "you are bent upon obliging me to talk in a harsher manner than I intended. But as I have shewn you what may be hoped from my friendship, it may not be improper to represent what may be the consequences of my resentment. My attorney, to whom your late bond has been transferred, threatens hard, nor do I know how to prevent the course of justice, except by paying the money myself, which, as I have been at some expences lately, previous to my intended marriage, is not so easy to be done. And then my steward talks of driving for the rent: it is certain he knows his duty; for I never trouble myself with affairs of that nature. Yet still I could wish to serve you, and even to have you and your daughter present at my marriage, which is shortly to be solemnized with Miss Wilmot; it is even the request of my charming Arabella herself, whom I hope you will not refuse."

"Mr. Thornhill," replied I, "hear me once for all: as to your marriage with any but my daughter, that I never will consent to; and though your friendship could raise me to a throne, or your resentment sink me to the grave, yet would I despise both. Thou hast once woefully, irreparably deceived me. I reposed my heart upon thine honour, and have found its baseness. Never more therefore expect friendship from me. Go, and possess what fortune has given thee, beauty, riches, health, and pleasure. Go, and leave me to want, infamy, disease, and sorrow. Yet humbled as I am, shall my heart still vindicate its dignity, and though thou hast my forgiveness, thou shalt ever have my contempt."

"If so," returned he, "depend upon it you shall feel the effects of this insolence, and we shall shortly see which is the fittest object of scorn, you or me."—Upon which he departed abruptly.

My wife and son, who were present at this interview, seemed terrified with the apprehension. My daughters also, finding that he was gone, came out to be informed of the result of our conference, which, when known, alarmed them not less than the rest. But as to myself I disregarded the utmost stretch of his malevolence: he had already struck the blow, and now I stood prepared to repel every new effort. Like one of those instruments used in the art of war, which however thrown still presents a point to receive the enemy.

We soon, however, found that he had not threatened in vain; for the very next morning his steward came to demand my annual rent, which, by the train of accidents already related, I was unable to pay. The consequence of my incapacity was his driving my cattle that evening, and their being appraised and sold the next day for less than half their value. My wife and children now therefore entreated me to comply upon any terms, rather than incur certain destruction. They even begged of me to admit his visits once more, and used all their little eloquence to paint the calamities I was going to endure: the terrors of a prison, in so rigorous a season as the present, with the danger that threatened my health from the late accident that happened by the fire. But I continued inflexible.

"Why, my treasures," cried I, "why will you thus attempt to persuade me to the thing that is not right? My duty has taught me to forgive him; but my conscience will not permit me to approve. Would you have me applaud to the world what my heart must internally condemn? Would you have me tamely sit down and flatter our infamous betrayer; and to avoid a prison continually suffer the more galling bonds of mental confinement? No, never. If we are to be taken from this abode, only let us hold to the right, and wherever we are thrown we can still retire to a charming apartment, when we can look round our own hearts with intrepidity and with pleasure!"

In this manner we spent that evening. Early the next morning, as the snow had fallen in great abundance in the night, my son was employed in clearing it away, and opening a passage before the door. He had not been thus engaged long when he came running in, with looks all pale, to tell us that two strangers, whom he knew to be officers of justice, were making towards the house.

Just as he spoke they came in, and approaching the bed where I lay, after previously informing me of their employment and business, made me their prisoner, bidding me prepare to go with them to the county gaol, which was eleven miles off.

"My friends," said I, "this is severe weather in which you have come to take me to a prison; and it is particularly unfortunate at this time, as one of my arms has lately been burnt in a terrible manner, and it has thrown me into a slight fever, and I want clothes to cover me, and I am now too weak and old to walk far in such deep snow: but if it must be so—"

I then turned to my wife and children, and directed them to get together what few things were left us, and to prepare immediately for leaving this place. I entreated them to be expeditious, and desired my son to assist his eldest sister, who, from a consciousness that she was the cause of all our calamities, was fallen, and had lost anguish in insensibility. I encouraged my wife, who, pale and trembling, clasped our affrighted little ones in her arms, that clung to her bosom in silence, dreading to look round at the strangers. In the mean time my youngest daughter prepared for our departure, and as she received several hints to use dispatch, in about an hour we were ready to depart.

*. . . two strangers, whom he knew to be officers
of justice . . .*

25

No situation, however wretched it seems, but has some sort of comfort attending it.

WE set forward from this peaceful neighbourhood and walked on slowly. My eldest daughter being enfeebled by a slow fever, which had begun for some days to undermine her constitution, one of the officers, who had an horse, kindly took her behind him; for even these men cannot entirely divest themselves of humanity. My son led one of the little ones by the hand, and my wife the other, while I leaned upon my youngest girl, whose tears fell not for her own but my distresses.

We were now got from my late dwelling about two miles, when we saw a crowd running and shouting behind us consisting of about fifty of my poorest parishioners. These, with dreadful imprecations, soon seized upon the two officers of justice, and swearing they would never see their minister go to a gaol while they had a drop of blood to shed in his defence, were going to use them with great severity. The consequence might have been fatal, had I not immediately interposed, and with some difficulty rescued the officers from the hands of the enraged multitude. My children, who looked upon my delivery now as certain, appeared transported with joy, and were incapable of containing their raptures. But they were soon undeceived, upon hearing me address the poor deluded people who came, as they imagined, to do me service.

"What! my friends," cried I, "and is this the way you love me! Is this the manner you obey the instructions I have given you from the pulpit! Thus to fly in the face of justice, and bring down ruin on yourselves and me! Which is your ring-leader? Shew me the man that has thus seduced you. As sure as he lives he shall feel my resentment. Alas! my dear deluded flock, return back to the duty you owe to God, to your country, and to me. I shall yet perhaps one day see you in greater felicity here, and contribute to make your lives more happy. But let it at least be my comfort when I pen my fold for immortality, that not one here shall be wanting."

They now seemed all repentance, and melting into tears came one after the other to bid me farewell. I shook each tenderly by the hand, and leaving them my blessing, proceeded forward without meeting any farther interruption. Some hours before night we reached the town or rather village; for it consisted but of a few mean houses, having lost all its former opulence, and retaining no marks of its ancient superiority but the gaol.

Upon entering, we put up at an inn, where we had such refreshments as could most readily be procured, and I supped with my family with my usual cheerfulness. After seeing them properly accommodated for that night, I next attended the sheriff's officers to the prison, which had formerly been built for the purposes of war, and consisted of one large apartment, strongly grated and paved with stone, common to both felons and debtors at certain hours in the four and twenty. Besides this, every prisoner had a separate cell where he was locked in for the night.

I expected upon my entrance to find nothing but lamentations and various sounds of misery; but it was very different. The prisoners seemed all employed in one common design, that of forgetting thought in merriment or clamour. I was apprized of the usual perquisite required upon these occasions, and immediately complied with the demand, though the little money I had was very near being all exhausted. This was immediately sent away for liquor, and the whole prison soon was filled with riot, laughter and prophaneness.

"How," cried I to myself, "shall men so very wicked be cheerful, and shall I be melancholy! I feel only the same confinement with them, and I think I have more reason to be happy."

With such reflections I laboured to become cheerful; but cheerfulness was never yet produced by effort, which is itself painful. As I was sitting therefore in a corner of the gaol, in a pensive posture, one of my fellow-prisoners came up, and sitting by me, entered into conversation. It was my constant rule in life never to avoid the conversation of any man who seemed to desire it: for if good I might profit by his instruction; if bad he might be assisted by mine. I found this to be a knowing man of strong unlettered sense; but a thorough knowledge of the world as it is called, or, more properly speaking, of human nature on the wrong side. He asked me if I had taken care to provide myself with a bed, which was a circumstance I had never once attended to.

"That's unfortunate," cried he, "as you are allowed here nothing but straw, and your apartment is very large and cold. However you seem to be something of a gentleman, and as I have been one myself in my time, part of my bed-clothes are heartily at your service."

I thanked him, professing my surprise at finding such humanity in a gaol in misfortunes; adding, to let him see that I was a scholar, "That the sage ancient seemed to understand the value of company in affliction when he said, Ton kosmon aire, ei dos ton etairon; and in fact," continued I, "what is the World if it affords only solitude?"

"You talk of the World, Sir," returned my fellow-prisoner; "*the world is in its dotage, and yet the cosmogony or creation of the world has puzzled the philosophers of every age. What a medley of opinions have they not broached upon the creation of the world. Sanchoniathon, Manetho, Berosus, and Ocellus Lucanus have all attempted it in vain. The latter has these words, Anarchon ara kai atelutaion to pan, which implies*"—"I ask pardon, Sir," cried I, "for interrupting so much learning; but I think I have heard all this before. Have I not had the pleasure of once seeing you at Welbridge fair, and is not your name Ephraim Jenkinson?" At this demand he only sighed. "I suppose you must recollect," resumed I, "one Doctor Primrose, from whom you bought a horse."

He now at once recollected me; for the gloominess of the place and the approaching night had prevented his distinguishing my features before.—"Yes, Sir," returned Mr. Jenkinson, "I remember you perfectly well; I bought a horse but forgot to pay for him. Your neighbour Flamborough is the only prosecutor I am any way afraid of at the next assizes: for he intends to swear positively against me as a coiner. I am heartily sorry, Sir, I ever deceived you, or indeed any man; for you see," continued he, shewing his hackles, "what my tricks have brought me to."

"Well, Sir," replied I, "your kindness in offering me assistance when you could expect no return, shall be repaid with my endeavours to soften or totally suppress Mr. Flamborough's evidence, and I will send my son to him for that purpose the first opportunity; nor do I in the least doubt but he will comply with my request, and as to my own evidence you need be under no uneasiness about that."

"Well, Sir," cried he, "all the return I can make shall be yours. You shall have more than half my bed-clothes to-night, and I'll take care to stand your friend in the prison, where I think I have some influence."

I thanked him, and could not avoid being surprised at the present youthful change in his aspect; for at the time I had seen him before he appeared at least sixty.—"Sir," answered he, "you are little acquainted with the world; I had at that time false hair, and have learnt the art of counterfeiting every age from seventeen to seventy. Ah, Sir, had I but bestowed half the pains in learning a trade that I have in learning to be a scoundrel, I might have been a rich man at this day. But rogue as I am, still I may be your friend, and that perhaps when you least expect it."

We were now prevented from further conversation by the arrival of the gaoler's servants, who came to call over the prisoners' names, and lock up for the night. A fellow also, with a bundle of straw for my bed, attended, who led me along a dark narrow passage into a room paved like the common prison, and in one corner of this I spread my bed and the clothes given me by my fellow-prisoner; which done, my conductor, who was civil enough, bade me a good night. After my usual meditations, and having praised my heavenly corrector, I laid myself down and slept with the utmost tranquillity till morning.

A reformation in the gaol. To make laws compleat they should reward as well as punish.

THE next morning early I was awakened by my family, whom I found in tears at my bed-side. The gloomy strength of everything about us, it seems, had daunted them. I gently rebuked their sorrow, assuring them I had never slept with greater tranquillity, and next enquired after my eldest daughter who was not among them. They informed me that yesterday's uneasiness and fatigue had increased her fever, and it was judged proper to leave her behind. My next care was to send my son to procure a room or two to lodge the family in, as near the prison as conveniently could be found. He obeyed; but could only find one apartment, which was hired at a small expence for his mother and sisters, the gaoler with humanity consenting to let him and his two little brothers lie in the prison with me. A bed was therefore prepared for them in a corner of the room, which I thought answered very conveniently. I was willing, however, previously to know whether my little children chose to lie in a place which seemed to fright them upon entrance.

"Well," cried I, "my good boys, how do you like your bed? I hope you are not afraid to lie in this room, dark as it appears."

"No, papa," say Dick, "I am not afraid to lie anywhere where you are."

"And I," says Bill, who was yet but four years old, "love every place best that my papa is in."

After this I allotted to each of the family what they were to do. My daughter was particularly directed to watch her declining sister's health; my wife was to attend me; my little boys were to read to me: "And as for you my son," continued I, "it is by the labour of your hands we must all hope to be supported. Your wages, as a day-labourer, will be fully sufficient with proper frugality to maintain us all, and comfortably too. Thou are now sixteen years old, and hast strength, and it was given thee, my son, for very useful purposes; for it must save from famine your helpless parents and family. Prepare then this evening to look out for work against to-morrow, and bring home every night what money you earn, for our support."

Having thus instructed him, and settled the rest, I walked down to the common prison, where I could enjoy more air and room. But I was not long there when the execrations, lewdness, and brutality that invaded me on every side drove me back to my apartment again. Here I sat for some time pondering upon the strange infatuation of wretches who, finding all mankind in open arms against them, were labouring to make themselves a future and a tremendous enemy.

Their insensibility excited my highest compassion, and blotted my own uneasiness from my mind. It even appeared a duty incumbent upon me to attempt to reclaim them. I resolved therefore once more to return, and in spite of their contempt to give them my advice, and conquer them by perseverance. Going therefore among them again, I informed Mr. Jenkinson of my design, at which he laughed heartily, but communicated it to the rest. The proposal was received with the greatest good-humour, as it promised to afford a new fund of entertainment to persons who had now no other resource for mirth, but what could be derived from ridicule or debauchery.

I therefore read them a portion of the service with a loud unaffected voice, and found my audience perfectly merry upon the occasion. Lewd whispers, groans of contrition burlesqued, winking and coughing alternately excited laughter. However, I continued with my natural solemnity to read on, sensible that what I did might mend some, but could itself receive no contamination from any.

After reading, I entered upon my exhortation, which was rather calculated at first to amuse them than to reprove. I previously observed, that no other motive but their welfare could induce me to this; that I was their fellow prisoner, and now got nothing by preaching. I was sorry, I said, to hear them so very profane; because they got nothing by it, but might lose a great deal: "For be assured, my friends," cried I, "for you are my friends, however the world may disclaim your friendship, though you swore twelve thousand oaths in a day, it would not put one penny in your purse. Then what signifies calling every moment upon the devil, and courting his friendship, since you find how scurvily he uses you. He has given you nothing here, you find, but a mouthful of oaths and an empty belly; and by the best accounts I have of him, he will give you nothing that's good hereafter.

"If used ill in our dealings with one man we naturally go elsewhere. Were it not worth your while then just to try how you may like the usage of another master, who gives you fair promises at least to come to him? Surely, my friends, of all stupidity in the world, his must be the greatest, who after robbing a house runs to the thief-takers for protection. And yet how are you more wise? You are all seeking comfort from one that has already betrayed you, applying to a more malicious being than any thieftaker of them all; for they only decoy and then hang you; but he decoys and hangs, and what is worst of all, will not let you loose after the hangman has done."

When I had concluded, I received the compliments of my audience, some of whom came and shook me by the hand, swearing that I was a very honest fellow, and that they desired my further acquaintance. I therefore promised to repeat my lecture next day, and actually conceived some hopes of making a reformation here; for it had ever been my opinion that no man was past the hour of amendment, every heart lying open to the shafts of reproof if the archer could but take a proper aim. When I had thus satisfied my mind, I went back to my apartment, where my wife prepared a frugal meal, while Mr. Jenkinson begged leave to add his dinner to ours and partake of the pleasure, as he was kind enough to express it, of my conversation. He had not yet seen my family, for as they came to my apartment by a door in the narrow passage already described, by this means they avoided the common prison. Jenkinson at the first interview therefore seemed not a little struck with the beauty of my youngest daughter, which her pensive air contributed to heighten, and my little ones did not pass unnoticed.

"Alas, Doctor," cried he, "these children are too handsome and too good for such a place as this!"

"Why, Mr. Jenkinson," replied I, "thank heaven my children are pretty tolerable in morals, and if they be good, it matters little for the rest."

"I fancy, Sir," returned my fellow-prisoner, "that it must give you great comfort to have this little family about you."

"A comfort, Mr. Jenkinson," replied I; "yes it is indeed a comfort, and I would not be without them for all the world; for they can make a dungeon seem a palace. There is but one way in this life of wounding my happiness, and that is by injuring them."

"I am afraid then, Sir," cried he, "that I am in some measure culpable; for I think I see here" (looking at my son Moses) "one that I have injured, and by whom I wish to be forgiven."

My son immediately recollected his voice and features, though he had before seen him in disguise, and taking him by the hand, with a smile forgave him. "Yet," continued he, "I can't help wondering at what you could see in my face to think me a proper mark for deception."

"My dear Sir," returned the other, "it was not your face, but your white stockings and the black ribband in your hair that allured me. But no disparagement to your parts, I have deceived wiser men than you in my time; and yet with all my tricks, the blockheads have been too many for me at last."

"I suppose," cried my son, "that the narrative of such a life as yours must be extremely instructive and amusing."

"Not much of either," returned Mr. Jenkinson. "Those relations which describe the tricks and vices only of mankind, by increasing our suspicion in life, retard our success. The traveller that distrusts every person he meets, and turns back upon the appearance of every man that looks like a robber, seldom arrives in time at his journey's end.

"Indeed I think from my own experience, that the knowing one is the silliest fellow under the sun. I was thought cunning from my very childhood; when but seven years old the ladies would say that I was a perfect little man; at fourteen I knew the world, cocked my hat, and loved the ladies; at twenty, though I was perfectly honest, yet every one thought me so cunning that not one would trust me. Thus I was at last obliged to turn sharper in my own defence, and have lived ever since, my head throbbing with schemes to deceive, and my heart palpitating with fears of detection. I used often to laugh at your honest simple neighbour Flamborough, and one way or another generally cheated him once a year. Yet still the honest man went forward without suspicion, and grew rich while I still continued tricksy and cunning, and was poor, without the consolation of being honest. However," continued he, "let me know your case, and what has brought you here; perhaps, though I have not skill to avoid a gaol myself, I may extricate my friends."

In compliance with this curiosity, I informed him of the whole train of accidents and follies that had plunged me into my present troubles, and my utter inability to get free.

After hearing my story, and pausing some minutes, he slapt his forehead as if he had hit upon something material, and took his leave, saying he would try what could be done.

The same subject continued.

THE next morning I communicated to my wife and children the scheme I had planned of reforming the prisoners, which they received with universal disapprobation, alleging the impossibility and impropriety of it; adding, that my endeavours would no way contribute to their amendment, but might probably disgrace my calling.

"Excuse me," returned I, "these people, however fallen, are still men, and that is a very good title to my affections. Good counsel rejected returns to enrich the giver's bosom; and though the instruction I communicate may not mend them, yet it will assuredly mend myself. If these wretches, my children, were princes, there would be thousands ready to offer their ministry; but in my opinion, the heart that is buried in a dungeon is as precious as that seated upon a throne. Yes, my treasures, if I can mend them I will; perhaps they will not all despise me. Perhaps I may catch up even one from the gulph, and that will be great gain; for is there upon earth a gem so precious as the human soul?"

Thus saying I left them, and descended to the common prison, where I found the prisoners very merry, expecting my arrival; and each prepared with some gaol trick to play upon the doctor. Thus, as I was going to begin, one turned my wig awry, as if by accident, and then asked my pardon. A second, who stood at some distance, had a knack of spitting through his teeth, which fell in showers upon my book. A third would cry Amen in such an affected tone as gave the rest great delight. A fourth had slily picked my pocket of my spectacles. But there was one whose trick gave more universal pleasure than all the rest; for observing the manner in which I had disposed my books on the table before me, he very dextrously displaced one of them, and put an obscene jest-book of his own in the place. However, I took no notice of all that this mischievous group of little beings could do; but went on, perfectly sensible that what was ridiculous in my attempt would excite mirth only the first or second time, while what was serious would be permanent. My design succeeded, and in less than six days some were penitent, and all attentive.

It was now that I applauded my perseverance and address, at thus giving sensibility to wretches divested of every moral feeling, and now began to think of doing them temporal services also, by rendering their situation somewhat more comfortable. Their time had hitherto been divided between famine and excess, tumultuous riot and bitter repining. Their only employment was quarrelling among each other, playing at cribbage, and cutting tobacco stoppers. From this last mode of idle industry I took the hint of setting such as chose to work at cutting pegs for tobacconists and shoemakers, the proper wood being bought by a general subscription, and when manufactured, sold by my appointment; so that each earned something every day: a trifle indeed, but sufficient to maintain him.

I did not stop here, but instituted fines for the punishment of immorality, and rewards for peculiar industry. Thus in less than a fortnight I had formed them into something social and humane, and had the pleasure of regarding myself as a legislator, who had brought men from their native ferocity into friendship and obedience.

And it were highly to be wished, that legislative power would thus direct the law rather to reformation than severity: that it would seem convinced that the work of eradicating crimes is not by making punishments familiar, but formidable. Then instead of our present prisons, which find or make men guilty, which enclose wretches for the commission of one crime, and return them, if returned alive, fitted for the perpetration of thousands; we should see, as in other parts of Europe, places of penitence and solitude, where the accused might be attended by such as could give them repentance if guilty, or new motives to virtue, if innocent. And this, but not the increasing punishments, is the way to mend a state; nor can I avoid even questioning the validity of that right which social combinations have assumed of capitally punishing offences of a slight nature. In cases of murder their right is obvious, as it is the duty of us all, from the law of self-defence, to cut off that man who has shewn a disregard for the life of another. Against such all nature rises in arms; but it is not so against him who steals my property. Natural law gives me no right to take away his life, as by that the horse he steals is as much his property as mine. If then I have any right, it must be from a compact made between us, that he who deprives the other of his horse shall die. But this is a false compact; because no man has a right to barter his life any more than to take it away, as it is not his own. And besides, the compact is inadequate, and would be set aside even in a court of modern equity, as there is a great penalty for a very trifling convenience, since it is far better that two men should live than that one man should ride. But a compact that is false between two men is equally so between an hundred, or an hundred thousand; for as ten millions of circles can never make a square, so the united voice of myriads cannot lend the smallest foundation to falsehood. It is thus that reason speaks, and untutored nature says the same thing. Savages that are directed by natural law alone are very tender of the lives of each other; they seldom shed blood but to retaliate former cruelty.

Our Saxon ancestors, fierce as they were in war, had but few executions in times of peace; and in all commencing governments that have the print of nature still strong upon them, scarce any crime is held capital.

It is among the citizens of a refined community that penal laws, which are in the hands of the rich, are laid upon the poor. Government, while it grows older, seems to acquire the moroseness of age; and as if our property were become dearer in proportion as it increased, as if the more enormous our wealth, the more extensive our fears, all our possessions are paled up with new edicts every day, and hung round with gibbets to scare every invader.

I cannot tell whether it is from the number of our penal laws, or the licentiousness of our people, that this country should shew more convicts in a year than half the dominions of Europe united. Perhaps it is owing to both; for they mutually produce each other. When by indiscriminate penal laws a nation beholds the same punishment affixed to dissimilar degrees of guilt, from perceiving no distinction in the penalty the people are led to lose all sense of distinction in the crime, and this distinction is the bulwark of all morality; thus the multitude of laws produce new vices, and new vices call for fresh restraints.

It were to be wished then that power, instead of contriving new laws to punish vice, instead of drawing hard the cords of society till a convulsion come to burst them, instead of cutting away wretches as useless before we have tried their utility, instead of converting correction into vengeance, it were to be wished that we tried the restrictive arts of government, and made law the protector, but not the tyrant of the people. We should then find that creatures, whose souls are held as dross, only wanted the hand of a refiner; we should then find that creatures, now stuck up for long tortures, lest luxury should feel a momentary pang, might, if properly treated, serve to sinew the state in times of danger; that as their faces are like ours, their hearts are so too; that few minds are so base as that perseverance cannot amend; that a man may see his last crime without dying for it; and that very little blood will serve to cement our security.

27

Happiness and misery rather the result of prudence than of virtue in this life. Temporal evils or felicities being regarded by heaven as things merely in themselves trifling, and unworthy its care in the distribution.

I HAD now been confined more than a fortnight, but had not since my arrival been visited by my dear Olivia and I greatly longed to see her. Having communicated my wishes to my wife, the next morning the poor girl entered my apartment leaning on her sister's arm. The change which I saw in her countenance struck me. The numberless graces that once resided there were now fled, and the hand of death seemed to have moulded every feature to alarm me. Her temples were sunk, her forehead was tense, and a fatal paleness sat upon her cheek.

"I am glad to see thee, my dear," cried I; "but why this dejection, Livy? I hope, my love, you have too great a regard for me to permit disappointment thus to undermine a life which I prize as my own. Be cheerful, child, and we yet may see happier days."

"You have ever, Sir," replied she, "been kind to me, and it adds to my pain that I shall never have an opportunity of sharing that happiness you promise. Happiness, I fear, is no longer reserved for me here; and I long to be rid of a place where I have only found distress. Indeed, Sir, I wish you would make a proper submission to Mr. Thornhill; it may in some measure induce him to pity you, and it will give me relief in dying."

"Never, child," replied I, "never will I be brought to acknowledge my daughter a prostitute; for though the world may look upon your offence with scorn, let it be mine to regard it as a mark of credulity, not of guilt. My dear, I am no way miserable in this place, however dismal it may seem; and be assured that while you continue to bless me by living, he shall never have my consent to make you more wretched by marrying another."

After the departure of my daughter, my fellow-prisoner, who was by at this interview, sensibly enough expostulated upon my obstinacy in refusing a submission which promised to give me freedom. He observed, that the rest of my family was not to be sacrificed to the peace of one child alone, and she the only one who had offended me. "Beside," added he, "I don't know if it be just thus to obstruct the union of man and wife, which you do at present by refusing to consent to a match you cannot hinder, but may render unhappy."

"Sir," replied I, "you are unacquainted with the man that oppresses us. I am very sensible that no submission I can make could procure me liberty even for an hour. I am told that even in this very room a debtor of his no later than last year died for want. But though my submission and approbation could transfer me from hence to the most beautiful apartment he is possessed of; yet I would grant neither, as something whispers me that it would be giving a sanction to adultery. While my daughter lives, no other marriage of his shall ever be legal in my eye. Were she removed, indeed, I should be the basest of men, from any resentment of my own, to attempt putting asunder those who wish for an union. No, villain as he is, I should then wish him married to prevent the consequences of his future debaucheries. But now should I not be the most cruel of all fathers, to sign an instrument which must send my child to the grave, merely to avoid a prison myself: and thus to escape one pang break my child's heart with a thousand?"

He acquiesced in the justice of this answer, but could not avoid observing, that he feared my daughter's life was already too much wasted to keep me long a prisoner. "However," continued he, "though you refuse to submit to the nephew, I hope you have no objections to laying your case before the uncle, who has the first character in the kingdom for every thing that is just and good. I would advise you to send him a letter by the post, intimating all his nephew's ill usage, and my life for it, that in three days you shall have an answer." I thanked him for the hint, and instantly set about complying; but I wanted paper, and unluckily all our money had been laid out that morning in provisions: however, he supplied me.

For the three ensuing days I was in a state of anxiety to know what reception my letter might meet with; but in the mean time was frequently solicited by my wife to submit to any conditions rather than remain here, and every hour received repeated accounts of the decline of my daughter's health. The third day and the fourth arrived, but I received no answer to my letter; the complaints of a stranger against a favourite nephew were no way likely to succeed; so that these hopes soon vanished like all my former. My mind, however, still supported itself, though confinement and bad air began to make a visible alteration in my health, and my arm that had suffered in the fire grew worse. My children, however, sat by me, and while I was stretched on my straw read to me by turns, or listened and wept at my instructions. But my daughter's health declined faster than mine; every message from her contributed to increase my apprehensions and pain. The fifth morning after I had written the letter which was sent to Sir William Thornhill, I was alarmed with an account that she was speechless. Now it was, that confinement was truly painful to me; my soul was bursting from its prison to be near the pillow of my child, to comfort, to strengthen her, to receive her last wishes, and teach her soul the way to heaven! Another account came. She was expiring, and yet I was debarred the small comfort of weeping by her. My fellow-prisoner some time after came with the last account. He bade me be patient. She was dead!—The next morning he returned, and found me with my two little ones, now my only companions, who were using all their innocent efforts to comfort me. They entreated to read to me, and bade me not to cry, for I was now too old to weep. "And is not my sister an angel now, papa?" cried the eldest, "and why then are you sorry for her? I wish I were an angel out of this frightful place, if my papa were with me." "Yes," added my youngest darling, "Heaven, where my sister is, is a finer place than this, and there are none but good people there, and the people here are very bad."

Mr. Jenkinson interrupted their harmless prattle, by observing that now my daughter was no more, I should seriously think of the rest of my family, and attempt to save my own life, which was every day declining for want of necessaries and wholesome air. He added, that it was now incumbent on me to sacrifice any pride or resentment of my own, to the welfare of those who depended on me for support; and that I was now, both by reason and justice, obliged to try to reconcile my landlord.

"Heaven be praised," replied I, "there is no pride left me now, I should detest my own heart if I saw either pride or resentment lurking there. On the contrary, as my oppressor has been once my parishioner, I hope one day to present him up an unpolluted soul at the eternal tribunal. No, Sir, I have no resentment now, and though he has taken from me what I held dearer than all his treasures, though he has wrung my heart, for I am sick almost to fainting, very sick, my fellow-prisoner, yet that shall never inspire me with vengeance. I am now willing to approve his marriage, and if this submission can do him any pleasure, let him know, that, if I have done him any injury, I am sorry for it."

Mr. Jenkinson took pen and ink and wrote down my submission nearly as I have expressed it, to which I signed my name. My son was employed to carry the letter to Mr. Thornhill, who was then at his seat in the country. He went, and in about six hours returned with a verbal answer. He had some difficulty, he said, to get a sight of his landlord, as the servants were insolent and suspicious; but he accidentally saw him as he was going out upon business, preparing for his marriage, which was to be in three days. He continued to inform us that he stept up in the humblest manner and delivered the letter, which, when Mr. Thornhill had read, he said that all submission was now too late and unnecessary; that he had heard of our application to his uncle, which met with the contempt it deserved; and as for the rest, that all future applications should be directed to his attorney, not to him. He observed, however, that as he had a very good opinion of the discretion of the two young ladies, they might have been the most agreeable intercessors.

"Well, Sir," said I to my fellow-prisoner, "you now discover the temper of the man who oppresses me. He can at once be facetious and cruel; but let him use me as he will, I shall soon be free, in spite of all his bolts to restrain me. I am now drawing towards an abode that looks brighter as I approach it; this expectation cheers my afflictions, and though I leave an helpless family of orphans behind me, yet they will not be utterly forsaken; some friend perhaps will be found to assist them for the sake of their poor father, and some may charitably relieve them for the sake of their heavenly Father."

Just as I spoke, my wife, whom I had not seen that day before, appeared with looks of terror, and making efforts, but unable to speak. "Why, my love," cried I, "why will you thus increase my afflictions by your own, what though no submissions can turn our severe master, though he has doomed me to die in this place of wretchedness, and though we have lost a darling child, yet still you will find comfort in your other children when I shall be no more." "We have indeed lost," returned she, "a darling child. My Sophia, my dearest is gone, snatched from us, carried off by ruffians!"

"How, madam," cried my fellow-prisoner, "Miss Sophia carried off by villains, sure it cannot be?"

She could only answer with a fixed look and a flood of tears. But one of the prisoners' wives who was present, and came in with her, gave us a more distinct account: she informed us that as my wife, my daughter, and herself were taking a walk together on the great road a little way out of the village, a post-chaise and pair drove up to them and instantly stopt. Upon which a well-drest man, but not Mr. Thornhill, stepping out, clasped my daughter round the waist, and forcing her in, bid the postillion drive on, so that they were out of sight in a moment.

"Now," cried I, "the sum of my miseries is made up, nor is it in the power of any thing on earth to give me another pang. What! not one left! not to leave me one! the monster! the child that was next my heart! she had the beauty of an angel, and almost the wisdom of an angel. But support that woman, nor let her fall. Not to leave me one!"

"Alas! my husband," said my wife, "you seem to want comfort even more than I. Our distresses are great; but I could bear this and more, if I saw you but easy. They may take away my children, and all the world, if they leave me but you."

My son, who was present, endeavoured to moderate our grief; he bade us take comfort, for he hoped that we might still have reason to be thankful.—"My child," cried I, "look round the world, and see if there be any happiness left me now. Is not every ray of comfort shut out; while all our bright prospects only lie beyond the grave!"—"My dear father," returned he, "I hope there is still something that will give you an interval of satisfaction; for I have a letter from my brother George."— "What of him, child," interrupted I, "does he know our misery? I hope my boy is exempt from any part of what his wretched family suffers?"—"Yes, Sir," returned he, "he is perfectly gay, cheerful, and happy. His letter brings nothing but good news; he is the favourite of his colonel, who promises to procure him the very next lieutenancy that becomes vacant!"

"And are you sure of all this," cried my wife, "are you sure that nothing ill has befallen my boy?"—"Nothing indeed, Madam," returned my son, "you shall see the letter, which will give you the highest pleasure; and if any thing can procure you comfort I am sure that will." "But are you sure," still repeated she, "that the letter is from himself, and that he is really so happy?"—"Yes, Madam," replied he, "it is certainly his, and he will one day be the credit and the support of our family!"— "Then I thank Providence," cried she, "that my last letter to him has miscarried.—Yes, my dear," continued she, turning to me, "I will now confess, that though the hand of heaven is sore upon us in other instances, it has been favourable here. By the last letter I wrote my son, which was in the bitterness of anger, I desired him, upon his mother's blessing, and if he had the heart of a man, to see justice done his father and sister, and avenge our cause. But thanks be to Him that directs all things, it has miscarried, and I am at rest," "Woman," cried I, "thou hast done very ill, and at another time my reproaches might have been more severe. Oh! what a tremendous gulph hast thou escaped, that would have buried both thee and him in endless ruin. Providence indeed, has here been kinder to us than we to ourselves. It has reserved that son to be the father and protector of my children when I shall be away. How unjustly did I complain of being stript of every comfort, when still I hear that he is happy and insensible of our afflictions; still kept in reserve to support his widowed mother, and to protect his brothers and sisters. But what sisters has he left? he has no sisters now, they are all gone, robbed from me, and I am undone."— "Father," interrupted my son, "I beg you will give me leave to read this letter, I know it will please you." Upon which, with my permission, he read as follows.

Honoured Sir,

I have called off my imagination a few moments from the pleasures that surround me, to fix it upon objects that are still more pleasing, the dear little fire-side at home. My fancy draws that harmless group as listening to every line of this with great composure. I view those faces with delight which never felt the deforming hand of ambition or distress! But whatever your happiness may be at home, I am sure it will be some addition to it to hear that I am perfectly pleased with my situation, and every way happy here.

Our regiment is countermanded, and is not to leave the kingdom; the colonel, who professes himself my friend, takes me with him to all companies where he is acquainted, and after my first visit I generally find myself received with increased respect upon repeating it. I danced last night with Lady G——, and could I forget you know whom, I might be perhaps successful. But it is my fate still to remember others while I am myself forgotten by most of my absent friends, and in this number I fear, Sir, that I must consider you; for I have long expected the pleasure of a letter from home, to no purpose. Olivia and Sophia too promised to write, but seem to have forgotten me. Tell them they are two arrant little baggages, and that I am this moment in a most violent passion with them: yet still I know not how; though I want to bluster a little, my heart is respondent only to softer emotions. Then tell them, Sir, that after all, I love them affectionately, and be assured of my ever remaining

Your dutiful son.

"In all our miseries," cried I, "what thanks have we not to return, that one at least of our family is exempted from what we suffer. Heaven be his guard, and keep my boy thus happy to be the support of his widowed mother, and the father of these two babes, which is all the patrimony I can now bequeath him. May he keep their innocence from the temptations of want, and be their conductor in the paths of honour." I had scarce said these words when a noise, like that of a tumult, seemed to proceed from the prison below; it died away soon after, and a clanking of fetters was heard along the passage that led to my apartment. The keeper of the prison entered, holding a man all bloody, wounded and fettered with the heaviest irons. I looked with compassion on the wretch as he approached me, but with horror when I found it was my own son.—"My George! My George! and do I behold thee thus. Wounded! Fettered! Is this thy happiness? Is this the manner you return to me? O that this sight could break my heart at once and let me die!"

"Where, Sir, is your fortitude?" returned my son with an intrepid voice. "I must suffer, my life is forfeited, and let them take it."

I tried to restrain my passions for a few minutes in silence, but I thought I should have died with the effort. —"O, my boy, my heart weeps to behold thee thus, and I cannot, cannot help it. In the moment that I thought thee blest, and prayed for thy safety, to behold thee thus again! Chained, wounded! And yet the death of the youthful is happy. But I am old, a very old man, and have lived to see this day. To see my children all untimely falling about me, while I continue a wretched survivor in the midst of ruin! May all the curses that ever sunk a soul fall heavy upon the murderer of my children. May he live, like me, to see—"

"Hold, Sir," replied my son, "or I shall blush for thee. How, Sir, forgetful of your age, your holy calling, thus to arrogate the justice of heaven, and fling those curses upward that must soon descend to crush thy own grey head with destruction! No, Sir, let it be your care now to fit me for that vile death I must shortly suffer, to arm me with hope and resolution, to give me courage to drink of that bitterness which must shortly be my portion."

"My child, you must not die: I am sure no offence of thine can deserve so vile a punishment. My George could never be guilty of any crime to make his ancestors ashamed of him."

"Mine, Sir," returned my son, "is I fear an unpardonable one. When I received my mother's letter from home, I immediately came down, determined to punish

185

the betrayer of our honour, and sent him an order to meet me, which he answered not in person, but by his dispatching four of his domestics to seize me. I wounded one who first assaulted me, and I fear desperately; but the rest made me their prisoner. The coward is determined to put the law in execution against me; the proofs are undeniable; I have sent a challenge, and as I am the first transgressor upon the statute, I see no hopes of pardon. But you have often charmed me with your lessons of fortitude, let me now, Sir, find them in your example."

"And, my son, you shall find them. I am now raised above this world, and all the pleasures it can produce. From this moment I break from my heart all the ties that held it down to earth, and will prepare to fit us both for eternity. Yes, my son, I will point out the way, and my soul shall guide yours in the ascent, for we will take our flight together. I now see and am convinced you can expect no pardon here, and I can only exhort you to seek it at that greatest tribunal where we both shall shortly answer. But let us not be niggardly in our exhortation, but let all our fellow-prisoners have a share: good gaoler, let them be permitted to stand here while I attempt to improve them." Thus saying, I made an effort to rise from my straw, but wanted strength, and was able only to recline against the wall. The prisoners assembled themselves according to my directions, for they loved to hear my counsel; my son and his mother supported me on either side; I looked and saw that none were wanting, and then addressed them with the following exhortation.

29

The equal dealings of Providence demonstrated with regard to the happy and the miserable here below. That from the nature of pleasure and pain, the wretched must be repaid the balance of their sufferings in the life hereafter.

My friends, my children, and fellow sufferers, when I reflect on the distribution of good and evil here below, I find that much has been given man to enjoy, yet still more to suffer. Though we should examine the whole world, we shall not find one man so happy as to have nothing left to wish for; but we daily see thousands who by suicide shew us they have nothing left to hope. In this life then it appears that we cannot be entirely blest, but yet we may be completely miserable.

Why man should thus feel pain, why our wretchedness should be requisite in the formation of universal felicity; why, when all other systems are made perfect by the perfection of their subordinate parts, the great system should require for its perfection parts that are not only subordinate to others, but imperfect in themselves; these are questions that never can be explained, and might be useless if known. On this subject Providence has thought fit to elude our curiosity, satisfied with granting us motives to consolation.

In this situation, man has called in the friendly assistance of philosophy, and heaven, seeing the incapacity of that to console him, has given him the aid of religion. The consolations of philosophy are very amusing, but often fallacious. It tells us that life is filled with comforts, if we will but enjoy them; and on the other hand, that though we unavoidably have miseries here, life is short, and they will soon be over. Thus do these consolations destroy each other; for if life is a place of comfort, its shortness must be misery, and if it be long, our griefs are protracted. Thus philosophy is weak; but religion comforts in an higher strain. Man is here, it tells us, fitting up his mind, and preparing it for another abode. When the good man leaves the body, and is all a glorious mind, he will find he has been making himself a heaven of happiness here; while the wretch that has been maimed and contaminated by his vices, shrinks from his body with terror, and finds that he has anticipated the vengeance of heaven. To religion then we must hold in every circumstance of life for our truest comfort; for if already we are happy, it is a pleasure to think that we can make that happiness unending; and if we are miserable, it is very consoling to think that there is a place of rest. Thus to the fortunate religion holds out a continuance of bliss, to the wretched a change from pain.

But though religion is very kind to all men, it has promised peculiar rewards to the unhappy; the sick, the naked, the houseless, the heavy-laden, and the prisoner, have ever most frequent promises in our sacred law. The Author of our religion everywhere professes himself the wretch's friend, and unlike the false ones of this world, bestows all his caresses upon the forlorn. The unthinking have censured this as partiality, as a preference without merit to deserve it. But they never reflect that it is not in the power even of Heaven itself to make the offer of unceasing felicity as great a gift to the happy as to the miserable. To the first eternity is but a single blessing, since at most it but increases what they already possess. To the latter it is a double advantage; for it diminishes their pain here, and rewards them with heavenly bliss hereafter.

But Providence is in another respect kinder to the poor than the rich; for as it thus makes the life after death more desirable, so it smoothes the passage there. The wretched have had a long familiarity with every face of terror. The man of sorrows lays himself quietly down, without possessions to regret, and but few ties to stop his departure: he feels only nature's pang in the final separation, and this is no way greater than he has often fainted under before; for after a certain degree of pain, every new breach that death opens in the constitution, nature kindly covers with insensibility.

Thus Providence has given the wretched two advantages over the happy in this life, greater felicity in dying, and in heaven all that superiority of pleasure which arises from contrasted enjoyment. And this superiority, my friends, is no small advantage, and seems to be one of the pleasures of the poor man in the parable; for though he was already in heaven, and felt all the raptures it could give, yet it was mentioned as an addition to his happiness, that he had once been wretched, and now was comforted; that he had known what it was to be miserable, and now felt what it was to be happy.

Thus, my friends, you see religion does what philosophy could never do; it shews the equal dealings of heaven to the happy and the unhappy, and levels all human enjoyments to nearly the same standard. It gives to both rich and poor the same happiness hereafter, and equal hopes to aspire after it; but if the rich have the advantage of enjoying pleasure here, the poor have the endless satisfaction of knowing what it was once to be miserable, when crowned with endless felicity hereafter; and even though this should be called a small advantage, yet being an eternal one, it must make up by duration what the temporal happiness of the great may have exceeded by intenseness.

These are therefore the consolations which the wretched have peculiar to themselves, and in which they are above the rest of mankind; in other respects they are below them. They who would know the miseries of the poor, must see life and endure it. To declaim on the temporal advantages they enjoy is only repeating what none either believe or practise. The men who have the necessaries of living are not poor, and they who want them must be miserable. Yes my friends, we must be miserable. No vain efforts of a refined imagination can soothe the wants of nature, can give elastic sweetness to the dank vapour of a dungeon, or ease the throbbings of a broken heart. Let the philosopher from his couch of softness tell us that we can resist all these. Alas! the effort by which we resist them is still the greatest pain! Death is slight, and any man may sustain it; but torments are dreadful, and these no man can endure.

To us then my friends the promises of happiness in heaven should be peculiarly dear; for if our reward be in this life alone, we are then indeed of all men the most miserable. When I look round these gloomy walls, made to terrify as well as to confine us; this light that only serves to show the horrors of the place, those shackles that tyranny has imposed or crime made necessary; when I survey these emaciated looks, and hear those groans, O! my friends, what a glorious exchange would heaven be for these. To fly through regions unconfined as air, to bask in the sunshine of eternal bliss, to carol over endless hymns of praise, to have no master to threaten or insult us, but the form of Goodness himself for ever in our eyes; when I think of these things, death becomes the messenger of very glad tidings; when I think of these things his sharpest arrow becomes the staff of my support; when I think of these things, what is there in life worth having? when I think of these things what is there that should not be spurned away? kings in their palaces should groan for such advantages; but we, humbled as we are, should yearn for them.

And shall these things be ours? Ours they will certainly be if we but try for them; and what is a comfort, we are shut out from many temptations that would retard our pursuit. Only let us try for them and they will certainly be ours, and what is still a comfort, shortly too; for if we look back on a past life it appears by a very short span, and whatever we may think of the rest of life, it will yet be found of less duration; as we grow older the days seem to grow shorter, and our intimacy with time ever lessens the perception of his stay. Then let us

. . . religion does what philosophy could never do . . .

take comfort now, for we shall soon be at our journey's end; we shall soon lay down the heavy burthen laid by heaven upon us; and though death, the only friend of the wretched, for a little while mocks the weary traveller with the view, and, like his horizon still flies before him; yet the time will certainly and shortly come when we shall cease from our toil; when the luxuriant great ones of the world shall no more tread us to the earth; when we shall think with pleasure on our sufferings below; when we shall be surrounded with all our friends, or such as deserved our friendship; when our bliss shall be unutterable, and still to crown all, unending.

30

Happier prospects begin to appear. Let us be inflexible, and fortune will at last change in our favour.

WHEN I had thus finished, and my audience was retired, the gaoler, who was one of the most humane of his profession, hoped I would not be displeased, as what he did was but his duty, observing that he must be obliged to remove my son into a stronger cell, but that he should be permitted to visit me every morning. I thanked him for his clemency, and grasping my boy's hand bade him farewell, and be mindful of the great duty that was before him.

I again therefore laid me down, and one of my little ones sate by my bed-side reading, when Mr. Jenkinson entering, informed me that there was news of my daughter; for that she was seen by a person about two hours before in a strange gentleman's company, and that they had stopt at a neighbouring village for refreshment, and seemed as if returning to town. He had scarcely delivered this news, when the gaoler came with looks of haste and pleasure to inform me that my daughter was found. Moses came running in a moment after, crying out that his sister Sophy was below, and coming up with our old friend Mr. Burchell.

Just as he delivered this news my dearest girl entered, and with looks almost wild with pleasure ran to kiss me in a transport of affection. Her mother's tears and silence also shewed her pleasure.—"Here, papa," cried the charming girl, "here is the brave man to whom I owe my delivery; to this gentleman's intrepidity I am indebted for my happiness and safety—" A kiss from Mr. Buchell, whose pleasure seemed even greater than hers, interrupted what she was going to add.

"Ah, Mr. Burchell," cried I, "this is but a wretched

habitation you now find us in; and we are now very different from what you last saw us. You were ever our friend: we have long discovered our errors with regard to you, and repented of our ingratitude. After the vile usage you then received at my hands, I am almost ashamed to behold your face; yet I hope you'll forgive me, as I was deceived by a base ungenerous wretch, who under the mask of friendship has undone me."

"It is impossible," cried Mr. Burchell, "that I should forgive you, as you never deserved my resentment. I partly saw your delusion then, and as it was out of my power to restrain, I could only pity it!"

"It was ever my conjecture," cried I, "that your mind was noble, but now I find it so. But tell me, my dear child, how hast thou been relieved, or who the ruffians were who carried thee away."

"Indeed, Sir," replied she, "as to the villain who carried me off, I am yet ignorant. For as my mamma and I were walking out, he came behind us, and almost before I could call for help, forced me into the post-chaise, and in an instant the horses drove away. I met several on the road to whom I cried out for assistance; but they disregarded my entreaties. In the mean time the ruffian himself used every art to hinder me from crying out: he flattered and threatened by turns, and swore that if I continued but silent he intended no harm. In the mean time I had broken the canvas that he had drawn up, and whom should I perceive at some distance but your old friend Mr. Burchell, walking along with his usual swiftness, with the great stick for which we used so much to ridicule him. As soon as we came within hearing, I called out to him by name and entreated his help. I repeated my exclamation several times, upon which with a very loud voice he bid the postillion stop; but the boy took no notice, but drove on with still greater speed. I now thought he could never overtake us, when in less than a minute I saw Mr. Burchell come running up by the side of the horses, and with one blow knock the postillion to the ground. The horses when he was fallen soon stopt of themselves, and the ruffian, stepping out, with oaths and menaces drew his sword, and ordered him at his peril to retire; but Mr. Burchell running up shivered his sword to pieces, and then pursued him for near a quarter of a mile; but he made his escape. I was at this time come out myself, willing to assist my deliverer; but he soon returned to me in triumph. The postillion, who was recovered, was going to make his escape too; but Mr. Burchell ordered him at his peril to mount again and drive back to town. Finding it impossible to resist, he reluctantly complied, though the wound he had received seemed, to me at least, to be dangerous. He continued to complain of the pain as we drove along, so that he at last excited Mr. Burchell's compassion, who at my request exchanged him for another at an inn where we called on our return."

"Welcome, then," cried I, "my child, and thou her gallant deliverer, a thousand welcomes. Though our cheer is but wretched yet our hearts are ready to receive you. And now, Mr. Burchell, as you have delivered my girl, if you think her a recompence she is yours; if you can stoop to an alliance with a family so poor as mine, take her, obtain her consent, as I know you have her heart, and you have mine. And let me tell you, Sir, that I give you no small treasure; she has been celebrated for beauty it is true, but that is not my meaning, I give you up a treasure in her mind."

"But I suppose, Sir," cried Mr. Burchell, "that you are apprized of my circumstances, and of my incapacity to support her as she deserves?"

"If your present objection," replied I, "be meant as an evasion of my offer, I desist: but I know no man so worthy to deserve her as you: and if I could give her thousands, and thousands sought her from me, yet my honest brave Burchell should be my dearest choice."

To all this his silence alone seemed to give a mortifying refusal, and without the least reply to my offer, he demanded if he could not be furnished with refreshments from the next inn, to which being answered in the affirmative, he ordered them to send in the best dinner that could be provided upon such short notice. He bespoke also a dozen of their best wine, and some cordials for me, adding, with a smile, that he would stretch a little for once, and though in a prison asserted he was never better disposed to be merry. The waiter soon made his appearance with preparations for dinner; a table was lent us by the gaoler, who seemed remarkably assiduous, the wine was disposed in order, and two very well-drest dishes were brought in.

My daughter had not yet heard of her poor brother's melancholy situation, and we all seemed unwilling to damp her cheerfulness by the relation. But it was in vain that I attempted to appear cheerful, the circumstances of my unfortunate son broke through all efforts to dissemble; so that I was at last obliged to damp our mirth by relating his misfortunes, and wishing that he might be permitted to share with us in this little interval of satisfaction. After my guests were recovered from the consternation my account had produced, I requested also that Mr. Jenkinson, a fellow-prisoner, might be admitted, and the gaoler granted my request with an air of unusual submission. The clanking of my son's irons was no sooner heard along the passage than his sister ran impatiently to meet him; while Mr. Burchell in the mean time asked me if my son's name were George, to which replying in the affirmative he still continued silent. As soon as my boy entered the room, I could perceive he regarded Mr. Burchell with a look of astonishment and reverence. "Come on," cried I, "my son, though we are fallen very low, yet Providence has been pleased to grant us some small relaxation from pain. Thy sister is restored to us, and there is her deliverer: to that brave man it is that I am indebted for yet having a daughter; give him, my boy, the hand of friendship, he deserves our warmest gratitude."

My son seemed all this while regardless of what I said, and still continued fixed at a respectful distance.—"My dear brother," cried his sister, "why don't you thank my good deliverer? the brave should ever love each other."

He still continued his silence and astonishment, till our guest at last perceived himself to be known, and assuming all his native dignity desired my son to come forward. Never before had I seen any thing so truly majestic as the air he assumed upon this occasion. The greatest object in the universe, says a certain philosopher, is a good man struggling with adversity; yet there is still a greater, which is the good man that comes to relieve it. After he had regarded my son for some time with a superior air, "I again find," said he, "unthinking boy, that the same crime"—But here he was interrupted by one of the gaoler's servants, who came to inform us that a person of distinction, who had driven into town with a chariot and several attendants, sent his respects to the gentleman that was with us and begged to know when he should think proper to be waited upon.—"Bid the fellow wait," cried our guest, "till I shall have leisure to receive him;" and then turning to my son, "I again find, Sir," proceeded he, "that you are guilty of the same offence, for which you once had my reproof, and for which the law is now preparing its justest punishments. You imagine, perhaps, that a contempt for your own life gives you a right to take that of another: but where, Sir, is the difference between a duellist who hazards a life of no value, and the murderer who acts with greater security? Is it any diminution of the gamester's fraud when he alleges that he has staked a counter?"

"Alas, Sir," cried I, "whoever you are, pity the poor misguided creature; for what he has done was in obedience to a deluded mother, who in the bitterness of her resentment required him upon her blessing to avenge her quarrel. Here, Sir, is the letter which will serve to convince you of her imprudence and diminish his guilt."

He took the letter and hastily read it over. "This," says

he, "though not a perfect excuse, is such a palliation of his fault, as induces me to forgive him. And now, Sir," continued he, kindly taking my son by the hand, "I see you are surprised at finding me here; but I have often visited prisons upon occasions less interesting. I am now come to see justice done a worthy man, for whom I have the most sincere esteem. I have long been a disguised spectator of thy father's benevolence. I have at his little dwelling enjoyed respect uncontaminated by flattery, and have received that happiness that courts could not give, from the amusing simplicity round his fireside. My nephew has been apprized of my intentions of coming here, and I find is arrived; it would be wronging him and you to condemn him without examination: if there be injury there shall be redress; and this I may say without boasting, that none have ever taxed the injustice of Sir William Thornhill."

We now found the personage whom we had so long entertained as an harmless amusing companion was no other than the celebrated Sir William Thornhill, to whose virtues and singularities scarce any were strangers. The poor Mr. Burchell was in reality a man of large fortune and great interest, to whom senates listened with applause, and whom partly heard with conviction; who was the friend of his country, but loyal to his king. My poor wife recollecting her former familiarity seemed to shrink with apprehension; but Sophia, who a few moments before thought him her own, now perceiving the immense distance to which he was removed by fortune, was unable to conceal her tears.

"Ah, Sir," cried my wife with a piteous aspect, "how is it possible that I can ever have your forgiveness? The slights you received from me the last time I had the honour of seeing you at our house, and the jokes which I audaciously threw out, these jokes, Sir, I fear can never be forgiven."

"My dear good lady," returned he with a smile, "if you had your joke I had my answer: I'll leave it to all the company if mine were not as good as yours. To say the truth I know nobody whom I am disposed to be angry with at present but the fellow who so frighted my little girl here. I had not even time to examine the rascal's person so as to describe him in an advertisement. Can you tell me, Sophia, my dear, whether you should know him again?"

"Indeed, Sir," replied she, "I can't be positive; yet now I recollect he had a large mark over one of his eye-brows." "I ask pardon, Madam," interrupted Jenkin-son, who was by, "but be so good as to inform me if the fellow wore his own red hair?"—"Yes, I think so," cried Sophia.—"And did your honour," continued he, turning to Sir William, "observe the length of his legs?"—"I can't be sure of their length," cried the Baronet, "but I am convinced of their swiftness; for he outran me, which is what I thought few men in the kingdom could have done."—"Please your honour," cried Jenkinson, "I know the man: it is certainly the same; the best runner in England; he has beaten Pinwire of Newcastle. Timothy Baxter is his name, I know him perfectly, and the very place of his retreat this moment. If your honour will bid Mr. Gaoler let two of his men go with me, I'll engage to produce him to you in an hour at farthest." Upon this the gaoler was called, who instantly appearing, Sir William demanded if he knew him. "Yes, please your honour," replied the gaoler, "I know Sir William Thornhill well, and everybody that knows any thing of him will desire to know more of him."—"Well, then," said the Baronet, "my request is, that you will permit this man and two of your servants to go upon a message by my authority, and as I am in the Commission of the Peace, I undertake to secure you."—"Your promise is sufficient," replied the other, "and you may at a minute's warning send them over England whenever your honour thinks fit."

In pursuance of the gaoler's compliance, Jenkinson was dispatched in search of Timothy Baxter, while we were amused with the assiduity of our youngest boy Bill, who had just come in and climbed up to Sir William's neck in order to kiss him. His mother was immediately going to chastise his familiarity, but the worthy man prevented her; and taking the child, all ragged as he was, upon his knee, "What, Bill, you chubby rogue," cried he "do you remember your old friend Burchell? and Dick too, my honest veteran, are you here? you shall find I have not forgot you." So saying, he gave each a large piece of gingerbread, which the poor fellows ate very heartily, as they had got that morning but a very scanty breakfast.

We now sat down to dinner, which was almost cold; but previously, my arm still continuing painful, Sir William wrote a prescription, for he had made the study of physic his amusement, and was more than moderately skilled in the profession: this being sent to an apothecary who lived in the place, my arm was dressed, and I found almost instantaneous relief. We were waited upon at dinner by the gaoler himself, who was willing to do our guest all the honour in his power. But before we had well dined, another message was brought from his nephew, desiring permission to appear in order to vindicate his innocence and honour, with which request the Baronet complied, and desired Mr. Thornhill to be introduced.

31

Former benevolence now repaid with unexpected interest.

MR. THORNHILL made his appearance with a smile, which he seldom wanted, and was going to embrace his uncle, which the other repulsed with an air of disdain. "No fawning, Sir, at present," cried the Baronet, with a look of severity, "the only way to my heart is by the road of honour; but here I only see complicated instances of falsehood, cowardice, and oppression. How is it, Sir, that this poor man, for whom I know you professed a friend-ship, is used thus hardly? His daughter vilely seduced, as a recompense for his hospitality, and he himself thrown into a prison, perhaps but for resenting the insult? His son too whom you feared to face as a man—"

"Is it possible, Sir," interrupted his nephew, "that my uncle could object that as a crime, which his repeated instructions alone have persuaded me to avoid."

"Your rebuke," cried Sir William, "is just: you have acted in this instance prudently and well, though not quite as your father would have done: my brother indeed was the soul of honour; but thou—yes you have acted in this instance perfectly right, and it has my warmest approbation."

"And I hope," said his nephew, "that the rest of my conduct will not be found to deserve censure. I appeared, Sir, with this gentleman's daughter at some places of public amusement: thus, what was levity, scandal called by a harsher name, and it was reported that I had debauched her. I waited on her father in person, willing to clear the thing to his satisfaction, and he received me only with insult and abuse. As for the rest, with regard to his being here, my attorney and steward can best inform you, as I commit the management of business entirely to them. If he has contracted debts and is unwilling or even unable to pay them, it is their business to proceed in this manner, and I see no hardship or injustice in pursuing the most legal means of redress."

"If this," cried Sir William, "be as you have stated it, there is nothing unpardonable in your offence; and though your conduct might have been more generous in not suffering this gentleman to be oppressed by subordinate tyranny, yet it has been at least equitable."

"He cannot contradict a single particular," replied the 'Squire; "I defy him to do so, and several of my servants are ready to attest what I say. Thus, Sir," continued he, finding that I was silent, for in fact I could not contradict him, "thus, Sir, my own innocence is vindicated; but though at your entreaty I am ready to forgive this gentleman every other offence, yet his attempts to lessen me in your esteem excite a resentment that I cannot govern. And this too at a time when his son was actually preparing to take away my life; this I say was such guilt that I am determined to let the law take its course. I have here the challenge that was sent me, and two witnesses to prove it; one of my servants has been wounded dangerously, and even though my uncle himself should dissuade me, which I know he will not, yet I will see public justice done, and he shall suffer for it."

"Thou monster," cried my wife, "hast thou not had vengeance enough already, but must my poor boy feel thy cruelty? I hope that good Sir William will protect us, for my son is as innocent as a child; I am sure he is and never did harm to man."

"Madam," replied the good man, "your wishes for his safety are not greater than mine; but I am sorry to find his guilt too plain; and if my nephew persists"—But the appearance of Jenkinson and the gaoler's two servants now called off our attention, who entered hauling in a tall man very genteelly drest, and answering the description already given of the ruffian who had carried off my daughter—"Here," cried Jenkinson, pulling him in, "here we have him; and if ever there was a candidate for Tyburn this is one."

The moment Mr. Thornhill perceived the prisoner, and Jenkinson who had him in custody, he seemed to shrink back with terror. His face became pale with conscious guilt, and he would have withdrawn; but Jenkinson, who perceived his design, stopt him.— "What 'Squire," cried he, "are you ashamed of your two old acquaintances, Jenkinson and Baxter? but this is the way that all great men forget their friends, though I am resolved we will not forget you. Our prisoner, please your honour," continued he, turning to Sir William, "has already confessed all. This is the gentleman reported to be so dangerously wounded; he declares that it was Mr. Thornhill who first put him upon this affair, that he gave him the clothes he now wears to appear like a gentleman, and furnished him with the post-chaise. The plan was laid between them that he should carry off the young lady to a place of safety, and that there he should threaten and terrify her; but Mr. Thornhill was to come in in the meantime, as if by accident, to her rescue, and that they should fight a while, and then he was to run off, by which Mr. Thornhill would have the better opportunity of gaining her affections himself under the character of her defender."

Sir William remembered the coat to have been frequently worn by his nephew, and all the rest the prisoner himself confirmed by a more circumstantial account; concluding, that Mr. Thornhill had often declared to him that he was in love with both sisters at the same time.

"Heavens!" cried Sir William, "what a viper have I been fostering in my bosom! And so fond of public justice too as he seemed to be. But he shall have it; secure him, Mr. Gaoler—yet hold, I fear there is not legal evidence to detain him."

Upon this, Mr. Thornhill, with the utmost humility, entreated that two such abandoned wretches might not be admitted as evidences against him, but that his servants should be examined.—"Your servants!" replied Sir William, "wretch, call them yours no longer: but come, let us hear what those fellows have to say, let his butler be called."

When the butler was introduced, he soon perceived by his former master's looks that all his power was now over. "Tell me," cried Sir William sternly, "have you ever seen your master and that fellow drest up in his clothes in company together?" "Yes, please your honour," cried the butler, "a thousand times: he was the man that always brought him his ladies."—"How," interrupted young Mr. Thornhill, "this to my face!"—"Yes," replied the butler, "or to any man's face. To tell you a truth, Master Thornhill, I never either loved you or liked you, and I don't care if I tell you now a piece of my mind."—"Now then," cried Jenkinson, "tell his honour whether you know any thing of me."—"I can't say," replied the butler, "that I know much good of you. The night that gentleman's daughter was deluded to our house you were one of them."—"So then," cried Sir William, "I find you have brought a very fine witness to prove your innocence: thou stain to humanity! to associate with such wretches!" (But continuing his examination) "You tell me, Mr. Butler, that this was the person who brought him this old gentleman's daughter."—"No, please your honour," replied the butler, "he did not bring her, for the 'Squire himself undertook that business; but he brought the priest that pretended to marry them."—"It is but too true," cried Jenkinson, "I cannot deny it; that was the employment assigned me, and I confess it to my confusion."

"Good heavens!" exclaimed the Baronet, "how every new discovery of his villainy alarms me. All his guilt is now too plain, and I find his prosecution was dictated by tyranny, cowardice, and revenge; at my request, Mr. Gaoler, set this young officer, now your prisoner, free, and trust to me for the consequences. I'll make it my business to set the affair in a proper light to my friend the magistrate who has committed him. But where is the unfortunate young lady herself? let her appear to confront this wretch; I long to know by what arts he has seduced her. Entreat her to come in. Where is she?"

"Ah, Sir," said I, "that question stings me to the heart: I was once indeed happy in a daughter, but her miseries—" Another interruption here prevented me; for who should make her appearance but Miss Arabella Wilmot, who was next day to have been married to Mr. Thornhill. Nothing could equal her surprise at seeing Sir William and his nephew here before her; for her arrival was quite accidental. It happened that she and the old gentleman her father were passing through the town, on their way to her aunt's, who had insisted that her nuptials with Mr. Thornhill should be consummated at her house; but stopping for refreshment, they put up at an inn at the other end of the town. It was there from the window that the young lady happened to observe one of my little boys playing in the street, and instantly sending a footman to bring the child to her, she learnt from him some account of our misfortunes; but was still kept ignorant of young Mr. Thornhill's being the cause. Though her father made several remonstrances on the impropriety of going to a prison to visit us, yet they were ineffectual; she desired the child to conduct her, which he did, and it was thus she surprised us at a juncture so unexpected.

Nor can I go on, without a reflection on those accidental meetings, which, though they happen every day, seldom excite our surprise but upon some extraordinary occasion. To what a fortuitous occurrence do we not owe every pleasure and convenience of our lives. How many seeming accidents must unite before we can be clothed or fed. The peasant must be disposed to labour, the shower must fall, the wind fill the merchant's sail, or numbers must want the usual supply.

We all continued silent for some moments, while my

charming pupil, which was the name I generally gave this young lady, united in her looks compassion and astonishment, which gave new finishings to her beauty. "Indeed, my dear Mr. Thornhill," cried she to the 'Squire, who she supposed was come here to succour and not to oppress us, "I take it a little unkindly that you should come here without me, or never inform me of the situation of a family so dear to us both: you know I should take as much pleasure in contributing to the relief of my reverend old master here, whom I shall ever esteem, as you can. But I find that, like your uncle, you take pleasure in doing good in secret."

"*He* find pleasure in doing good!" cried Sir William, interrupting her. "No, my dear, his pleasures are as base as he is. You see in him, madam, as compleat a villain as ever disgraced humanity. A wretch, who after having deluded this poor man's daughter, after plotting against the innocence of her sister, has thrown the father into prison, and the eldest son into fetters, because he had courage to face her betrayer. And give me leave, madam, now to congratulate you upon an escape from the embraces of such a monster."

"Oh goodness," cried the lovely girl, "how have I been deceived! Mr. Thornhill informed me for certain that this gentleman's eldest son, Captain Primrose, was gone off to America with his new-married lady."

"My sweetest miss," cried my wife, "he has told you nothing but falsehoods. My son George never left the kingdom, nor never was married.—Though you have forsaken him, he has always loved you too well to think of any body else; and I have heard him say he would die a bachelor for your sake." She then proceeded to expatiate upon the sincerity of her son's passion, she set his duel with Mr. Thornhill in a proper light, from thence she made a rapid digression to the 'Squire's debaucheries, his pretended marriages, and ended with a most insulting picture of his cowardice.

"Good heaven!" cried Miss Wilmot, "how very near

have I been to the brink of ruin! But how great is my pleasure to have escaped it! Ten thousand falsehoods has this gentleman told me! He had at last art enough to persuade me that my promise to the only man I esteemed was no longer binding, since he had been unfaithful. By his falsehoods I was taught to detest one equally brave and generous!"

But by this time my son was freed from the incumbrances of justice, as the person supposed to be wounded was detected to be an impostor. Mr. Jenkinson also, who had acted as his valet-de-chambre, had drest up his hair, and furnished him with whatever was necessary to make a genteel appearance. He now therefore entered, handsomely drest in his regimentals, and, without vanity (for I am above it), he appeared as handsome a fellow as ever wore a military dress. As he entered, he made Miss Wilmot a modest and distant bow, for he was not as yet acquainted with the change which the eloquence of his mother had wrought in his favour. But no decorums could restrain the impatience of his blushing mistress to be forgiven. Her tears, her looks, all contributed to discover the real sensations of her heart for having forgotten her former promise, and having suffered herself to be deluded by an impostor. My son appeared amazed at her condescension, and could scarce believe it real.—"Sure, madam," cried he, "this is but delusion! I can never have merited this! To be blessed thus is to be too happy." —"No, Sir," replied she, "I have been deceived, basely deceived, else nothing could ever have made me unjust to my promise. You know my friendship, you have long known it; but forget what I have done, and as you once had my warmest vows of constancy, you shall now have them repeated; and be assured that if your Arabella cannot be yours she shall never be another's."—"And no other's you shall be," cried Sir William, "if I have any influence with your father."·

This hint was sufficient for my son Moses, who immediately flew to the inn where the old gentleman was, to inform him of every circumstance that had happened. But in the mean time the 'Squire perceiving that he was on every side undone, now finding that no hopes were left from flattery or dissimulation, concluded that his wisest way would be to turn and face his pursuers. Thus laying aside all shame, he appeared the open hardy villain. "I find then," cried he, "that I am to expect no justice here; but I am resolved it shall be done me. You shall know, Sir," turning to Sir William, "I am no longer a poor dependant upon your favours. I scorn them. Nothing can keep Miss Wilmot's fortune from me, which, I thank her father's assiduity, is pretty large. The articles, and a bond for her fortune, are signed, and safe in my possession. It was her fortune, not her person, that induced me to wish for this match; and possesst of the one, let who will take the other."

This was an alarming blow; Sir William was sensible of the justice of his claims, for he had been instrumental in drawing up the marriage articles himself. Miss Wilmot therefore, perceiving that her fortune was irretrievably lost, turning to my son, she asked if the loss of fortune could lessen her value to him. "Though fortune," said she, "is out of my power, at least I have my hand to give."

"And that, madam," cried her real lover, "was indeed all that you ever had to give; at least all that I ever thought worth the acceptance. And I now protest, my Arabella, by all that's happy, your want of fortune this moment encreases my pleasure, as it serves to convince my sweet girl of my sincerity."

Mr. Wilmot now entering, he seemed not a little pleased at the danger his daughter had just escaped, and readily consented to a dissolution of the match. But finding that her fortune, which was secured to Mr. Thornhill by bond, would not be given up, nothing could exceed his disappointment. He now saw that his money must all go to enrich one who had no fortune of his own. He could bear his being a rascal, but to want an equivalent to his daughter's fortune was wormwood. He sat therefore for

some minutes employed in the most mortifying speculations, till Sir William attempted to lessen his anxiety.—
"I must confess, Sir," cried he, "that your present disappointment does not entirely displease me. Your im-
moderate passion for wealth is now justly punished. But
though the young lady cannot be rich, she has still a
competence sufficient to give content. Here you see an
honest young soldier, who is willing to take her without
fortune; they have long loved each other, and for the
friendship I bear his father, my interest shall not be
wanting in his promotion. Leave then that ambition
which disappoints you, and for once admit that happiness which courts your acceptance."

"Sir William," replied the old gentleman, "be assured
I never yet forced her inclinations, nor will I now. If she
still continues to love this young gentleman, let her have
him with all my heart.—There is still, thank heaven,
some fortune left, and your promise will make it something more. Only let my old friend here (meaning me)
give me a promise of settling six thousand pounds upon
my girl if ever he should come to his fortune, and I am
ready this night to be the first to join them together."

As it now remained with me to make the young couple
happy, I readily gave a promise of making the settlement
he required, which, to one who had such little expectations as I, was no great favour.—We had now therefore
the satisfaction of seeing them fly into each other's arms
in a transport.—"After all my misfortunes," cried my son
George, "to be thus rewarded! Sure this is more than I
could ever have presumed to hope for. To be possesst of all
that's good, and after such an interval of pain! My
warmest wishes could never rise so high!"

"Yes, my George," returned his lovely bride, "now let
the wretch take my fortune; since you are happy without
it, so am I. Oh, what an exchange have I made, from the
basest of men to the dearest, best!—Let him enjoy our
fortune, I can now be happy even in indigence."—"And
I promise you," cried the 'Squire, with a malicious grin,

"that I shall be very happy with what you despise."
"Hold, hold, Sir," cried Jenkinson, "there are two words
to that bargain. As for that lady's fortune, Sir, you shall
never touch a single stiver of it. Pray your honour," continued he to Sir William, "can the 'Squire have this
lady's fortune if he be married to another?"—"How can
you make such a simple demand?" replied the Baronet;
"undoubtedly he cannot."—"I am sorry for that," cried
Jenkinson; "for as this gentleman and I have been old
fellow-sporters, I have a friendship for him. But I must
declare, well as I love him, that his contract is not worth
a tobacco stopper, for he is married already."—"You lie,
like a rascal," returned the 'Squire, who seemed roused by
this insult; "I never was legally married to any woman."

"Indeed, begging your honour's pardon," replied the
other, "you were; and I hope you will shew a proper
return of friendship to your own honest Jenkinson, who
brings you a wife, and if the company restrains their
curiosity a few minutes, they shall see her."—So saying he
went off with his usual celerity, and left us all unable to
form any probable conjecture as to his design.—"Ay let
him go," cried the 'Squire; "whatever else I may have
done I defy him there. I am too old now to be frightened
with squibs."

"I am surprised," said the Baronet, "what the fellow
can intend by this. Some low piece of humour I suppose!"—"Perhaps, Sir," replied I, "he may have a more
serious meaning. For when we reflect on the various
schemes this gentleman has laid to seduce innocence,
perhaps some one more artful than the rest has been
found able to deceive him. When we consider what
numbers he has ruined, how many parents now feel with
anguish the infamy and the contamination which he has
brought into their families, it would not surprise me if
some one of them—Amazement! Do I see my lost
daughter? Do I hold her? It is, it is my life, my happiness.
I thought thee lost, my Olivia, yet still I hold thee—and
still thou shalt live to bless me." The warmest transports

of the fondest lover were not greater than mine when I saw him introduce my child, and held my daughter in my arms, whose silence only spoke her raptures.

"And art thou returned to me, my darling," cried I, "to be my comfort in age!"—"That she is," cried Jenkinson, "and make much of her, for she is your own honourable child, and as honest a woman as any in the whole room, let the other be who she will. And as for you, 'Squire, as sure as you stand there, this young lady is your lawful wedded wife. And to convince you that I speak nothing but truth, here is the licence by which you were married together."—So saying he put the licence into the Baronet's hands, who read it and found it perfect in every respect. "And now, gentlemen," continued he, "I find you are surprised at all this; but a few words will explain the difficulty. That there 'Squire of renown, for whom I have a great friendship, but that's between ourselves, has often employed me in doing odd little things for him. Among the rest, he commissioned me to procure him a false licence and a false priest, in order to deceive this young lady. But as I was very much his friend, what did I do but went and got a true licence and a true priest, and married them both as fast as the cloth could make them? Perhaps you'll think it was generosity that made me do all this. But no. To my shame I confess it, my only design was to keep the licence and let the 'Squire know that I could prove it upon him whenever I thought proper, and so make him come down whenever I wanted money." A burst of pleasure now seemed to fill the whole apartment; our joy reached even to the common room, where the prisoners themselves sympathized,

> And shook their chains
> In transport and rude harmony.

Happiness was expanded upon every face, and even Olivia's cheek seemed flushed with pleasure. To be thus restored to reputation, to friends and fortune at once, was a rapture sufficient to stop the progress of decay and restore former health and vivacity. But perhaps among all there was not one who felt sincerer pleasure than I. Still holding the dear-loved child in my arms, I asked my heart if these transports were not delusion. "How could you," cried I, turning to Mr. Jenkinson, "how could you add to my miseries by the story of her death? But it matters not; my pleasure at finding her again is more than a recompence for the pain."

"As to your question," replied Jenkinson, "that is easily answered. I thought the only probable means of freeing you from prison, was by submitting to the 'Squire, and consenting to his marriage with the other young lady. But these you had vowed never to grant while your daughter was living; there was therefore no other method to bring things to bear but by persuading you that she was dead. I prevailed on your wife to join in the deceit, and we have not had a fit opportunity of undeceiving you till now."

In the whole assembly now there only appeared two faces that did not glow with transport. Mr. Thornhill's assurance had entirely forsaken him: he now saw the gulph of infamy and want before him, and trembled to take the plunge. He therefore fell on his knees before his uncle, and in a voice of piercing misery implored compassion. Sir William was going to spurn him away, but at my request he raised him, and after pausing a few moments, "Thy vices, crimes, and ingratitude," cried he, "deserve no tenderness; yet thou shalt not be entirely forsaken, a bare competence shall be supplied to support the wants of life, but not its follies. This young lady, thy wife, shall be put in possession of a third part of that fortune which once was thine, and from her tenderness alone thou art to expect any extraordinary supplies for the future." He was going to express his gratitude for such kindness in a set speech; but the Baronet prevented him by bidding him not aggravate his meanness, which was already but too apparent. He ordered him at the same time to be gone, and from all his former domestics to chuse one such as he should think proper, which was all that should be granted to attend him.

As soon as he left us, Sir William very politely stept up to his new niece with a smile and wished her joy. His example was followed by Miss Wilmot and her father; my wife too kissed her daughter with much affection, as, to use her own expression, she was now made an honest woman of. Sophia and Moses followed in turn, and even our benefactor Jenkinson desired to be admitted to that honour. Our satisfaction seemed scarce capable of encrease. Sir William, whose greatest pleasure was in doing good, now looked round with a countenance open as the sun, and saw nothing but joy in the looks of all except that of my daughter Sophia, who, for some reasons we could not comprehend, did not seem perfectly satisfied. "I think now," cried he with a smile, "that all the company except one or two seem perfectly happy. There only remains an act of justice for me to do. You are sensible, Sir," continued he, turning to me, "of the obligations we both owe Mr. Jenkinson. And it is but just we should both reward him for it. Miss Sophia will, I am sure, make him very happy, and he shall have from me five hundred pounds as her fortune, and upon this I am sure they can live very comfortably together. Come, Miss Sophia, what say you to this match of my making? Will you have him?"—My poor girl seemed almost sinking into her mother's arms at the hideous proposal.—"Have him, Sir!" cried she faintly. "No, Sir, never."—"What," cried he again, "not have Mr. Jenkinson, your bene-factor, a handsome young fellow with five hundred pounds and good expectations!"—"I beg, Sir," returned she, scarce able to speak, "that you'll desist, and not make me so very wretched."—"Was ever such obstinacy known," cried he again, "to refuse a man whom the family has such infinite obligations to, who has preserved your sister and who has five hundred pounds! What, not have him!"—"No, Sir, never," replied she angrily, "I'd sooner die first."—"If that be the case then," cried he,

No, Sir, never.

"if you will not have him—I think I must have you myself." And so saying he caught her to his breast with ardour. "My loveliest, my most sensible of girls," cried he, "how could you ever think your own Burchell could deceive you, or that Sir William Thornhill could ever cease to admire a mistress that loved him for himself alone? I have for some years sought for a woman, who, a stranger to my fortune, could think that I had merit as a man. After having tried in vain, even amongst the pert and the ugly, how great at last must be my rapture to have made a conquest over such sense and such heavenly beauty." Then turning to Jenkinson, "As I cannot, Sir, part with this young lady myself, for she has taken a fancy to the cut of my face, all the recompence I can make is to give you her fortune, and you may call upon my steward to-morrow for five hundred pounds." Thus we had all our compliments to repeat, and Lady Thornhill underwent the same round of ceremony that her sister had done before. In the mean time Sir William's gentleman appeared to tell us that the equipages were ready to carry us to the inn, where every thing was prepared for our reception. My wife and I led the van, and left those gloomy mansions of sorrow. The generous Baronet ordered forty pounds to be distributed among the prisoners, and Mr. Wilmot, induced by his example, gave half that sum. We were received below by the shouts of the villagers, and I saw and shook by the hand two or three of my honest parishioners who were among the number. They attended us to our inn, where a sumptuous entertainment was provided, and coarser provisions were distributed in great quantities among the populace.

After supper, as my spirits were exhausted by the alternation of pleasure and pain, which they had sustained during the day, I asked permission to withdraw, and leaving the company in the midst of their mirth, as soon as I found myself alone I poured out my heart in gratitude to the Giver of joy as well as of sorrow, and then slept undisturbed till morning.

32

The Conclusion.

THE next morning as soon as I awaked I found my eldest
son sitting by my bedside, who came to increase my joy
with another turn of fortune in my favour. First having
released me from the settlement that I had made the day
before in his favour, he let me know that my merchant
who had failed in town was arrested at Antwerp, and
there had given up effects to a much greater amount than
what was due to his creditors. My boy's generosity pleased
me almost as much as this unlooked for good fortune. But
I had some doubts whether I ought in justice to accept
his offer. While I was pondering upon this, Sir William
entered the room, to whom I communicated my doubts.
His opinion was, that as my son was already possessed of
a very affluent fortune by his marriage, I might accept
his offer without any hesitation. His business, however,
was to inform me that as he had the night before sent for
the licences, and expected them every hour, he hoped
that I would not refuse my assistance in making all the
company happy that morning. A footman entered while
we were speaking, to tell us that the messenger was
returned, and as I was by this time ready I went down,
where I found the whole company as merry as affluence
and innocence could make them. However, as they were
now preparing for a very solemn ceremony, their laughter
entirely displeased me. I told them of the grave, becoming, and sublime deportment they should assume upon
this mystical occasion, and read them two homilies and a
thesis of my own composing in order to prepare them.
Yet they still seemed perfectly refractory and ungovern-

able. Even as we were going along to church, to which I
led the way, all gravity had quite forsaken them, and I
was often tempted to turn back in indignation. In church
a new dilemma arose, which promised no easy solution.
This was, which couple should be married first; my son's
bride warmly insisted that Lady Thornhill (that was to
be) should take the lead; but this the other refused with
equal ardour, protesting she would not be guilty of such
rudeness for the world. The argument was supported for
some time between both with equal obstinacy and good
breeding. But as I stood all this time with my book ready,
I was at last quite tired of the contest, and shutting it,
"I perceive," cried I, "that none of you have a mind to
be married, and I think we had as good go back again;
for I suppose there will be no business done here to-day."
—This at once reduced them to reason. The Baronet and
his lady were first married, and then my son and his
lovely partner.

I had previously that morning given orders that a
coach should be sent for my honest neighbour Flamborough and his family, by which means, upon our return
to the inn, we had the pleasure of finding the two Miss
Flamboroughs alighted before us. Mr. Jenkinson gave
his hand to the eldest, and my son Moses led up the
other; (and I have since found that he has taken a real
liking to the girl, and my consent and bounty he shall
have, whenever he thinks proper to demand them). We
were no sooner returned to the inn, but numbers of my
parishioners, hearing of my success, came to congratulate
me, but among the rest were those who rose to rescue me,
and whom I formerly rebuked with such sharpness. I told
the story to Sir William, my son-in-law, who went out
and reproved them with great severity; but finding them
quite disheartened by his harsh reproof, he gave them
half a guinea apiece to drink his health and raise their
dejected spirits.

Soon after this we were called to a very genteel entertainment, which was drest by Mr. Thornhill's cook. And

it may not be improper to observe with respect to that gentleman, that he now resides in quality of companion, at a relation's house, being very well liked and seldom sitting at the side-table, except when there is no room at the other; for they make no stranger of him. His time is pretty much taken up in keeping his relation, who is a little melancholy, in spirits, and in learning to blow the French horn. My eldest daughter, however, still remembers him with regret; and she has even told me, though I make a great secret of it, that when he reforms she may be brought to relent.

But to return, for I am not apt to digress thus, when we were to sit down to dinner our ceremonies were going to be renewed. The question was whether my eldest daughter, as being a matron should not sit above the two young brides, but the debate was cut short by my son George, who proposed that the company should sit indiscriminately, every gentleman by his lady. This was received with great approbation by all, excepting my wife, who I could perceive was not perfectly satisfied, as she expected to have had the pleasure of sitting at the head of the table and carving all the meat for all the company. But notwithstanding this, it is impossible to describe our good humour. I can't say whether we had more wit amongst us now than usual, but I am certain we had more laughing, which answered the end as well. One jest I particularly remember; old Mr. Wilmot drinking to Moses, whose head was turned another way, my son replied, "Madam, I thank you." Upon which the old gentleman, winking upon the rest of the company, observed that he was thinking of his mistress. At which jest I thought the two Miss Flamboroughs would have died with laughing. As soon as dinner was over, according to my old custom, I requested that the table might be taken away to have the pleasure of seeing all my family assembled once more by a chearful fire-side. My two little ones sat upon each knee, the rest of the company by their partners. I had nothing now on this side of the grave to wish for ; all my cares were over, my pleasure was unspeakable. It now only remained that my gratitude in good fortune should exceed my former submission in adversity.

THE END

SHE STOOPS TO CONQUER

CONQUER

or, The Mistakes of a Night

DRAMATIS PERSONAE

MEN

Sir Charles Marlow
Young Marlow, *his son*
Hardcastle
Hastings
Tony Lumpkin
Diggory

WOMEN

Mrs. Hardcastle
Miss Hardcastle
Miss Neville
Maid
Landlords, Servants, *etc.*

SHE STOOPS TO CONQUER

OR, THE MISTAKES OF A NIGHT

———◆———

PROLOGUE

BY DAVID GARRICK, ESQ.

Enter Mr. Woodward, dressed in black, and holding a hand-kerchief to his eyes.

EXCUSE me, sirs, I pray—I can't yet speak—
  I'm crying now—and have been all the week.
"'Tis not alone this mourning suit," good masters;
  "I've that within"—for which there are no plasters!
Pray would you know the reason why I'm crying?
  The comic muse, long sick, is now a-dying!
And if she goes, my tears will never stop;
  For as a player, I can't squeeze out one drop:
I am undone, that's all—shall lose my bread—
  I'd rather, but that's nothing—lose my head.
When the sweet maid is laid upon the bier,
  Shuter and I shall be chief mourners here.
To her a mawkish drab of spurious breed,
  Who deal in Sentimentals will succeed!
Poor Ned and I are dead to all intents;
  We can as soon speak Greek as Sentiments.
Both nervous grown, to keep our spirits up,
  We now and then take down a hearty cup.
What shall we do?—If Comedy forsake us!
  They'll turn us out, and no one else will take us,
But, why can't I be moral?—Let me try—
  My heart thus pressing—fix'd my face and eye—
With a sententious look, that nothing means
  (Faces are blocks, in sentimental scenes),

Thus I begin—"All is not gold that glitters,
  "Pleasure seems sweet, but proves a glass of bitters.
"When ignorance enters, folly is at hand:
  "Learning is better far than house and land.
"Let nor your virtue trip, who trips may stumble,
  "And virtue is not virtue, if she tumble."
I give it up—morals won't do for me;
  To make you laugh, I must play tragedy.
One hope remains—hearing the maid was ill,
  A Doctor comes this night to show his skill.
To cheer her heart, and give your muscles motion,
  He in Five Draughts prepar'd, presents a potion:
A kind of magic charm—for be assur'd,
  If you will swallow it, the maid is cur'd.
But desperate the Doctor, and her case is,
  If you reject the dose, and make wry faces!
This truth he boasts, will boast it while he lives,
  No poisonous drugs are mix'd in what he gives.
Should he succeed, you'll give him his degree;
  If not, within he will receive no fee!
The college You, must his pretensions back,
  Pronounce him Regular, or dub 'him Quack.

ACT ONE, SCENE ONE

A Chamber in an old-fashioned house.

Enter Mrs. Hardcastle *and* Mr. Hardcastle.

mrs. hard. : I vow, Mr. Hardcastle, you're very particular. Is there a creature in the whole country, but ourselves, that does not take a trip to town now and then, to rub off the rust a little? There's the two Miss Hoggs, and our neighbour, Mrs. Grigsby, go to take a month's polishing every winter.

hard. : Ay, and bring back vanity and affectation to last them the whole year. I wonder why London cannot keep its own fools at home. In my time, the follies of the town crept slowly among us, but now they travel faster than a stage-coach. Its fopperies come down, not only as inside passengers, but in the very basket.

mrs. hard. : Ay, your times were fine times, indeed; you have been telling us of them for many a long year. Here we live in an old rambling mansion, that looks for all the world like an inn, but that we never see company. Our best visitors are old Mrs. Oddfish, the curate's wife, and little Cripplegate, the lame dancing-master : and all our entertainment your old stories of Prince Eugene and the Duke of Marlborough. I hate such old-fashioned trumpery.

hard. : And I love it. I love everything that's old : old friends, old times, old manners, old books, old wine; and, I believe, Dorothy (*taking her hand*), you'll own I have been pretty fond of an old wife.

mrs. hard. : Lord, Mr. Hardcastle, you're for ever at your Dorothys and your old wives. You may be a Darby, but I'll be no Joan, I promise you. I'm not so old as you'd make me, by more than one good year. Add twenty to twenty, and make money of that.

HARD.: Let me see; twenty added to twenty makes just fifty and seven.

MRS. HARD.: It's false, Mr. Hardcastle: I was but twenty when Tony was born, the son of Mr. Lumpkin, my first husband; and he's not come to years of discretion yet.

HARD.: Nor ever will, I dare answer for him. Ay, you have taught him finely!

MRS. HARD.: No matter, Tony Lumpkin has a good fortune. My son is not to live by his learning. I don't think a boy wants much learning to spend fifteen hundred a-year.

HARD.: Learning, quotha! a mere composition of tricks and mischief!

MRS. HARD.: Humour, my dear: nothing but humour. Come, Mr. Hardcastle, you must allow the boy a little humour.

HARD.: I'd sooner allow him a horse-pond! If burning the footmen's shoes, frightening the maids, and worrying the kittens be humour, he has it. It was but yesterday he fastened my wig to the back of my chair, and when I went to make a bow, I popt my bald head in Mrs. Frizzle's face!

MRS. HARD.: And am I to blame? The poor boy was always too sickly to do any good. A school would be his death. When he comes to be a little stronger, who knows what a year or two's Latin may do for him?

HARD.: Latin for him! A cat and fiddle! No, no, the alehouse and the stable are the only schools he'll ever go to.

MRS. HARD.: Well, we must not snub the poor boy now, for I believe we shan't have him long among us. Anybody that looks in his face may see he's consumptive.

HARD.: Ay, if growing too fat be one of the symptoms.

MRS. HARD.: He coughs sometimes.

HARD.: Yes, when his liquor goes the wrong way.

MRS. HARD.: I'm actually afraid of his lungs.

HARD.: And truly, so am I; for he sometimes whoops like

a speaking-trumpet—(*Tony hallooing behind the scenes*)—
O, there he goes—a very consumptive figure, truly!

Enter TONY, *crossing the stage.*

MRS. HARD.: Tony, where are going, my charmer? Won't
you give papa and I a little of your company, lovee?

TONY: I'm in haste, mother; I cannot stay.

MRS. HARD.: You shan't venture out this raw evening, my
dear; you look most shockingly.

TONY: I can't stay, I tell you. The Three Pigeons expects
me down every moment. There's some fun going
forward.

HARD.: Ay; the alehouse, the old place: I thought so.

MRS. HARD.: A low, paltry set of fellows.

TONY: Not so low, neither. There's Dick Muggins the
exciseman, Jack Slang the horse doctor, Little Amina-
dab that grinds the music-box, and Tom Twist that
spins the pewter platter.

MRS. HARD.: Pray, my dear, disappoint them for one
night, at least.

TONY: As for disappointing them, I should not so much
mind; but I can't abide to disappoint myself!

MRS. HARD.: (*Detaining him.*) You shan't go.

TONY: I will, I tell you.

MRS. HARD.: I say you shan't.

TONY: We'll see which is strongest, you or I.

[*Exit, hauling her out.*

HARDCASTLE *solus.*

HARD.: Ay, there goes a pair that only spoil each other.
But is not the whole age in a combination to drive
sense and discretion out of doors? There's my pretty
darling Kate! the fashions of the times have almost
infected her too. By living a year or two in town, she's
as fond of gauze and French frippery as the best of
them.

Enter MISS HARDCASTLE.

HARD.: Blessings on my pretty innocence! drest out as
usual, my Kate. Goodness! What a quantity of superfluous silk hast thou got about thee, girl! I could never

teach the fools of this age, that the indigent world could be clothed out of the trimmings of the vain.

MISS HARD.: You know our agreement, sir. You allow me the morning to receive and pay visits, and to dress in my own manner; and in the evening I put on my housewife's dress to please you.

HARD.: Well, remember, I insist on the terms of our agreement; and, by the by, I believe I shall have occasion to try your obedience this very evening.

MISS HARD.: I protest, sir, I don't comprehend your meaning.

HARD.: Then, to be plain with you, Kate, I expect the young gentleman I have chosen to be your husband from town this very day. I have his father's letter, in which he informs me his son is set out, and that he intends to follow himself shortly after.

MISS HARD.: Indeed! I wish I had known something of this before. Bless me, how shall I behave? It's a thousand to one I shan't like him; our meeting will be so formal, and so like a thing of business, that I shall find no room for friendship or esteem.

HARD.: Depend upon it, child, I never will control your choice; but Mr. Marlow, whom I have pitched upon, is the son of my old friend, Sir Charles Marlow, of whom you have heard me talk so often. The young gentleman has been bred a scholar, and is designed for an employment in the service of his country. I am told he's a man of an excellent understanding.

MISS HARD.: Is he?

HARD.: Very generous.

MISS HARD.: I believe I shall like him.

HARD.: Young and brave.

MISS HARD.: I am sure I shall like him.

HARD.: And very handsome.

MISS HARD.: My dear papa, say no more (*kissing his hand*). He's mine, I'll have him.

HARD.: And, to crown all, Kate, he's one of the most bashful and reserved young fellows in all the world.

MISS HARD. : Eh! you have frozen me to death again. That word *reserved* has undone all the rest of his accomplishments. A reserved lover, it is said, always makes a suspicious husband.

HARD. : On the contrary, modesty seldom resides in a breast that is not enriched with nobler virtues. It was the very feature in his character that first struck me.

MISS HARD. : He must have more striking features to catch me, I promise you. However, if he be so young, so handsome, and so everything as you mention, I believe he'll do still. I think I'll have him.

HARD. : Ay, Kate, but there is still an obstacle. It is more than an even wager, he may not have you.

MISS HARD. : My dear papa, why will you mortify one so? Well, if he refuses, instead of breaking my heart at his indifference, I'll only break my glass for its flattery, set my cap to some newer fashion, and look out for some less difficult admirer.

HARD. : Bravely resolved! In the meantime I'll go prepare the servants for his reception; as we seldom see company, they want as much training as a company of recruits the first day's muster.   [*Exit.*

MISS HARD. : (*Alone.*) Lud, this news of papa's puts me all in a flutter. Young, handsome; these he put last; but I put them foremost. Sensible, good-natured; I like all that. But then reserved, and sheepish, that's much against him. Yet can't he be cured of his timidity, by being taught to be proud of his wife? Yes, and can't I— but I vow I'm disposing of the husband before I have secured the lover.

Enter MISS NEVILLE.

MISS HARD. : I'm glad you're come, Neville, my dear. Tell me, Constance, how do I look this evening? Is there anything whimsical about me? Is it one of my well-looking days, child? Am I in face to-day?

MISS NEVILLE : Perfectly, my dear. Yet, now I look again— bless me!—sure no accident has happened among the canary birds or the goldfishes? Has your brother or the cat been meddling? Or has the last novel been too moving?

MISS HARD.: No; nothing of all this. I have been threatened—I can scarce get it out—I have been threatened with a lover.

MISS NEVILLE: And his name—

MISS HARD.: Is Marlow.

MISS NEVILLE: Indeed!

MISS HARD.: The son of Sir Charles Marlow.

MISS NEVILLE: As I live, the most intimate friend of Mr. Hastings, my admirer. They are never asunder. I believe you must have seen him when we lived in town.

MISS HARD.: Never.

MISS NEVILLE: He's a very singular character, I assure you. Among women of reputation he is the modestest man alive; but his acquaintance give him a very different character among creatures of another stamp: you understand me.

MISS HARD.: An odd character, indeed. I shall never be able to manage him. What shall I do? Pshaw, think no more of him, but trust to occurrences for success. But how goes on your own affair, my dear? Has my mother been courting you for my brother Tony as usual?

MISS NEVILLE: I have just come from one of our agreeable *tête-à-têtes*. She has been saying a hundred tender things, and setting off her pretty monster as the very pink of perfection.

MISS HARD.: And her partiality is such, that she actually thinks him so. A fortune like yours is no small temptation. Besides, as she has the sole management of it, I'm not surprised to see her unwilling to let it go out of the family.

MISS NEVILLE: A fortune like mine, which chiefly consists in jewels, is no such mighty temptation. But at any rate, if my dear Hastings be but constant, I make no doubt to be too hard for her at last. However, I let her suppose that I am in love with her son, and she never once dreams that my affections are fixed upon another.

MISS HARD.: My good brother holds out stoutly. I could almost love him for hating you so.

MISS NEVILLE: It is a good-natured creature at bottom, and I'm sure would wish to see me married to anybody but himself. But my aunt's bell rings for our afternoon's walk round the improvements. *Allons.* Courage is necessary, as our affairs are critical.

MISS HARD.: "Would it were bed-time and all were well."

[*Exeunt.*

ACT ONE, SCENE TWO

An Alehouse Room.

Several shabby fellows, with punch and tobacco. TONY *at the head of the table, a little higher than the rest, a mallet in his hand.*

OMNES: Hurrea! hurrea! hurrea! bravo!

FIRST FELLOW: Now, gentlemen, silence for a song. The 'squire is going to knock himself down for a song.

OMNES: Ay, a song, a song.

TONY: Then I'll sing you, gentlemen, a song I made upon this alehouse, the Three Pigeons.

Song

Let school-masters puzzle their brain,
    With grammar, and nonsense, and learning;
Good liquor, I stoutly maintain,
    Gives genius a better discerning.
Let them brag of their heathenish gods,
    Their Lethes, their Styxes, and Stygians;
Their Quis, and their Quæs, and their Quods,
    They're all but a parcel of pigeons.
            Toroddle, toroddle, toroll!

When Methodist preachers come down,
　A-preaching that drinking is sinful,
I'll wager the rascals a crown,
　They always preach best with a skinful.
But when you come down with your pence,
　For a slice of their scurvy religion,
I'll leave it to all men of sense,
　But you, my good friend, are the pigeon.
　　　　Toroddle, toroddle, toroll!

Then come, put the jorum about,
　And let us be merry and clever,
Our hearts and our liquors are stout,
　Here's the Three Jolly Pigeons for ever.
Let some cry up woodcock or hare,
　Your bustards, your ducks, and your widgeons;
But of all the birds in the air,
　Here's a health to the Three Jolly Pigeons.
　　　　Toroddle, toroddle, toroll!

OMNES: Bravo, bravo!

FIRST FELLOW: The 'squire has got spunk in him.

SECOND FELLOW: I loves to hear him sing, bekeays he never gives us nothing that's low.

THIRD FELLOW: O damn anything that's low, I cannot bear it.

FOURTH FELLOW: The genteel thing is the genteel thing at any time: if so be that a gentleman bees in a concatenation accordingly.

THIRD FELLOW: I like the maxum of it, Master Muggins. What, though I am obligated to dance a bear, a man may be a gentleman for all that. May this be my poison if my bear ever dances but to the very genteelest of tunes; Water Parted, or the minuet in "Ariadne."

SECOND FELLOW: What a pity it is the 'squire is not come to his own. It would be well for all the publicans within ten miles round of him.

TONY: Ecod, and so it would, Master Slang. I'd then show what it was to keep choice of company.

SECOND FELLOW: Oh, he takes after his own father for that. To be sure, old 'squire Lumpkin was the finest gentleman I ever set my eyes on. For winding the straight horn, or beating a thicket for a hare, or a wench, he never had his fellow. It was a saying in the place, that he kept the best horses, dogs, and girls, in the whole county.

TONY: Ecod, and when I'm of age I'll be no bastard, I promise you. I have been thinking of Bet Bouncer and the miller's grey mare to begin with. But come, my boys, drink about and be merry, for you pay no reckoning. Well, Stingo, what's the matter?

Enter LANDLORD.

LANDLORD: There be two gentlemen in a postchaise at the door. They have lost their way upo' the forest; and they are talking something about Mr. Hardcastle.

TONY: As sure as can be, one of them must be the gentleman that's coming down to court my sister. Do they seem to be Londoners?

LANDLORD: I believe they may. They look woundily like Frenchmen.

TONY: Then desire them to step this way, and I'll set them right in a twinkling. [*Exit Landlord.*] Gentlemen, as they mayn't be good enough company for you, step down for a moment, and I'll be with you in the squeezing of a lemon. [*Exeunt Mob.*

TONY: (*Alone.*) Father-in-law has been calling me whelp and hound this half-year. Now, if I pleased, I could be so revenged upon the old grumbletonian. But then I'm afraid—afraid of what? I shall soon be worth fifteen hundred a year, and let him frighten me out of that if he can!

Enter the LANDLORD, *conducting* MARLOW *and* HASTINGS.

MARLOW: What a tedious uncomfortable day have we had of it! We were told it was but forty miles across the country, and we have come above threescore!

HASTINGS: And all, Marlow, from that unaccountable

reserve of yours that would not let us inquire more frequently on the way.

MARLOW: I own, Hastings, I am unwilling to lay myself under an obligation to everyone I meet, and often stand the chance of an unmannerly answer.

HASTINGS: At present, however, we are not likely to receive any answer.

TONY: No offence, gentlemen. But I'm told you have been inquiring for one Mr. Hardcastle in these parts. Do you know what part of the country you are in?

HASTINGS: Not in the least, sir, but should thank you for information.

TONY: Nor the way you came?

HASTINGS: No, sir; but if you can inform us—

TONY: Why, gentlemen, if you know neither the road you are going, nor where you are, nor the road you came, the first thing I have to inform you is, that—you have lost your way.

MARLOW: We wanted no ghost to tell us that.

TONY: Pray, gentlemen, may I be so bold as to ask the place from whence you came?

MARLOW: That's not necessary towards directing us where we are to go.

TONY: No offence; but question for question is all fair, you know.—Pray, gentlemen, is not this same Hard-castle a cross-grained, old-fashioned, whimsical fellow with an ugly face, a daughter, and a pretty son?

HASTINGS: We have not seen the gentleman; but he has the family you mention.

TONY: The daughter, a tall, trapesing, trolloping, talka-tive maypole—the son, a pretty, well-bred, agreeable youth, that everybody is fond of?

MARLOW: Our information differs in this. The daughter is said to be well-bred, and beautiful; the son, an awk-ward booby, reared up and spoiled at his mother's apron-string.

TONY: He-he-hem!—Then, gentlemen, all I have to tell

you is, that you won't reach Mr. Hardcastle's house
this night, I believe.

HASTINGS: Unfortunate!

TONY: It's a damned long, dark, boggy, dirty, dangerous
way. Stingo, tell the gentlemen the way to Mr. Hardcastle's. (*Winking upon the Landlord.*) Mr. Hardcastle's
of Quagmire Marsh, you understand me.

LANDLORD: Master Hardcastle's! Lock-a-daisy, my
masters, you're come a deadly deal wrong! When you
came to the bottom of the hill, you should have crossed
down Squash Lane.

MARLOW: Cross down Squash Lane!

LANDLORD: Then you were to keep straight forward,
until you came to four roads.

MARLOW: Come to where four roads meet!

TONY: Ay, but you must be sure to take only one of them.

MARLOW: O, sir, you're facetious!

TONY: Then, keeping to the right, you are to go sideways
till you come upon Crack-skull common: there you
must look sharp for the track of the wheel, and go forward, till you come to Farmer Murrain's barn. Coming
to the farmer's barn, you are to turn to the right, and
then to the left, and then to the right about again, till
you find out the old mill.

MARLOW: Zounds, man! we could as soon find out the
longitude!

HASTINGS: What's to be done, Marlow?

MARLOW: This house promises but a poor reception;
though perhaps the landlord can accommodate us.

LANDLORD: Alack, master, we have but one spare bed in
the whole house.

TONY: And to my knowledge, that's taken up by three
lodgers already. (*After a pause, in which the rest seem disconcerted.*) I have hit it. Don't you think, Stingo, our
landlady could accommodate the gentlemen by the
fireside, with—three chairs and a bolster?

HASTINGS: I hate sleeping by the fireside.

MARLOW: And I detest your three chairs and a bolster.

TONY : You do, do you?—then let me see—what if you go on a mile farther, to the Buck's Head; the old Buck's Head on the hill, one of the best inns in the whole county?

HASTINGS : Oho! so we have escaped an adventure for this night, however.

LANDLORD : (*Apart to Tony.*) Sure, you ben't sending them to your father's as an inn, be you?

TONY : Mum, you fool, you. Let them find that out. (*To them.*) You have only to keep on straight forward, till you come to a large old house by the roadside. You'll see a pair of large horns over the door. That's the sign. Drive up the yard, and call stoutly about you.

HASTINGS : Sir, we are obliged to you. The servants can't miss the way?

TONY : No, no: but I tell you, though, the landlord is rich, and going to leave off business; so he wants to be thought a gentleman, saving your presence, he! he! he! He'll be for giving you his company, and, ecod, if you mind him, he'll persuade you that his mother was an alderman, and his aunt a justice of peace!

LANDLORD : A troublesome old blade, to be sure; but 'a keeps as good wines and beds as any in the whole country.

MARLOW : Well, if he supplies us with these, we shall want no further connexion. We are to turn to the right, did you say?

TONY : No, no; straight forward. I'll just step myself, and show you a piece of the way. (*To the Landlord.*) Mum.

LANDLORD : Ah, bless your heart for a sweet, pleasant— damned, mischievous son of a whore.

ACT TWO

An Old-fashioned House.

(HARDCASTLE, *followed by three or four awkward Servants.*)

HARDCASTLE: Well, I hope you're perfect in the table exercise I have been teaching you these three days. You all know your posts and your places, and can shew that you have been used to good company, without ever stirring from home.

OMNES: Ay, ay.

HARD.: When company comes, you are not to pop out and stare, and then run in again, like frightened rabbits in a warren.

OMNES: No, no.

HARD.: You, Diggory, whom I have taken from the barn, are to make a shew at the side-table; and you, Roger, whom I have advanced from the plough, are to place yourself behind my chair. But you're not to stand so, with your hands in your pockets. Take your hands from your pockets, Roger; and from your head, you blockhead, you. See how Diggory carries his hands. They're a little too stiff, indeed, but that's no great matter.

DIGGORY: Ay, mind how I hold them. I learned to hold my hands this way, when I was upon drill for the militia. And so being upon drill—

HARD.: You must not be so talkative, Diggory. You must be all attention to the guests. You must hear us talk, and not think of talking; you must see us drink, and not think of drinking; you must see us eat, and not think of eating.

DIGGORY: By the laws, your worship, that's parfectly unpossible. Whenever Diggory sees yeating going forward, ecod, he's always wishing for a mouthful himself.

235

HARD.: Blockhead! Is not a bellyful in the kitchen as good as a bellyful in the parlour? Stay your stomach with that reflection.

DIGGORY: Ecod, I thank your worship, I'll make a shift to stay my stomach with a slice of cold beef in the pantry.

HARD.: Diggory, you are too talkative.—Then, if I happen to say a good thing, or tell a good story at table, you must not all burst out a-laughing, as if you made part of the company.

DIGGORY: Then, ecod, your worship must not tell the story of old Grouse in the gun-room: I can't help laughing at that—he! he! he!—for the soul of me! We have laughed at that these twenty years—ha! ha! ha!

HARD.: Ha! ha! ha! The story is a good one. Well, honest Diggory, you may laugh at that—but still remember to be attentive. Suppose one of the company should call for a glass of wine, how will you behave? A glass of wine, sir, if you please (*To Diggory*)—Eh, why don't you move?

DIGGORY: Ecod, your worship, I never have courage till I see the eatables and drinkables brought upo' the table, and then I'm as bauld as a lion.

HARD.: What, will nobody move?

FIRST SERVANT: I'm not to leave this pleace.

SECOND SERVANT: I'm sure it's no pleace of mine.

THIRD SERVANT: Nor mine, for sartain.

DIGGORY: Wauns, and I'm sure it canna be mine.

HARD.: You numskulls! and so while, like your betters, you are quarrelling for places, the guests must be starved. O, you dunces! I find I must begin all over again.—But don't I hear a coach drive into the yard? To your posts, you blockheads. I'll go in the meantime and give my old friend's son a hearty reception at the gate.   [*Exit Hardcastle.*

DIGGORY: By the elevens, my pleace is gone quite out of my head.

ROGER: I know that my pleace is to be everywhere!

FIRST SERVANT: Where the devil is mine?

SECOND SERVANT: My pleace is to be nowhere at all; and so I'ze go about my business!

[*Exeunt Servants, running about as if frighted, different ways.*

Enter Servant with lighted candles, showing in MARLOW *and* HASTINGS.

SERVANT: Welcome, gentlemen, very welcome! This way.

HASTINGS: After the disappointments of the day, welcome once more, Charles, to the comforts of a clean room and a good fire. Upon my word, a very well-looking house; antique but creditable.

MARLOW: The usual fate of a large mansion. Having first ruined the master by good house-keeping, it at last comes to levy contributions as an inn.

HASTINGS: As you say, we passengers are to be taxed to pay for all these fineries. I have often seen a good side-board, or a marble chimney-piece, though not actually put in the bill, inflame a reckoning confoundedly.

MARLOW: Travellers, George, must pay in all places. The only difference is, that in good inns you pay dearly for luxuries, in bad inns, you are fleeced and starved.

HASTINGS: You have lived pretty much among them. In truth, I have been often surprised, that you who have seen so much of the world, with your natural good sense, and your many opportunities, could never yet acquire a requisite share of assurance.

MARLOW: The Englishman's malady. But tell me, George, where could I have learned that assurance you talk of? My life has been chiefly spent in a college or an inn, in seclusion from that lovely part of the creation that chiefly teach men confidence. I don't know that I was ever familiarly acquainted with a single modest woman—except my mother—but among females of another class, you know—

HASTINGS: Ay, among them you are impudent enough of all conscience!

MARLOW: They are of *us*, you know.

HASTINGS: But in the company of women of reputation I

never saw such an idiot, such a trembler; you look for all the world as if you wanted an opportunity of stealing out of the room.

MARLOW: Why, man, that's because I do want to steal out of the room. Faith, I have often formed a resolution to break the ice, and rattle away at any rate. But I don't know how, a single glance from a pair of fine eyes has totally overset my resolution. An impudent fellow may counterfeit modesty, but I'll be hanged if a modest man can ever counterfeit impudence.

HASTINGS: If you could but say half the fine things to them, that I have heard you lavish upon the barmaid of an inn, or even a college bed-maker—

MARLOW: Why, George, I can't say fine things to them. They freeze, they petrify me. They may talk of a comet, or a burning mountain, or some such bagatelle; but to me, a modest woman, drest out in all her finery, is the most tremendous object of the whole creation.

HASTINGS: Ha! ha! ha! At this rate, man, how can you ever expect to marry!

MARLOW: Never; unless, as among kings and princes, my bride were to be courted by proxy. If, indeed, like an eastern bridegroom, one were to be introduced to a wife he never saw before, it might be endured. But to go through all the terrors of a formal courtship, together with the episode of aunts, grandmothers and cousins, and at last to blurt out the broad staring question of, Madam, will you marry me? No, no, that's a strain much above me, I assure you!

HASTINGS: I pity you. But how do you intend behaving to the lady you are come down to visit at the request of your father?

MARLOW: As I behave to all other ladies. Bow very low; answer yes, or no, to all her demands.—But for the rest, I don't think I shall venture to look in her face, till I see my father's again.

HASTINGS: I'm surprised that one who is so warm a friend can be so cool a lover.

MARLOW: To be explicit, my dear Hastings, my chief inducement down was to be instrumental in forwarding
your happiness, not my own. Miss Neville loves you,
the family don't know you; as my friend you are sure
of a reception, and let honour do the rest.

HASTINGS: My dear Marlow! But I'll suppress the emotion. Were I a wretch, meanly seeking to carry off a
fortune, you should be the last man in the world I
would apply to for assistance. But Miss Neville's person
is all I ask, and that is mine, both from her deceased
father's consent, and her own inclination.

MARLOW: Happy man! You have talents and art to
captivate any woman. I'm doomed to adore the sex,
and yet to converse with the only part of it I despise.
This stammer in my address, and this awkward unpre-
possessing visage of mine, can never permit me to soar
above the reach of a milliner's apprentice, or one of the
duchesses of Drury-Lane. Pshaw! this fellow here to
interrupt us.

Enter HARDCASTLE.

HARD.: Gentlemen, once more you are heartily welcome.
Which is Mr. Marlow? Sir, you're heartily welcome.
It's not my way, you see, to receive my friends with my
back to the fire. I like to give them a hearty reception
in the old style at my gate. I like to see their horses and
trunks taken care of.

MARLOW: (*Aside.*) He has got our names from the servants
already. (*To him.*) We approve your caution and
hospitality, sir. (*To Hastings.*) I have been thinking,
George, of changing our travelling dresses in the
morning. I am grown confoundedly ashamed of mine.

HARD.: I beg, Mr. Marlow, you'll use no ceremony in
this house.   [*Both ignore him.*

HASTINGS: I fancy, George, you're right: the first blow is
half the battle. I intend opening the campaign with the
white and gold.

HARD.: Mr. Marlow—Mr. Hastings—gentlemen—pray
be under no constraint in this house. This is Liberty

239

Hall, gentlemen. You may do just as you please here.

MARLOW: Yet, George, if we open the campaign too fiercely at first, we may want ammunition before it is over. I think to reserve the embroidery to secure a retreat.

HARD.: Your talking of a retreat, Mr. Marlow, puts me in mind of the Duke of Marlborough, when we went to besiege Denain. He first summoned the garrison—

MARLOW: Don't you think the *ventre d'or* waistcoat will do with the plain brown?

HARD.: He first summoned the garrison, which might consist of about five thousand men—

HASTINGS: I think not: brown and yellow mix but very poorly.

HARD.: I say, gentlemen, as I was telling you, he summoned the garrison, which might consist of about five thousand men—

MARLOW: The girls like finery.

HARD.: Which might consist of about five thousand men, well appointed with stores, ammunition, and other implements of war. "Now," says the Duke of Marlborough to George Brooks, that stood next to him—you must have heard of George Brooks; "I'll pawn my Dukedom," says he, "but I take that garrison without spilling a drop of blood." So—

MARLOW: What, my good friend, if you gave us a glass of punch in the meantime, it would help us to carry on the siege with vigour.

HARD.: Punch, sir! (*Aside.*) This is the most unaccountable kind of modesty I ever met with.

MARLOW: Yes, sir, punch! A glass of warm punch, after our journey, will be comfortable. This is Liberty Hall, you know.

HARD.: Here's a cup, sir.

MARLOW: (*Aside.*) So this fellow, in his Liberty Hall, will only let us have just what he pleases.

HARD.: (*Taking the cup.*) I hope you'll find it to your mind. I have prepared it with my own hands, and I believe

you'll own the ingredients are tolerable. Will you be so
good as to pledge me, sir? Here, Mr. Marlow, here is
our better acquaintance!   [*Drinks.*

MARLOW: (*Aside.*) A very impudent fellow this! but he's a
character, and I'll humour him a little. Sir, my service
to you.   [*Drinks.*

HASTINGS: (*Aside.*) I see this fellow wants to give us his
company, and forgets that he's an innkeeper, before he
has learned to be a gentleman.

MARLOW: From the excellence of your cup, my old friend,
I suppose you have a good deal of business in this part
of the country. Warm work, now and then, at elections,
I suppose?

HARD.: No, sir, I have long given that work over. Since
our betters have hit upon the expedient of electing each
other, there's no business "for us that sell ale."

HASTINGS: So, then you have no turn for politics, I find.

HARD.: Not in the least. There was a time, indeed, I
fretted myself about the mistakes of government, like
other people; but, finding myself every day grow more
angry, and the government growing no better, I left it
to mend itself. Since that, I no more trouble my head
about Heyder Ally or Ally Cawn, than about Ally
Croaker. Sir, my service to you.

HASTINGS: So that, with eating above stairs, and drinking
below, with receiving your friends within, and amusing
them without, you lead a good pleasant bustling life
of it.

HARD.: I do stir about a great deal, that's certain. Half
the differences of the parish are adjusted in this very
parlour.

MARLOW: (*After drinking.*) And you have an argument in
your cup, old gentleman, better than any in Westminster Hall.

HARD.: Ay, young gentleman, that, and a little philosophy.

MARLOW: (*Aside.*) Well, this is the first time I ever heard
of an innkeeper's philosophy.

HASTINGS: So then, like an experienced general, you attack them on every quarter. If you find their reason manageable, you attack it with your philosophy; if you find they have no reason, you attack them with this. Here's your health, my philosopher. [*Drinks.*

HARD.: Good, very good, thank you; ha! ha! Your generalship puts me in mind of Prince Eugene, when he fought the Turks at the battle of Belgrade. You shall hear.

MARLOW: Instead of the battle of Belgrade, I believe it's almost time to talk about supper. What has your philosophy got in the house for supper?

HARD.: For supper, sir! (*Aside.*) Was ever such a request to a man in his own house!

MARLOW: Yes, sir, supper, sir; I begin to feel an appetite. I shall make devilish work to-night in the larder, I promise you.

HARD.: (*Aside.*) Such a brazen dog sure never my eyes beheld. (*To him.*) Why, really, sir, as for supper I can't well tell. My Dorothy, and the cook-maid, settle these things between them. I leave these kind of things entirely to them.

MARLOW: You do, do you?

HARD.: Entirely. By the by, I believe they are in actual consultation upon what's for supper this moment in the kitchen.

MARLOW: Then I beg they'll admit me as one of their privy council. It's a way I have got. When I travel I always choose to regulate my own supper. Let the cook be called. No offence, I hope, sir.

HARD.: Oh no, sir, none in the least; yet, I don't know how: our Bridget, the cook maid, is not very communicative upon these occasions. Should we send for her, she might scold us all out of the house.

HASTINGS: Let's see your list of the larder, then. I ask it as a favour. I always match my appetite to my bill of fare.

MARLOW: (*To Hardcastle, who looks at them with surprise.*) Sir, he's very right, and it's my way, too.

HARD.: Sir, you have a right to command here. Here, Roger, bring us the bill of fare for to-night's supper. I believe it's drawn out.—Your manner, Mr. Hastings, puts me in mind of my uncle, Colonel Wallop. It was a saying of his, that no man was sure of his supper till he had eaten it.

HASTINGS: (*Aside.*) All upon the high rope! His uncle a colonel! We shall soon hear of his mother being a justice of peace. (*Hardcastle gives the paper to Marlow.*) But let's hear the bill of fare.

MARLOW: (*Perusing.*) What's here? For the first course; for the second course; for the dessert. The devil, sir, do you think we have brought down the whole Joiners' Company, or the Corporation of Bedford, to eat up such a supper? Two or three little things, clean and comfortable, will do.

HASTINGS: But let's hear it.

MARLOW: (*Reading.*) For the first course at the top, a pig, and pruin sauce.

HASTINGS: Damn your pig, I say!

MARLOW: And damn your pruin sauce, say I!

HARD.: And yet, gentlemen, to men that are hungry, pig with pruin sauce is very good eating.

MARLOW: At the bottom a calf's tongue and brains.

HASTINGS: Let your brains be knocked out, my good sir, I don't like them.

MARLOW: Or you may clap them on a plate by themselves. I do.

HARD.: (*Aside.*) Their impudence confounds me. (*To them.*) Gentlemen, you are my guests, make what alterations you please. Is there anything else you wish to retrench or alter, gentlemen?

MARLOW: A pork pie, a boiled rabbit and sausages, a Florentine, a shaking pudding, and a dish of tiff—taff—taffety cream!

HASTINGS: Confound your made dishes; I shall be as much at a loss in this house as at a green and yellow dinner at the French ambassador's table, I'm for plain eating.

HARD. : I'm sorry, gentlemen, that I have nothing you like, but if there be anything you have a particular fancy to—

MARLOW : Why really, sir, your bill of fare is so exquisite, that any one part of it is full as good as another. Send us what you please. So much for supper. And now to see that our beds are aired, and properly taken care of.

HARD. : I entreat you'll leave all that to me. You shall not stir a step.

MARLOW : Leave that to you! I protest, sir, you must excuse me, I always look to these things myself.

HARD. : I must insist, sir, you'll make yourself easy on that head.

MARLOW : You see I'm resolved on it. (*Aside.*) A very troublesome fellow this, as ever I met with.

HARD. : Well, sir, I'm resolved at least to attend you. (*Aside.*) This may be modern modesty, but I never saw anything look so like old-fashioned impudence.

[*Exeunt Marlow and Hardcastle.*

HASTINGS : (*Alone.*) So I find this fellow's civilities begin to grow troublesome. But who can be angry at those assiduities which are meant to please him? Ha! what do I see! Miss Neville, by all that's happy!

Enter MISS NEVILLE.

MISS NEVILLE : My dear Hastings! To what unexpected good fortune, to what accident, am I to ascribe this happy meeting?

HASTINGS : Rather let me ask the same question, as I could never have hoped to meet my dearest Constance at an inn.

MISS NEVILLE : An inn! sure you mistake: my aunt, my guardian, lives here. What could induce you to think this house an inn?

HASTINGS : My friend, Mr. Marlow, with whom I came down, and I, have been sent here as to an inn, I assure you. A young fellow, whom we accidentally met at a house hard by, directed us thither.

MISS NEVILLE: Certainly it must be one of my hopeful cousin's tricks, of whom you have heard me talk so often: ha! ha! ha!

HASTINGS: He whom your aunt intends for you? He of whom I have such just apprehensions?

MISS NEVILLE: You have nothing to fear from him, I assure you. You'd adore him if you knew how heartily he despises me. My aunt knows it, too, and has undertaken to court me for him, and actually begins to think she has made a conquest.

HASTINGS: Thou dear dissembler! You must know, my Constance, I have just seized this happy opportunity of my friend's visit here to get admittance into the family. The horses that carried us down are now fatigued with their journey, but they'll soon be refreshed; and then, if my dearest girl will trust in her faithful Hastings, we shall soon be landed in France, where even among slaves the laws of marriage are respected.

MISS NEVILLE: I have often told you, that though ready to obey you, I yet should leave my little fortune behind with reluctance. The greatest part of it was left me by my uncle, the India Director, and chiefly consists in jewels. I have been for some time persuading my aunt to let me wear them. I fancy I'm very near succeeding. The instant they are put into my possession you shall find me ready to make them and myself yours.

HASTINGS: Perish the baubles! Your person is all I desire. In the meantime, my friend Marlow must not be let into his mistake. I know the strange reserve of his temper is such that, if abruptly informed of it, he would instantly quit the house before our plan was ripe for execution.

MISS NEVILLE: But how shall we keep him in the deception? Miss Hardcastle is just returned from walking; what if we still continue to deceive him?—This, this way—   [*They confer.*

Enter MARLOW.

245

MARLOW: The assiduities of these good people tease me beyond bearing. My host seems to think it ill manners to leave me alone, and so he claps not only himself, but his old-fashioned wife on my back. They talk of coming to sup with us, too; and then, I suppose, we are to run the gauntlet through all the rest of the family.—What have we got here?—

HASTINGS: My dear Charles! Let me congratulate you!—The most fortunate accident!—Who do you think is just alighted?

MARLOW: Cannot guess.

HASTINGS: Our mistresses, boy, Miss Hardcastle and Miss Neville. Give me leave to introduce Miss Constance Neville to your acquaintance. Happening to dine in the neighbourhood, they called, on their return, to take fresh horses here. Miss Hardcastle has just stept into the next room, and will be back in an instant. Wasn't it lucky? eh!

MARLOW: (*Aside.*) I have just been mortified enough of all conscience, and here comes something to complete my embarrassment.

HASTINGS: Well! but wasn't it the most fortunate thing in the world?

MARLOW: Oh! yes. Very fortunate—a most joyful encounter.—But our dresses, George, you know, are in disorder.—What if we should postpone the happiness till to-morrow?—To-morrow at her own house.—It will be every bit as convenient—and rather more respectful.—To-morrow let it be.   [*Offering to go.*

MISS NEVILLE: By no means, sir. Your ceremony will displease her. The disorder of your dress will shew the ardour of your impatience. Besides, she knows you are in the house, and will permit you to see her.

MARLOW: Oh! the devil! how shall I support it? Hem! hem! Hastings, you must not go. You are to assist me, you know. I shall be confoundedly ridiculous. Yet, hang it! I'll take courage. Hem!

HASTINGS: Pshaw, man! it's but the first plunge, and all's over. She's but a woman, you know.

MARLOW: And of all women, she that I dread most to encounter!

Enter MISS HARDCASTLE, *as returned from walking.*

HASTINGS: (*Introducing them.*) Miss Hardcastle. Mr. Marlow. I'm proud of bringing two persons of such merit together, that only want to know, to esteem each other.

MISS HARD.: (*Aside.*) Now, for meeting my modest gentleman with a demure face, and quite in his own manner. (*After a pause, in which he appears very uneasy and disconcerted.*) I'm glad of your safe arrival, sir—I'm told you had some accidents by the way.

MARLOW: Only a few, madam. Yes, we had some. Yes, madam, a good many accidents, but should be sorry— madam—or rather glad of any accidents—that are so agreeably concluded. Hem!

HASTINGS: (*To him.*) You never spoke better in your whole life. Keep it up, and I'll insure you the victory.

MISS HARD.: I'm afraid you flatter, sir. You that have seen so much of the finest company can find little entertainment in an obscure corner of the country.

MARLOW: (*Gathering courage.*) I have lived, indeed, in the world, madam; but I have kept very little company. I have been but an observer upon life, madam, while others were enjoying it.

MISS NEVILLE: But that, I am told, is the way to enjoy it at last.

HASTINGS: (*To him.*) Cicero never spoke better. Once more, and you are confirmed in assurance for ever.

MARLOW: (*To him.*) Hem! Stand by me, then, and when I'm down, throw in a word or two to set me up again.

MISS HARD.: An observer, like you, upon life, were, I fear, disagreeably employed, since you must have had much more to censure than to approve.

MARLOW: Pardon me, madam. I was always willing to be amused. The folly of most people is rather an object of mirth than uneasiness.

247

HASTINGS: (*To him.*) Bravo, bravo. Never spoke so well in your whole life. Well, Miss Hardcastle, I see that you and Mr. Marlow are going to be very good company. I believe our being here will but embarrass the interview.

MARLOW: Not in the least, Mr. Hastings. We like your company of all things. (*To him.*) Zounds! George, sure you won't go? How can you leave us?

HASTINGS: Our presence will but soil conversation, so we'll retire to the next room. (*To him.*) You don't consider, man, that we are to manage a little *tête-à-tête* of our own. [*Exeunt.*

MISS HARD.: (*After a pause.*) But you have not been wholly an observer, I presume, sir: the ladies, I should hope, have employed some part of your addresses.

MARLOW: (*Relapsing into timidity.*) Pardon me, madam, I—I—I—as yet have studied—only—to—deserve them.

MISS HARD.: And that some say is the very worst way to obtain them.

MARLOW: Perhaps so, madam. But I love to converse only with the more grave and sensible part of the sex.—But I'm afraid I grow tiresome.

MISS HARD.: Not at all, sir; there is nothing I like so much as grave conversation myself: I could hear it for ever. Indeed, I have often been surprised how a man of sentiment could ever admire those light airy pleasures, where nothing reaches the heart.

MARLOW: It's—a disease—of the mind, madam. In the variety of tastes there must be some who, wanting a relish for—um-a-um.

MISS HARD.: I understand you, sir. There must be some, who, wanting a relish for refined pleasures, pretend to despise what they are incapable of tasting.

MARLOW: My meaning, madam, but infinitely better expressed. And I can't help observing—a—

MISS HARD.: (*Aside.*) Who could ever suppose this fellow impudent upon some occasions. (*To him.*) You were going to observe, sir—

Who could ever suppose this fellow impudent
upon some occasions.

MARLOW: I was observing, madam—I protest, madam, I forget what I was going to observe.

MISS HARD.: (*Aside.*) I vow and so do I. (*To him.*) You were observing, sir, that in this age of hypocrisy—something about hypocrisy, sir.

MARLOW: Yes, madam, In this age of hypocrisy, there are few who upon strict inquiry do not—a—a—a—

MISS HARD.: I understand you perfectly, sir.

MARLOW: (*Aside.*) Egad! and that's more than I do myself!

MISS HARD.: You mean that in this hypocritical age there are few that do not condemn in public what they practise in private, and think they pay every debt to virtue when they praise it.

MARLOW: True, madam; those who have most virtue in their mouths, have least of it in their bosoms. But I'm sure I tire you, madam.

MISS HARD.: Not in the least, sir; there's something so agreeable and spirited in your manner, such life and force—pray, sir, go on.

MARLOW: Yes, madam. I was saying—that there are some occasions—when a total want of courage, madam, destroys all the—and puts us—upon a—a—a—

MISS HARD.: I agree with you entirely, a want of courage upon some occasions assumes the appearance of ignorance, and betrays us when we most want to excel. I beg you'll proceed.

MARLOW: Yes, madam. Morally speaking, madam—but I see Miss Neville expecting us in the next room. I would not intrude for the world.

MISS HARD.: I protest, sir, I never was more agreeably entertained in all my life. Pray go on.

MARLOW: Yes, madam. I was—but she beckons us to join her. Madam, shall I do myself the honour to attend you?

MISS HARD.: Well then, I'll follow.

MARLOW: (*Aside.*) This pretty smooth dialogue has done for me.   [*Exit.*

MISS HARD.: (*Alone.*) Ha! ha! ha! Was there ever such a sober sentimental interview? I'm certain he scarce looked in my face the whole time. Yet the fellow, but for his unaccountable bashfulness, is pretty well, too. He has good sense, but then so buried in his fears, that it fatigues one more than ignorance. If I could teach him a little confidence, it would be doing somebody that I know of a piece of service. But who is that somebody?—that, faith, is a question I can scarce answer.

[*Exit.*

Enter TONY *and* MISS NEVILLE, *followed by*
MRS. HARDCASTLE *and* HASTINGS.

TONY: What do you follow me for, cousin Con? I wonder you're not ashamed to be so very engaging.

MISS NEVILLE: I hope, cousin, one may speak to one's own relations, and not be to blame.

TONY: Ay, but I know what sort of a relation you want to make me, though; but it won't do. I tell you, cousin Con, it won't do; so I beg you'll keep your distance, I want no nearer relationship.

[*She follows, coquetting him to the back scene.*

MRS. HARD.: Well! I vow, Mr. Hastings, you are very entertaining. There's nothing in the world I love to talk of so much as London, and the fashions, though I was never there myself.

HASTINGS: Never there! You amaze me! From your air and manner, I concluded you had been bred all your life either at Ranelagh, St. James's, or Tower Wharf.

MRS. HARD.: Oh! sir, you're only pleased to say so. We country persons can have no manner at all. I'm in love with the town, and that serves to raise me above some of our neighbouring rustics; but who can have a manner, that has never seen the Pantheon, the Grotto Gardens, the Borough, and such places where the nobility chiefly resort? All I can do is to enjoy London at second-hand. I take care to know every *tête-à-tête* from the Scandalous Magazine, and have all the fashions as they come out, in a letter from the two Miss

Rickets of Crooked Lane. Pray how do you like this head, Mr. Hastings?

HASTINGS: Extremely elegant and *dégagée*, upon my word, madam. Your friseur is a Frenchman, I suppose?

MRS. HARD.: I protest, I dressed it myself from a print in the Ladies' Memorandum-book for the last year.

HASTINGS: Indeed. Such a head in a side-box, at the play-house, would draw as many gazers as my Lady Mayoress at a city ball.

MRS. HARD.: I vow, since inoculation began, there is no such thing to be seen as a plain woman; so one must dress a little particular, or one may escape in the crowd.

HASTINGS: But that can never be your case, madam, in any dress! (*Bowing.*)

MRS. HARD.: Yet, what signifies my dressing when I have such a piece of antiquity by my side as Mr. Hardcastle: all I can say will never argue down a single button from his clothes. I have often wanted him to throw off his great flaxen wig, and where he was bald, to plaster it over like my Lord Pately, with powder.

HASTINGS: You are right, madam; for, as among the ladies there are none ugly, so among the men there are none old.

MRS. HARD.: But what do you think his answer was? Why, with his usual Gothic vivacity, he said I only wanted him to throw off his wig to convert it into a *tête* for my own wearing!

HASTINGS: Intolerable! At your age you may wear what you please, and it must become you.

MRS. HARD.: Pray, Mr. Hastings, what do you take to be the most fashionable age about town?

HASTINGS: Some time ago forty was all the mode; but I'm told the ladies intend to bring up fifty for the ensuing winter.

MRS. HARD.: Seriously? Then I shall be too young for the fashion!

HASTINGS: No lady begins now to put on jewels till she's past forty. For instance, Miss there, in a polite circle, would be considered as a child, as a mere maker of samplers.

MRS. HARD.: And yet Mrs. Niece thinks herself as much a woman, and is as fond of jewels as the oldest of us all.

HASTINGS: Your niece, is she? And that young gentleman, a brother of yours, I should presume?

MRS. HARD.: My son, sir. They are contracted to each other. Observe their little sports. They fall in and out ten times a day, as if they were man and wife already. (*To them.*) Well, Tony child, what soft things are you saying to your cousin Constance this evening?

TONY: I have been saying no soft things; but that it's very hard to be followed about so! Ecod! I've not a place in the house now that's left to myself but the stable.

MRS. HARD.: Never mind him, Con, my dear. He's in another story behind your back.

MISS NEVILLE: There's something generous in my cousin's manner. He falls out before faces to be forgiven in private.

TONY: That's a damned confounded—crack.

MRS. HARD.: Ah! he's a sly one. Don't you think they're like each other about the mouth, Mr. Hastings? The Blenkinsop mouth to a T. They're of a size, too. Back to back, my pretties, that Mr. Hastings may see you. Come, Tony.

TONY: You had as good not make me, I tell you.

(*Measuring.*)

MISS NEVILLE: Oh lud! he has almost cracked my head.

MRS. HARD.: Oh, the monster! For shame, Tony. You a man, and behave so!

TONY: If I'm a man, let me have my fortin. Ecod! I'll not be made a fool of no longer.

MRS. HARD.: Is this, ungrateful boy, all that I'm to get for the pains I have taken in your education? I that have rocked you in your cradle, and fed that pretty mouth with a spoon! Did not I work that waistcoat to make you genteel? Did not I prescribe for you every day, and weep while the receipt was operating?

TONY: Ecod! you had reason to weep, for you have been dosing me ever since I was born. I have gone through every receipt in the complete housewife ten times over; and you have thoughts of coursing me through Quincy next spring. But, ecod! I tell you, I'll not be made a fool of no longer.

MRS. HARD.: Wasn't it all for your good, viper? Wasn't it all for your good?

TONY: I wish you'd let me and my good alone, then. Snubbing this way when I'm in spirits. If I'm to have any good, let it come of itself; not to keep dinging it, dinging it into one so.

MRS. HARD.: That's false; I never see you when you're in spirits. No, Tony, you then go to the alehouse or kennel. I'm never to be delighted with your agreeable wild notes, unfeeling monster!

TONY: Ecod! Mamma, your own notes are the wildest of the two.

MRS. HARD.: Was ever the like? But I see he wants to break my heart, I see he does.

HASTINGS: Dear Madam, permit me to lecture the young gentleman a little. I'm certain I can persuade him to his duty.

MRS. HARD.: Well, I must retire. Come, Constance, my love. You see, Mr. Hastings, the wretchedness of my situation. Was ever poor woman so plagued with a dear, sweet, pretty, provoking, undutiful boy.

[*Exeunt* MRS. HARDCASTLE *and* MISS NEVILLE.
HASTINGS, TONY.

TONY: (*Singing.*) "There was a young man riding by, and fain would have his will. Rang do didlo dee."
Don't mind her. Let her cry. It's the comfort of her heart. I have seen her and sister cry over a book for an hour together, and they said they liked the book the better the more it made them cry.

HASTINGS: Then you're no friend to the ladies, I find, my pretty young gentleman?

TONY: That's as I find 'um.

HASTINGS: Not to her of your mother's choosing, I dare answer! And yet she appears to me a pretty, well-tempered girl.

TONY: That's because you don't know her as well as I. Ecod! I know every inch about her; and there's not a more bitter cantankerous toad in all Christendom!

HASTINGS: (*Aside.*) Pretty encouragement this for a lover!

TONY: I have seen her since the height of that. She has as many tricks as a hare in a thicket, or a colt the first day's breaking.

HASTINGS: To me she appears sensible and silent.

TONY: Ay, before company. But when she's with her playmates, she's as loud as a hog in a gate.

HASTINGS: But there is a meek modesty about her that charms me.

TONY: Yes, but curb her never so little, she kicks up, and you're flung in a ditch.

HASTINGS: Well, but you must allow her a little beauty.— Yes, you must allow her some beauty.

TONY: Bandbox! She's all a made-up thing, mun. Ah! could you but see Bet Bouncer of these parts, you might then talk of beauty. Ecod, she has two eyes as black as sloes, and cheeks as broad and red as a pulpit cushion. She'd make two of she.

HASTINGS: Well, what say you of a friend that would take this bitter bargain off your hands?

TONY: Anon?

HASTINGS: Would you thank him that would take Miss Neville, and leave you to happiness and your dear Betsy?

TONY: Ay; but where is there such a friend, for who would take her?

HASTINGS: I am he. If you but assist me, I'll engage to whip her off to France, and you shall never hear more of her.

TONY: Assist you! Ecod, I will, to the last drop of my blood. I'll clap a pair of horses to your chaise that shall trundle you off in a twinkling, and may be get you a part of her fortin beside in jewels that you little dream of.

HASTINGS: My dear 'squire, this looks like a lad of spirit.

TONY: Come along then, and you shall see more of my spirit before you have done with me.

(*Singing*)

> We're the boys
> That fears no noise
> Where the thundering cannons roar.

[*Exeunt.*

ACT THREE

Enter HARDCASTLE *alone.*

HARD. : What could my old friend Sir Charles mean by
recommending his son as the modestest young man in
town? To me he appears the most impudent piece of
brass that ever spoke with a tongue. He has taken
possession of the easy chair by the fireside already. He
took off his boots in the parlour, and desired me to see
them taken care of. I'm desirous to know how his
impudence affects my daughter.—She will certainly
be shocked at it.

Enter MISS HARDCASTLE *plainly dressed.*

HARD. : Well, my Kate, I see you have changed your
dress, as I bid you; and yet, I believe, there was no
great occasion.

MISS HARD. : I find such a pleasure, sir, in obeying your
commands, that I take care to observe them without
ever debating their propriety.

HARD. : And yet, Kate, I sometimes give you some cause,
particularly when I recommended my modest gentleman to you as a lover to-day.

MISS HARD. : You taught me to expect something extraordinary, and I find the original exceeds the description!

HARD. : I was never so surprised in my life! He has quite
confounded all my faculties!

MISS HARD. : I never saw anything like it: and a man of
the world, too!

HARD. : Ay, he learned it all abroad,—what a fool was I,
to think a young man could learn modesty by travelling. He might as soon learn wit at a masquerade.

MISS HARD. : It seems all natural to him.

HARD. : A good deal assisted by bad company and a
French dancing-master.

MISS HARD. : Sure, you mistake, papa! A French dancing-master could never have taught him that timid look—that awkward address—that bashful manner—

HARD. : Whose look? whose manner, child?

MISS HARD. : Mr. Marlow's : his *mauvaise honte*, his timidity, struck me at the first sight.

HARD. : Then your first sight deceived you; for I think him one of the most brazen first sights that ever astonished my senses!

MISS HARD. : Sure, sir, you rally! I never saw anyone so modest.

HARD. : And can you be serious! I never saw such a bouncing swaggering puppy since I was born. Bully Dawson was but a fool to him.

MISS HARD. : Surprising! He met me with a respectful bow, a stammering voice, and a look fixed on the ground.

HARD. : He met me with a loud voice, a lordly air, and a familiarity that made my blood freeze again.

MISS HARD. : He treated me with diffidence and respect; censured the manners of the age; admired the prudence of girls that never laughed; tired me with apologies for being tiresome; then left the room with a bow, and "Madam, I would not for the world detain you."

HARD. : He spoke to me as if he knew me all his life before; asked twenty questions, and never waited for an answer; interrupted my best remarks with some silly pun, and when I was in my best story of the Duke of Marlborough and Prince Eugene, he asked if I had not a good hand at making punch. Yes, Kate, he asked your father if he was a maker of punch!

MISS HARD. : One of us must certainly be mistaken.

HARD. : If he be what he has shown himself, I'm determined he shall never have my consent.

MISS HARD. : And if he be the sullen thing I take him, he shall never have mine.

HARD. : In one thing then we are agreed—to reject him.

MISS HARD. : Yes : but upon conditions. For if you should

find him less impudent, and I more presuming; if you
find him more respectful, and I more importunate—
I don't know—the fellow is well enough for a man.—
Certainly we don't meet many such at a horse-race in
the country.

HARD.: If we should find him so—but that's impossible.
The first appearance has done my business. I'm seldom
deceived in that.

MISS HARD.: And yet there may be many good qualities
under that first appearance.

HARD.: Ay, when a girl finds a fellow's outside to her
taste, she then sets about guessing the rest of his furniture. With her, a smooth face stands for good sense, and
a genteel figure for every virtue.

MISS HARD.: I hope, sir, a conversation begun with a compliment to my good sense won't end with a sneer at my
understanding?

HARD.: Pardon me, Kate. But if young Mr. Brazen can
find the art of reconciling contradictions, he may
please us both, perhaps.

MISS HARD.: And as one of us must be mistaken, what if
we go to make further discoveries?

HARD.: Agreed. But depend on't I'm in the right.

MISS HARD.: And depend on't I'm not much in the wrong.
[*Exeunt.*

Enter TONY, *running in with a casket.*

TONY: Ecod! I have got them. Here they are. My cousin
Con's necklaces, bobs and all. My mother shan't cheat
the poor souls out of their fortin neither. Oh! my
genius, is that you?

Enter HASTINGS.

HASTINGS: My dear friend, how have you managed with
your mother? I hope you have amused her with pretending love for your cousin, and that you are willing
to be reconciled at last? Our horses will be refreshed in
a short time, and we shall soon be ready to set off.

TONY: And here's something to bear your charges by the
way. (*Giving the casket.*) Your sweetheart's jewels. Keep

them, and hang those, I say, that would rob you of one of them.

HASTINGS: But how have you procured them from your mother?

TONY: Ask me no questions, and I'll tell you no fibs. I procured them by the rule of thumb. If I had not a key to every drawer in mother's bureau, how could I go to the alehouse so often as I do? An honest man may rob himself of his own at any time.

HASTINGS: Thousands do it every day. But to be plain with you, Miss Neville is endeavouring to procure them from her aunt this very instant. If she succeeds, it will be the most delicate way at least of obtaining them.

TONY: Well, keep them, till you know how it will be. But I know how it will be well enough; she'd as soon part with the only sound tooth in her head!

HASTINGS: But I dread the effects of her resentment, when she finds she has lost them.

TONY: Never you mind her resentment, leave *me* to manage that. I don't value her resentment the bounce of a cracker. Zounds! here they are! Morrice! prance!
[*Exit* HASTINGS.

TONY, MRS. HARDCASTLE, *and* MISS NEVILLE.

MRS. HARD.: Indeed, Constance, you amaze me. Such a girl as you want jewels? It will be time enough for jewels, my dear, twenty years hence, when your beauty begins to want repairs.

MISS NEVILLE: But what will repair beauty at forty, will certainly improve it at twenty, madam.

MRS. HARD.: Yours, my dear, can admit of none. That natural blush is beyond a thousand ornaments. Besides, child, jewels are quite out at present. Don't you see half the ladies of our acquaintance, my Lady Killdaylight, and Mrs. Crump, and the rest of them, carry their jewels to town, and bring nothing but paste and marcasites back?

MISS NEVILLE: But who knows, madam, but somebody

that shall be nameless would like me best with all my little finery about me?

MRS. HARD.: Consult your glass, my dear, and then see, if with such a pair of eyes, you want any better sparklers. What do you think, Tony, my dear, does your cousin Con want any jewels, in your eyes, to set off her beauty?

TONY: That's as thereafter may be.

MISS NEVILLE: My dear aunt, if you knew how it would oblige me.

MRS. HARD.: A parcel of old-fashioned rose and table-cut things. They would make you look like the court of King Solomon at a puppet-shew. Besides, I believe I can't readily come at them. They may be missing, for aught I know to the contrary.

TONY: (*Apart to Mrs. Hard.*) Then why don't you tell her so at once, as she's so longing for them. Tell her they're lost. It's the only way to quiet her. Say they're lost, and call me to bear witness.

MRS. HARD.: (*Apart to Tony.*) You know, my dear, I'm only keeping them for you. So if I say they're gone, you'll bear me witness, will you? He! he! he!

TONY: Never fear me. Ecod! I'll say I saw them taken out with my own eyes.

MISS NEVILLE: I desire them but for a day, madam. Just to be permitted to shew them as relics, and then they may be locked up again.

MRS. HARD.: To be plain with you, my dear Constance, if I could find them, you should have them. They're missing, I assure you. Lost, for aught I know; but we must have patience wherever they are.

MISS NEVILLE: I'll not believe it; this is but a shallow pretence to deny me. I know they're too valuable to be so slightly kept, and as you are to answer for the loss—

MRS. HARD.: Don't be alarmed, Constance. If they be lost, I must restore an equivalent. But my son knows they are missing, and not to be found.

TONY: That I can bear witness to. They are missing, and not to be found, I'll take my oath on't.

MRS. HARD.: You must learn resignation, my dear; for though we lose our fortune, yet we should not lose our patience. See me, how calm I am.

MISS NEVILLE: Ay, people are generally calm at the misfortunes of others.

MRS. HARD.: Now, I wonder a girl of your good sense should waste a thought upon such trumpery. We shall soon find them; and, in the meantime, you shall make use of my garnets till your jewels be found.

MISS NEVILLE: I detest garnets.

MRS. HARD.: The most becoming things in the world to set off a clear complexion. You have often seen how well they look upon me. You shall have them.   [*Exit.*

MISS NEVILLE: (*Trying to detain her.*) I dislike them of all things. You shan't stir. Was ever anything so provoking to mislay my own jewels, and force me to wear her trumpery.

TONY: Don't be a fool. If she gives you the garnets, take what you can get. The jewels are your own already. I have stolen them out of her bureau, and she does not know it. Fly to your spark, he'll tell you more of the matter. Leave me to manage her.

MISS NEVILLE: My dear cousin!

TONY: Vanish. She's here, and has missed them already. Zounds! how she fidgets and spits about like a catherine wheel!

Enter MRS. HARDCASTLE.

MRS. HARD.: Confusion! thieves! robbers! We are cheated, plundered, broke open, undone!

TONY: What's the matter, what's the matter, mamma? I hope nothing has happened to any of the good family!

MRS. HARD.: We are robbed. My bureau has been broke open, the jewels taken out, and I'm undone!

TONY: Oh! is that all? Ha! ha! ha! By the laws, I never saw it better acted in my life. Ecod, I thought you was ruined in earnest, ha, ha ha!

MRS. HARD.: Why, boy, I am ruined in earnest. My bureau has been broke open, and all taken away.

TONY: Stick to that; ha, ha, ha! stick to that. I'll bear witness, you know, call me to bear witness.

MRS. HARD.: I tell you, Tony, by all that's precious, the jewels are gone, and I shall be ruined for ever.

TONY: Sure I know they're gone, and I am to say so.

MRS. HARD.: My dearest Tony, but hear me. They're gone, I say.

TONY: By the laws, mamma, you make me for to laugh, ha! ha! I know who took them well enough, ha! ha! ha!

MRS. HARD.: Was there ever such a blockhead, that can't tell the difference between jest and earnest. I tell you I'm not in jest, booby!

TONY: That's right, that's right: you must be in a bitter passion, and then nobody will suspect either of us. I'll bear witness that they are gone.

MRS. HARD.: Was there ever such a cross-grained brute, that won't hear me! Can you bear witness that you're no better than a fool? Was ever poor woman so beset with fools on one hand, and thieves on the other?

TONY: I can bear witness to that.

MRS. HARD.: Bear witness again, you blockhead you, and I'll turn you out of the room directly. My poor niece, what will become of her? Do you laugh, you unfeeling brute, as if you enjoy my distress?

TONY: I can bear witness to that.

MRS. HARD.: Do you insult me, monster? I'll teach you to vex your mother, I will.

TONY: I can bear witness to that.

[*He runs off, she follows him.*
Enter MISS HARDCASTLE *and Maid.*

MISS HARD.: What an unaccountable creature is that brother of mine, to send them to the house as an inn, ha! ha! I don't wonder at his impudence.

MAID: But what is more, madam, the young gentleman as you passed by in your present dress, asked me if you were the barmaid. He mistook you for the barmaid, madam!

MISS HARD.: Did he? Then as I live I'm resolved to keep up the delusion. Tell me, Pimple, how do you like my present dress? Don't you think I look something like Cherry in the *Beaux' Stratagem*?

MAID: It's the dress, madam, that every lady wears in the country, but when she visits or receives company.

MISS HARD.: And are you sure he does not remember my face or person?

MAID: Certain of it.

MISS HARD.: I vow, I thought so; for though we spoke for some time together, yet his fears were such, that he never once looked up during the interview. Indeed, if he had, my bonnet would have kept him from seeing me.

MAID: But what do you hope from keeping him in his mistake?

MISS HARD.: In the first place, I shall be seen, and that is no small advantage to a girl who brings her face to market. Then I shall perhaps make an acquaintance, and that's no small victory gained over one who never addresses any but the wildest of her sex. But my chief aim is to take my gentleman off his guard, and like an invisible champion of romance, examine the giant's force before I offer to combat.

MAID: But you are sure you can act your part, and disguise your voice, so that he may mistake that, as he has already mistaken your person?

MISS HARD.: Never fear me. I think I have got the true bar cant. Did you honour call?—Attend the Lion there.—Pipes and tobacco for the Angel.—The Lamb has been outrageous this half-hour.

MAID: It will do, madam, But he's here.   [*Exit Maid.*
                        Enter MARLOW.

MARLOW: What a bawling in every part of the house; I have scarce a moment's repose. If I go to the best room, there I find my host and his story. If I fly to the gallery, there we have my hostess with her curtsy down to the ground. I have at last got a moment to myself, and now for recollection. [*Walks and muses.*

MISS HARD.: Did you call, sir? Did your honour call?

MARLOW: (*Musing.*) As for Miss Hardcastle, she's too grave and sentimental for me. [*Paces to left.*

MISS HARD.: Did your honour call?

[*She still places herself before him, he turning away.*

MARLOW: No, child. (*Musing.*) Besides from the glimpse I had of her, I think she squints.

MISS HARD.: I'm sure, sir, I heard the bell ring.

MARLOW: No, no. (*Musing.*) I have pleased my father, however, by coming down, and I'll to-morrow please myself by returning. [*Taking out his tablets, and perusing.*

MISS HARD.: Perhaps the other gentleman called, sir?

MARLOW: I tell you, no.

MISS HARD.: I should be glad to know, sir. We have such a parcel of servants.

MARLOW: No, no, I tell you. (*Looks full in her face.*) Yes, child, I think I did call. I wanted—I wanted—I vow, child, you are vastly handsome.

MISS HARD.: O la, sir, you'll make one ashamed.

MARLOW: Never saw a more sprightly malicious eye. Yes, yes, my dear, I did call. Have you got any of your— a—what d'ye call it in the house?

MISS HARD.: No, sir, we have been out of that these ten days.

MARLOW: One may call in this house, I find, to very little purpose. Suppose I should call for a taste, just by way of trial, of the nectar of your lips; perhaps I might be disappointed in that, too.

MISS HARD.: Nectar! nectar! that's a liquor there's no call for in these parts. French, I suppose. We keep no French wines here, sir.

MARLOW: Of true English growth, I assure you.

MISS HARD.: Then it's odd I should not know it. We brew all sorts of wines in this house, and I have lived here these eighteen years.

264

MARLOW: Eighteen years! Why one would think, child, you kept the bar before you were born. How old are you?

MISS HARD.: O! sir, I must not tell my age. They say women and music should never be dated.

MARLOW: To guess at this distance, you can't be much above forty. (*Approaching.*) Yet nearer I don't think so much. (*Approaching.*) By coming close to some women they look younger still; but when we come very close indeed— [*Attempting to kiss her.*

MISS HARD.: Pray, sir, keep your distance. One would think you wanted to know one's age as they do horses, by mark of mouth.

MARLOW: I protest, child, you use me extremely ill. If you keep me at this distance, how is it possible you and I can ever be acquainted?

MISS HARD.: And who wants to be acquainted with you? I want no such acquaintance, not I. I'm sure you did not treat Miss Hardcastle that was here awhile ago in this obstropalous manner. I'll warrant me, before her you looked dashed, and kept bowing to the ground, and talked, for all the world, as if you was before a justice of peace.

MARLOW: (*Aside.*) Egad! she has hit it, sure enough. (*To her.*) In awe of her, child? Ha! ha! ha! A mere awkward, squinting thing, no, no. I find you don't know me. I laughed, and rallied her a little; but I was unwilling to be too severe. No, I could not be too severe, curse me!

MISS HARD.: Oh! then, sir, you are a favourite, I find, among the ladies?

MARLOW: Yes, my dear, a great favourite. And yet, hang me, I don't see what they find in me to follow. At the ladies' club in town I'm called their agreeable Rattle. Rattle, child, is not my real name, but one I'm known by. My name is Solomons. Mr. Solomons, my dear, at you service. [*Offering to salute her.*

MISS HARD.: Hold, sir; you are introducing me to your

club, not to yourself. And you're so great a favourite
there, you say?

MARLOW: Yes, my dear. There's Mrs. Mantrap, Lady
Betty Blackleg, the Countess of Sligo, Mrs. Langhorns,
old Miss Biddy Buckskin and your humble servant,
keep up the spirit of the place.

MISS HARD.: Then it's a very merry place, I suppose?

MARLOW: Yes, as merry as cards, suppers, wine, and old
women can make us.

MISS HARD.: And their agreeable Rattle, ha! ha! ha!

MARLOW: (*Aside.*) Egad! I don't quite like this chit. She
looks knowing, methinks. You laugh, child!

MISS HARD.: I can't but laugh to think what time they all
have for minding their work or their family.

MARLOW: (*Aside.*) All's well, she don't laugh at me. (*To
her.*) Do you ever work, child?

MISS HARD.: Ay, sure. There's not a screen or a quilt in
the whole house but what can bear witness to that.

MARLOW: Odso! Then you must show me your embroidery. I embroider and draw patterns myself a little. If
you want a judge of your work you must apply to me.
[*Seizing her hand.*

MISS HARD.: Ay, but the colours don't look well by candle-
light. You shall see all in the morning.   [*Struggling.*

MARLOW: And why not now, my angel? Such beauty fires
beyond the power of resistance.—Pshaw! the father
here! My old luck: I never nicked seven that I did not
throw ames-ace three times following.   [*Exit Marlow.*
(*Enter* HARDCASTLE, *who stands in surprise.*)

HARD.: So, madam. So I find this is your modest lover.
This is your humble admirer that kept his eyes fixed on
the ground, and only adored at humble distance. Kate,
Kate, art thou not ashamed to deceive your father so?

MISS HARD.: Never trust me, dear papa, but he's still the
modest man I first took him for, you'll be convinced of
it as well as I.

HARD.: By the hand of my body. I believe his impudence
is infectious! Didn't I see him seize your hand? Didn't

266

I see him haul you about like a milkmaid? and now you talk of his respect and his modesty, forsooth!

MISS HARD.: But, if I shortly convince you of his modesty, that he has only the faults that will pass off with time, and the virtues that will improve with age, I hope you'll forgive him.

HARD.: The girl would actually make one run mad! I tell you I'll not be convinced. I am convinced. He has scarcely been three hours in the house, and he has already encroached on all my prerogatives. You may like his impudence, and call it modesty. But my son-in-law, madam, must have very different qualifications.

MISS HARD.: Sir, I ask but this night to convince you.

HARD.: You shall not have half the time, for I have thoughts of turning him out this very hour.

MISS HARD.: Give me that hour then, and I hope to satisfy you.

HARD.: Well, an hour let it be then. But I'll have no trifling with your father. All fair and open, do you mind me?

MISS HARD.: I hope, sir, you have ever found that I considered your commands as my pride; for your kindness is such, that my duty as yet has been inclination.

ACT FOUR

Enter HASTINGS AND MISS NEVILLE.

HASTINGS: You surprise me! Sir Charles Marlow expected here this night? Where have you had your information?

MISS NEVILLE: You may depend upon it. I just saw his letter to Mr. Hardcastle, in which he tells him he intends setting out a few hours after his son.

HASTINGS: Then, my Constance, all must be completed before he arrives. He knows me; and should he find me here, would discover my name, and perhaps my designs, to the rest of the family.

MISS NEVILLE: The jewels, I hope, are safe.

HASTINGS: Yes, yes. I have sent them to Marlow, who keeps the keys of our baggage. In the meantime, I'll go to prepare matters for our elopement. I have had the 'squire's promise of a fresh pair of horses; and, if I should not see him again, will write him further directions. [*Exit.*

MISS NEVILLE: Well! success attend you. In the meantime, I'll go amuse my aunt with the old pretence of a violent passion for my cousin. [*Exit.*

Enter MARLOW *followed by a servant.*

MARLOW: I wonder what Hastings could mean by sending me so valuable a thing as a casket to keep for him, when he knows the only place I have is the seat of a post-coach at an inn-door. Have you deposited the casket with the landlady, as I ordered you? Have you put it into her own hands?

SERVANT: Yes, your honour.

MARLOW: She said she'd keep it safe, did she?

SERVANT: Yes, she said she'd keep it safe enough; she asked me how I came by it, and she said she had a great mind to make me give an account of myself.

[*Exit Servant.*

MARLOW: Ha! ha! ha! They're safe, however. What an unaccountable set of beings have we got amongst! This little barmaid, though, runs in my head most strangely, and drives out the absurdities of all the rest of the family. She's mine, she must be mine, or I'm greatly mistaken.

Enter HASTINGS.

HASTINGS: Bless me! I quite forgot to tell her that I intended to prepare at the bottom of the garden. Marlow here, and in spirits too!

MARLOW: Give me joy, George! Crown me, shadow me with laurels! Well, George, after all, we modest fellows don't want for success among the women.

HASTINGS: Some women, you mean. But what success has your honour's modesty been crowned with now, that it grows so insolent upon us?

MARLOW: Didn't you see the tempting, brisk, lovely little thing that runs about the house with a bunch of keys to its girdle?

HASTINGS: Well! and what then?

MARLOW: She's mine, you rogue you. Such fire, such motions, such eyes, such lips—but, egad! she would not let me kiss them though.

HASTINGS: But are you so sure, so very sure of her?

MARLOW: Why man, she talked of showing me her work above stairs and I am to improve the pattern.

HASTINGS: But how can you, Charles, go about to rob a woman of her honour?

MARLOW: Pshaw! pshaw! We all know the honour of a barmaid of an inn. I don't intend to rob her, take my word for it, there's nothing in this house I shan't honestly pay for.

HASTINGS: I believe the girl has virtue.

MARLOW: And if she has, I should be the last man in the world that would attempt to corrupt it.

HASTINGS: You have taken care, I hope, of the casket I sent you to lock up? It's in safety?

MARLOW: Yes, yes. It's safe enough. I have taken care of it. But how could you think the seat of a post-coach at an inn-door a place of safety? Ah! numbskull! I have taken better precautions for you than you did for yourself.—I have—

HASTINGS: What?

MARLOW: I have sent it to the landlady to keep for you.

HASTINGS: To the landlady!

MARLOW: The landlady.

HASTINGS: You did?

MARLOW: I did. She's to be answerable for its forthcoming, you know.

HASTINGS: Yes, she'll bring it forth with a witness.

MARLOW: Wasn't I right? I believe you'll allow that I acted prudently upon this occasion?

HASTINGS: (*Aside*) He must not see my uneasiness.

MARLOW: You seem a little disconcerted, though, methinks. Sure nothing has happened?

HASTINGS: No, nothing. Never was in better spirits in all my life. And so you left it with the landlady, who, no doubt, very readily undertook the charge?

MARLOW: Rather too readily. For she not only kept the casket, but, through her great precaution, was going to keep the messenger too. Ha! ha! ha!

HASTINGS: He! he! he! They're safe, however.

MARLOW: As a guinea in a miser's purse.

HASTINGS: (*Aside*.) So now all hopes of fortune are at an end, and we must set off without it. (*To him.*) Well, Charles, I'll leave you to your meditations on the pretty barmaid, and, he! he! he! may you be as successful for yourself as you have been for me.   [*Exit.*

Enter HARDCASTLE.

HARD.: I no longer know my own house. It's turned all topsy-turvy. His servants have got drunk already. I'll bear it no longer, and yet, from my respect for his father, I'll be calm. (*To him.*) Mr. Marlow, your servant. I'm your very humble servant.   [*Bowing low.*

MARLOW: Sir, your humble servant. (*Aside.*) What's to be the wonder now?

HARD.: I believe, sir, you must be sensible, sir, that no

man alive ought to be more welcome than your father's son, sir. I hope you think so?

MARLOW: I do, from my soul, sir. I don't want much entreaty. I generally make my father's son welcome wherever he goes.

HARD.: I believe you do, from my soul, sir. But though I say nothing to your own conduct, that of your servants is insufferable. Their manner of drinking is setting a very bad example in this house, I assure you.

MARLOW: I protest, my very good sir, that's no fault of mine. If they don't drink as they ought they are to blame. I ordered them not to spare the cellar. I did, I assure you. (*To the side scene.*) Here, let one of my servants come up. (*To him.*) My positive directions were, that as I did not drink myself, they should make up for my deficiencies below.

HARD.: Then they had your orders for what they do! I'm satisfied!

MARLOW: They had, I assure you. You shall hear from one of themselves.

Enter SERVANT, *drunk.*

MARLOW: You, Jeremy! Come forward, sirrah! What were my orders? Were you not told to drink freely, and call for what you thought fit, for the good of the house?

HARD.: (*Aside.*) I begin to lose my patience.

JEREMY: (*Staggering forward.*) Please your honour, liberty and Fleet Street for ever! Though I'm but a servant, I'm as good as another man. I'll drink for no man before supper, sir, dammy! Good liquor will sit upon a good supper, but a good supper will not sit upon—hiccup—upon my conscience, sir.

MARLOW: You see, my old friend, the fellow is as drunk as he can possibly be. I don't know what you'd have more, unless you'd have the poor devil soused in a beer-barrel.

HARD.: Zounds! He'll drive me distracted if I contain myself any longer. Mr. Marlow, Sir; I have submitted to your insolence for more than four hours, and I see no likelihood of its coming to an end. I'm now resolved to be master here, sir, and I desire that you and your drunken pack may leave my house directly.

MARLOW: Leave your house!—Sure, you jest, my good friend! What, when I'm doing what I can to please you!

HARD.: I tell you, sir, you don't please me; so I desire you'll leave my house.

MARLOW: Sure, you cannot be serious! At this time o' night, and such a night! You only mean to banter me!

HARD.: I tell you, sir, I'm serious; and, now that my passions are roused, I say this house is mine, sir; this house is mine, and I command you to leave it directly.

MARLOW: Ha! ha! ha! A puddle in a storm. I shan't stir a step, I assure you. (*In a serious tone.*) This your house, fellow! It's my house. This is my house. Mine, while I choose to stay. What right have you to bid me leave this house, sir? I never met with such impudence, curse me, never in my whole life before.

HARD.: Nor I, confound me if ever I did! To come to my house, to call for what he likes, to turn me out of my own chair, to insult the family, to order his servants to get drunk, and then to tell me *This house is mine, sir*. By all that's impudent, it makes me laugh. Ha! ha! ha! Pray sir, (*bantering*) as you take the house, what think you of taking the rest of the furniture? There's a pair of silver candlesticks, and there's a firescreen, and here's a pair of brazen-nosed bellows, perhaps you may take a fancy to them?

MARLOW: Bring me your bill, sir, bring me your bill, and let's make no more words about it.

HARD.: There are a set of prints, too. What think you of the Rake's Progress for your own apartment?

MARLOW: Bring me your bill, I say; and I'll leave you and your infernal house directly.

HARD.: Then there's a mahogany table, that you may see your own face in.

MARLOW: My bill, I say.

HARD.: I had forgot the great chair, for your own particular slumbers, after a hearty meal.

MARLOW: Zounds! bring me my bill, I say, and let's hear no more on't.

HARD.: Young man, young man, from your father's letter to me, I was taught to expect a well-bred modest man, as a visitor here, but now I find him no better than a coxcomb and a bully; but he will be down here presently, and shall hear more of it. [*Exit.*

MARLOW: How's this! Sure I have not mistaken the house! Everything looks like an inn. The servants cry "coming." The attendance is awkward; the barmaid, too, to attend us. But she's here, and will further inform me. Whither so fast, child? A word with you.

Enter MISS HARDCASTLE.

MISS HARD.: Let it be short, then. I'm in a hurry. (*Aside.*) I believe he begins to find out his mistake, but it's too soon quite to undeceive him.

MARLOW: Pray, child, answer me one question. What are you, and what may your business in this house be?

MISS HARD.: A relation of the family, sir.

MARLOW: What, a poor relation?

MISS HARD.: Yes, sir. A poor relation appointed to keep the keys, and to see that the guests want nothing in my power to give them.

MARLOW: That is, you act as the barmaid of this inn.

MISS HARD.: Inn. O law!—What brought that in your head? One of the best families in the country keep an inn! Ha, ha, ha, old Mr. Hardcastle's house an inn!

MARLOW: Mr. Hardcastle's house! Is this house Mr. Hardcastle's house, child?

MISS HARD.: Ay, sure. Whose else should it be?

MARLOW: So then all's out, and I have been damnably imposed on. O, confound my stupid head, I shall be laughed at over the whole town. I shall be stuck up in caricatura in all the print-shops. The Dullissimo Maccaroni. To mistake this house of all others for an inn, and my father's old friend for an innkeeper. What a swaggering puppy must he take me for. What a silly puppy do I find myself. There again, may I be hanged, my dear, but I mistook you for the barmaid.

MISS HARD.: Dear me! dear me! I'm sure there's nothing in my behaviour to put me upon a level with one of that stamp.

MARLOW: Nothing, my dear, nothing. But I was in for a list of blunders, and could not help making you a subscriber. My stupidity saw everything the wrong way. I mistook your assiduity for assurance, and your simplicity for allurement. But it's over.—This house I no more show my face in!

MISS HARD.: I hope, sir, I have done nothing to disoblige you. I'm sure I should be sorry to affront any gentleman who has been so polite, and said so many civil things to me. I'm sure I should be sorry (*pretending to cry*) if he left the family upon my account. I'm sure I should be sorry people said anything amiss, since I have no fortune but my character.

MARLOW: (*Aside.*) By heaven, she weeps. This is the first mark of tenderness I ever had from a modest woman, and it touches me. (*To her.*) Excuse me, my lovely girl, you are the only part of the family I leave with reluctance. But to be plain with you, the difference of our birth, fortune and education, make an honourable connection impossible.

MISS HARD.: (*Aside.*) Generous man! I now begin to admire him. (*To him.*) But I'm sure my family is as good as Miss Hardcastle's, and though I'm poor, that's no great misfortune to a contented mind, and, until this moment, I never thought that it was bad to want fortune.

MARLOW: And why now, my pretty simplicity?

MISS HARD.: Because it puts me at a distance from one that if I had a thousand pound I would give it all to.

MARLOW: (*Aside.*) This simplicity bewitches me, so that if I stay I'm undone. I must make one bold effort, and leave her. (*To her.*) Your partiality in my favour, my

274

dear, touches me most sensibly, and were I to live for myself alone, I could easily fix my choice. But I owe too much to the opinion of the world, too much to the authority of a father, so that—I can scarcely speak it— it affects me. Farewell. [*Exit.*

MISS HARD. : I never knew half his merit till now. He shall not go, if I have power or art to detain him. I'll still preserve the character in which I stooped to conquer, but will undeceive my papa, who, perhaps, may laugh him out of his resolution. [*Exit.*

Enter TONY, MISS NEVILLE.

TONY : Ay, you may steal for yourselves the next time. I have done my duty. She has got the jewels again, that's a sure thing; but she believes it was all a mistake of the servants.

MISS NEVILLE : But, my dear cousin, sure, you won't forsake us in this distress. If she in the least suspects that I am going off, I shall certainly be locked up, or sent to my Aunt Pedigree's which is ten times worse.

TONY : To be sure, aunts of all kinds are damned bad things. But what can I do? I have got you a pair of horses that will fly like Whistlejacket, and I'm sure you can't say but I have courted you nicely before her face. Here she comes, we must court a bit or two more, for fear she should suspect us. [*They retire, and seem to fondle.*

Enter MRS. HARDCASTLE.

MRS. HARD. : Well, I was greatly fluttered, to be sure. But my son tells me it was all a mistake of the servants. I shan't be easy, however, till they are fairly married, and then let her keep her own fortune. But what do I see? Fondling together, as I'm alive! I never saw Tony so sprightly before. Ah! have I caught you, my pretty doves! What, billing, exchanging stolen glances, and broken murmurs! Ah!

TONY : As for murmurs, mother, we grumble a little now and then, to be sure. But there's no love lost between us.

MRS. HARD. : A mere sprinkling, Tony, upon the flame, only to make it burn brighter.

MISS NEVILLE: Cousin Tony promises to give us more of his company at home. Indeed, he shan't leave us any more. It won't leave us, cousin Tony, will it?

TONY: O! it's a pretty creature. No, I'd sooner leave my horse in a pound, than leave you when you smile upon one so. Your laugh makes you so becoming.

MISS NEVILLE: Agreeable cousin! Who can help admiring that natural humour, that pleasant, broad, red, thoughtless (*patting his cheek*) ah! it's a bold face.

MRS. HARD.: Pretty innocence!

TONY: I'm sure I always loved cousin Con's hazel eyes, and her pretty long fingers, that she twists this way and that, over the haspicholls, like a parcel of bobbins.

MRS. HARD.: Ah, he would charm the bird from the tree. I was never so happy before. My boy takes after his father, poor Mr. Lumpkin, exactly. The jewels, my dear Con, shall be yours incontinently. You shall have them. Isn't he a sweet boy, my dear? You shall be married to-morrow, and we'll put off the rest of his education, like Dr. Drowsy's sermons, to a fitter opportunity.

Enter DIGGORY.

DIGGORY: Where's the Squire? I have got a letter for your worship.

TONY: Give it to my mamma. She reads all my letters first.

DIGGORY: I had orders to deliver it into your own hands.

TONY: Who does it come from?

DIGGORY: Your worship mun ask that o' the letter itself.

TONY: I could wish to know, though.

[*Turning the letter, and gazing on it.*

MISS NEVILLE: (*Aside.*) Undone, undone. A letter to him from Hastings. I know the hand. If my aunt sees it we are ruined for ever. I'll keep her employed a little if I can. (*To Mrs. Hardcastle.*) But I have not told you, madam, of my cousin's smart answer just now to Mr. Marlow. We so laughed.—You must know, madam— This way a little, for he must not hear us. [*They confer.*

276

TONY: (*Still gazing.*) A damned cramp piece of penman-
ship, as ever I saw in my life. I can read your print-
hand very well. But here there are such handles, and
shanks, and dashes, that one can scarce tell the head
from the tail. "To Anthony Lumpkin, Esquire." It's
very odd, I can read the outside of my letters, where
my own name is, well enough. But when I come to
open it, it's all—buzz. That's hard, very hard; for the
inside of the letter is always the cream of the corre-
spondence.

MRS. HARD.: Ha! ha! ha! Very well, very well. And so my
son was too hard for the philosopher.

MISS NEVILLE: Yes, madam; but you must hear the rest,
madam. A little more this way, or he may hear us.
You'll hear how he puzzled him again.

MRS. HARD.: He seems strangely puzzled now himself,
methinks.

TONY: (*Still gazing.*) A damned up and down hand, as if it
was disguised in liquor. (*Reading.*) Dear Sir. Ay, that's
that. Then there's an M, and a T, and an S, but
whether the next be an izzard or an R, confound me,
I cannot tell.

MRS. HARD.: What's that, my dear? Can I give you any
assistance?

MISS NEVILLE: Pray, aunt, let me read it. Nobody reads a
cramph and better than I. (*Twitching the letter from her.*)
Do you know who it is from?

TONY: Can't tell, except from Dick Ginger the feeder.

MISS NEVILLE: Ay, so it is. (*Pretending to read.*) Dear Squire,
Hoping that you're in health, as I am at this present.
The gentlemen of the Shakebag club has cut the
gentlemen of Goose-green quite out of feather. The
odds—um—odd battle—um—long fighting—um,
here, here, it's all about cocks, and fighting; it's of no
consequence, here, put it up, put it up.
[*Thrusting the crumpled letter upon him.*

TONY: But I tell you, miss, it's of all the consequence in
the world. I would not lose the rest of it for a guinea.

Here, mother, do you make it out? Of no consequence!

[*Giving Mrs. Hardcastle the letter.*

MRS. HARD.: How's this! (*reads*) "Dear 'Squire, I'm now waiting for Miss Neville, with a post-chaise and pair, at the bottom of the garden but I find my horses yet unable to perform the journey. I expect you'll assist us with a pair of fresh horses, as you promised. Dispatch is necessary, as the hag"—ay, the hag—"your mother, will otherwise suspect us. Yours, Hastings." Grant me patience. I shall run distracted. My rage chokes me.

MISS NEVILLE: I hope, madam, you'll suspend your resentment for a few moments, and not impute to me any impertinence, or sinister design, that belongs to another.

MRS. HARD.: (*Curtsying very low.*) Fine spoken, madam, you are most miraculously polite and engaging, and quite the very pink of courtesy and circumspection, madam. (*Changing her tone.*) And you, you great ill-fashioned oaf, with scarce sense enough to keep your mouth shut. Were you too joined against me? But I'll defeat all your plots in a moment. As for you, madam, since you have got a pair of fresh horses ready, it would be cruel to disappoint them. So, if you please, instead of running away with your spark, prepare, this very moment, to run off with me. Your old Aunt Pedigree will keep you secure, I'll warrant me. You too, sir, may mount your horse, and guard us upon the way. Here, Thomas, Roger, Diggory, I'll show you that I wish you better than you do yourselves. [*Exit.*

MISS NEVILLE: So now I'm completely ruined.

TONY: Ay, that's a sure thing.

MISS NEVILLE: What better could be expected from being connected with such a stupid fool, and after all the nods and signs I made him.

TONY: By the laws, miss, it was your own cleverness, and not my stupidity, that did your business. You were so nice and so busy with your Shake-bags and Goose-greens, that I thought you could never be making believe.

Enter HASTINGS.

HASTINGS: So, sir, I find by my servant, that you have shown my letter, and betrayed us. Was this well done, young gentleman?

TONY: Here's another. Ask Miss there who betrayed you. Ecod, it was her doing, not mine.

Enter MARLOW.

MARLOW: So I have been finely used here among you. Rendered contemptible, driven into ill manners, despised, insulted, laughed at.

TONY: Here's another. We shall have old Bedlam broke loose presently.

MISS NEVILLE: And there, sir, is the gentleman to whom we all owe every obligation.

MARLOW: What can I say to him, a mere boy, an idiot, whose ignorance and age are a protection.

HASTINGS: A poor contemptible booby, that would but disgrace correction.

MISS NEVILLE: Yet with cunning and malice enough to make himself merry with all our embarrassments.

HASTINGS: An insensible cub.

MARLOW: Replete with tricks and mischief.

TONY: Baw! damme, but I'll fight you both one after the other—with baskets.

MARLOW: As for him, he's below resentment. But your conduct, Mr. Hastings, requires an explanation. You knew of my mistakes, yet would not undeceive me.

HASTINGS: Tortured as I am with my own disappointments, is this a time for explanations? It is not friendly, Mr. Marlow.

MARLOW: But, sir—

MISS NEVILLE: Mr. Marlow, we never kept on your mistake, till it was too late to undeceive you. Be pacified.

Enter SERVANT.

SERVANT: My mistress desires you'll get ready immediately, madam. The horses are putting to. Your hat and things are in the next room. We are to go thirty miles before morning.   [*Exit Servant.*

MISS NEVILLE: Well, well; I'll come presently.

MARLOW: (*To Hastings*.) Was it well done, sir, to assist in rendering me ridiculous? To hang me out for the scorn of all my acquaintance? Depend upon it, sir, I shall expect an explanation.

HASTINGS: Was it well done, sir, if you're upon that subject, to deliver what I entrusted to yourself, to the care of another, sir?

MISS NEVILLE: Mr. Hastings, Mr. Marlow. Why will you increase my distress by this groundless dispute? I implore, I entreat you—

Enter SERVANT.

SERVANT: Your cloak, madam. My mistress is impatient.
[*Exit Servant.*

MISS NEVILLE: I come. Pray be pacified. If I leave you thus, I shall die with apprehension!

Enter SERVANT.

SERVANT: Your fan, muff, and gloves, madam. The horses are waiting.

MISS NEVILLE: O, Mr. Marlow! if you knew what a scene of constraint and ill-nature lies before me, I'm sure it would convert your resentment into pity.

MARLOW: I'm so distracted with a variety of passions, that I don't know what I do. Forgive me, madam. George, forgive me. You know my hasty temper, and should not exasperate it.

HASTINGS: The torture of my situation is my only excuse.

MISS NEVILLE: Well, my dear Hastings, if you have that esteem for me that I think, that I am sure you have, your constancy for three years will but increase the happiness of our future connection. If—

MRS. HARD.: (*Within*.) Miss Neville. Constance, why, Constance, I say.

MISS NEVILLE: I'm coming. Well, constancy. Remember. constancy is the word.   [*Exit.*

HASTINGS: My heart! How can I support this? To be so near happiness, and such happiness!

MARLOW: (*To Tony*.) You see now, young gentleman, the

effects of your folly. What might be amusement to you, is here disappointment, and even distress.

TONY: (*From a reverie.*) Ecod, I have hit it. It's here. Your hands. Yours and yours, my poor Sulky. My boots there, ho! Meet me two hours hence at the bottom of the garden; and if you don't find Tony Lumpkin a more good-natur'd fellow than you thought for, I'll give you leave to take my best horse, and Bet Bouncer into the bargain. Come along. My boots, ho! [*Exeunt.*

ACT FIVE

Scene Continues.

Enter HASTINGS *and* SERVANT.

HASTINGS: You saw the old lady and Miss Neville drive off, you say?

SERVANT: Yes, your honour. They went off in a post coach, and the young squire went on horseback. They're thirty miles off by this time.

HASTINGS: Then all my hopes are over.

SERVANT: Yes, Sir. Old Sir Charles is arrived. He and the old gentleman of the house have been laughing at Mr. Marlow's mistake this half-hour. They are coming this way.

HASTINGS: Then I must not be seen. So now to my fruitless appointment at the bottom of the garden. This is about the time. [*Exit.*

Enter SIR CHARLES *and* HARDCASTLE.

HARD.: Ha! ha! ha! the peremptory tones in which he sent forth his sublime commands.

SIR CHARLES: And the reserve with which I suppose he treated all your advances.

HARD.: And yet he might have seen something in me above a common innkeeper, too.

SIR CHARLES: Yes, Dick, but he mistook you for an uncommon innkeeper, ha! ha! ha!

HARD.: Well, I'm in too good spirits to think of anything but joy. Yes, my dear friend, this union of our families will make our personal friendship hereditary: and though my daughter's fortune is but small—

SIR CHARLES: Why, Dick, will you talk of fortune to me? My son is possessed of more than a competence already, and can want nothing but a good and virtuous girl to share his happiness and increase it. If they like each other, as you say they do—

282

HARD.: If, man! I tell you they do like each other. My daughter as good as told me so.

SIR CHARLES: But girls are apt to flatter themselves, you know.

HARD.: I saw him grasp her hand in the warmest manner myself; and here he comes to put you out of your ifs, I warrant him.

Enter MARLOW.

MARLOW: I come, sir, once more, to ask pardon for my strange conduct. I can scarce reflect on my insolence without confusion.

HARD.: Tut, boy, a trifle. You take it too gravely. An hour or two's laughing with my daughter will set all to rights again. She'll never like you the worse for it.

MARLOW: Sir, I shall be always proud of her approbation.

HARD.: Approbation is but a cold word, Mr. Marlow; if I am not deceived, you have something more than approbation thereabouts. You take me.

MARLOW: Really, sir, I have not that happiness.

HARD.: Come, boy, I'm an old fellow, and know what's what, as well as you that are younger. I know what has past between you; but mum.

MARLOW: Sure, sir, nothing has passed between us but the most profound respect on my side, and the most distant reserve on hers. You don't think, sir, that my impudence has been passed upon all the rest of the family.

HARD.: Impudence! No, I don't say that—not quite impudence—though girls like to be played with, and rumpled a little too, sometimes. But she has told no tales, I assure you.

MARLOW: I never gave her the slightest cause.

HARD.: Well, well, I like modesty in its place well enough. But this is over-acting, young gentleman. You may be open. Your father and I will like you the better for it.

MARLOW: May I die, sir, if I ever—

HARD.: I tell you, she don't dislike you; and as I'm sure you like her—

MARLOW: Dear sir—I protest, sir—

HARD.: I see no reason why you should not be joined as fast as the parson can tie you.

MARLOW: But hear me, sir—

HARD.: Your father approves the match, I admire it, every moment's delay will be doing mischief, so—

MARLOW: But why won't you hear me? By all that's just and true, I never gave Miss Hardcastle the slightest mark of my attachment, or even the most distant hint to suspect me of affection. We had but one interview, and that was formal, modest, and uninteresting.

HARD.: (*Aside.*) This fellow's formal modest impudence is beyond bearing.

SIR CHARLES: And you never grasped her hand, or made any protestations!

MARLOW: As heaven is my witness, I came down in obedience to your commands. I saw the lady without emotion, and parted without reluctance. I hope you'll exact no further proofs of my duty, nor prevent me from leaving a house in which I suffer so many mortifications. [*Exit.*

SIR CHARLES: I'm astonished at the air of sincerity with which he parted.

HARD.: And I'm astonished at the deliberate intrepidity of his assurance.

SIR CHARLES: I dare pledge my life and honour upon his truth.

HARD.: (*Looking out to right.*) Here comes my daughter, and I would stake my happiness upon her veracity.

Enter MISS HARDCASTLE.

HARD.: Kate, come hither, child. Answer us sincerely, and without reserve; has Mr. Marlow made you any professions of love and affection?

MISS HARD.: The question is very abrupt, sir! But since you require unreserved sincerity, I think he has.

HARD.: (*To Sir Charles.*) You see.

SIR CHARLES: And pray, madam, have you and my son had more than one interview?

MISS HARD.: Yes, sir, several.

HARD.: (*To Sir Charles.*) You see.

SIR CHARLES: But did he profess any attachment?

MISS HARD.: A lasting one.

SIR CHARLES: Did he talk of love?

MISS HARD.: Much, sir.

SIR CHARLES: Amazing! And all this formally?

MISS HARD.: Formally.

HARD.: Now, my friend, I hope you are satisfied.

SIR CHARLES: And how did he behave, madam?

MISS HARD.: As most professed admirers do. Said some civil things of my face, talked much of his want of merit, and the greatness of mine; mentioned his heart, gave a short tragedy speech, and ended with pretended rapture.

SIR CHARLES: Now I'm perfectly convinced, indeed. I know his conversation among women to be modest and submissive. This forward, canting, ranting manner by no means describes him, and I am confident he never sat for the picture.

MISS HARD.: Then what, sir, if I should convince you to your face of my sincerity? If you and my papa, in about half an hour, will place yourselves behind that screen, you shall hear him declare his passion to me in person.

SIR CHARLES: Agreed. And if I find him what you describe, all my happiness in him must have an end.
                                                        [*Exit.*

MISS HARD.: And if you don't find him what I describe— I fear my happiness must never have a beginning.
                                                        [*Exeunt.*

Scene changes to the back of the garden.

Enter HASTINGS.

HASTINGS: What an idiot am I, to wait here for a fellow, who probably takes a delight in mortifying me. He never intended to be punctual, and I'll wait no longer.

What do I see? It is he, and perhaps with news of my Constance.

Enter TONY, *booted and spattered.*

HASTINGS: My honest Squire! I now find you a man of your word. This looks like friendship.

TONY: Ay, I'm your friend, and the best friend you have in the world, if you knew but all. This riding by night, by the by, is cursedly tiresome. It has shook me worse than the basket of a stage-coach.

HASTINGS: But how? Where did you leave your fellow-travellers? Are they in safety? Are they housed?

TONY: Five and twenty miles in two hours and a half is no such bad driving. The poor beasts have smoked for it: rabbit me, but I'd rather ride forty miles after a fox, than ten with such varmint.

HASTINGS: Well, but where have you left the ladies? I die with impatience.

TONY: Left them? Why, where should I leave them, but where I found them?

HASTINGS: This is a riddle.

TONY: Riddle me this, then. What's that goes round the house, and round the house, and never touches the house?

HASTINGS: I'm still astray.

TONY: Why, that's it, mon. I have led them astray. By jingo, there's not a pond or slough within five miles of the place but they can tell the taste of.

HASTINGS. Ha, ha, ha, I understand; you took them in a round, while they supposed themselves going forward. And so you have at last brought them home again.

TONY: You shall hear. I first took them down Feather-Bed Lane, where we stuck fast in the mud. I then rattled them crack over the stones of Up-and-Down Hill—I then introduced them to the gibbet on Heavy-Tree Heath, and from that, with a circumbendibus, I fairly lodged them in the horsepond at the bottom of the garden.

HASTINGS: But no accident, I hope.

TONY: No, no. Only mother is confoundedly frightened. She thinks herself forty miles off. She's sick of the journey, and the cattle can scarce crawl. So if your own horses be ready, you may whip off with cousin, and I'll be bound that no soul here can budge a foot to follow you.

HASTINGS: My dear friend, how can I be grateful?

TONY: Ay, now it's dear friend, noble Squire. Just now, it was all idiot, cub, and run me through the guts. Damn your way of fighting, I say. After we take a knock in this part of the country, we kiss and be friends. But if you had run me through the guts, then I should be dead, and you might go kiss the hangman.

HASTINGS: The rebuke is just. But I must hasten to relieve Miss Neville; if you keep the old lady employed, I promise to take care of the young one. [*Exit Hastings.*

TONY: Never fear me. Here she comes. Vanish. She's got from the pond, and draggled up to the waist like a mermaid.

Enter MRS. HARDCASTLE.

MRS. HARD.: Oh, Tony, I'm killed. Shook. Battered to death. I shall never survive it. That last jolt that laid us against the quickset hedge has done my business.

TONY: Alack, mamma, it was all your own fault. You would be for running away by night, without knowing one inch of the way.

MRS. HARD.: I wish we were at home again. I never met so many accidents in so short a journey. Drenched in the mud, overturned in a ditch, stuck fast in a slough, jolted to a jelly, and at last to lose our way. Whereabouts do you think we are, Tony?

TONY: By my guess we should be upon Crackskull Common, about forty miles from home.

MRS. HARD.: O lud! O lud! the most notorious spot in all the country. We only want a robbery to make a complete night on't.

TONY: Don't be afraid, mamma, don't be afraid. Two of the five that kept here are hanged, and the other three may not find us. Don't be afraid. Is that a man that's galloping behind us? No; it's only a tree. Don't be afraid.

MRS. HARD.: The fright will certainly kill me.

TONY: Do you see any thing like a black hat moving behind the thicket?

MRS. HARD.: O death!

TONY: No, it's only a cow. Don't be afraid, mamma, don't be afraid.

MRS. HARD.: As I'm alive, Tony, I see a man coming towards us. Ah! I'm sure on't. If he perceives us, we are undone.

TONY: (*Aside.*) Father-in-law, by all that's unlucky, come to take one of his night walks. (*To her.*) Ah, it's a highwayman, with pistols as long as my arm. A damned ill-looking fellow.

MRS. HARD.: Good Heaven defend us! He approaches.

TONY: Do you hide yourself in that thicket and leave me to manage him. If there be any danger I'll cough and cry hem. When I cough be sure to keep close.

[*Mrs. Hardcastle hides behind a tree in the back scene.*
Enter HARDCASTLE.

HARD.: I'm mistaken, or I heard voices of people in want of help. Oh, Tony, is that you? I did not expect you so soon back. Are your mother and her charge in safety?

TONY: Very safe, sir, at my Aunt Pedigree's. Hem.

MRS. HARD.: (*From behind.*) Ah! I find there's danger.

HARD.: Forty miles in three hours; sure, that's too much, my youngster.

TONY: Stout horses and willing minds make short journeys, as they say. Hem.

MRS. HARD.: (*From behind.*) Sure he'll do the dear boy no harm.

HARD.: But I heard a voice here; I should be glad to know from whence it came?

TONY: It was I, sir, talking to myself, sir. I was saying that forty miles in four hours was very good going. Hem.

Ah! I find there's danger.

As to be sure it was. Hem. I have got a sort of cold by being out in the air. We'll go in if you please. Hem.

HARD.: But if you talked to yourself, you did not answer yourself. I am certain I heard two voices, and am resolved (*raising his voice*) to find the other out.

MRS. HARD. (*From behind.*) Oh! he's coming to find me out. Oh!

TONY: What need you go sir, if I tell you? Hem. I'll lay down my life for the truth—hem—I'll tell you all, sir.
[*Detaining him.*

HARD.: I tell you I will not be detained. I insist on seeing. It's in vain to expect I'll believe you.

MRS. HARD.: (*Running forward from behind.*) O lud, he'll murder my poor boy, my darling. Here, good gentleman, whet your rage upon me. Take my money, my life, but spare that young gentleman, spare my child, if you have any mercy.

HARD.: My wife! as I'm a Christian. From whence can she come, or what does she mean?

MRS. HARD.: (*Kneeling.*) Take compassion on us, good Mr. Highwayman. Take our money, our watches, all we have, but spare our lives. We will never bring you to justice, indeed we won't, good Mr. Highwayman.

HARD.: I believe the woman's out of her senses. What, Dorothy, don't you know me?

MRS. HARD.: Mr. Hardcastle, as I'm alive! My fears blinded me. But who, my dear, could have expected to meet you here, in this frightful place, so far from home. What has brought you to follow us?

HARD.: Sure, Dorothy, you have not lost your wits. So far from home, when you are within forty yards of your own door! (*To him.*) This is one of your old tricks, you graceless rogue, you! (*To her.*) Don't you know the gate, and the mulberry-tree; and don't you remember the horsepond, my dear?

MRS. HARD.: Yes, I shall remember the horsepond as long as I live; I have caught my death in it. (*To Tony.*) And is it to you, you graceless varlet, I owe all this? I'll teach you to abuse your mother, I will.

TONY: Ecod, mother, all the parish says you have spoiled me, and so you may take the fruits on't.

MRS. HARD.: I'll spoil you, I will. [*Follows him off stage.*

HARD.: There's morality, however, in his reply. [*Exit.*

Enter HASTINGS AND MISS NEVILLE.

HASTINGS: My dear Constance, why will you deliberate thus? If we delay a moment, all is lost for ever. Pluck up a little resolution, and we shall soon be out of the reach of her malignity.

MISS NEVILLE: I find it impossible. My spirits are so sunk with the agitations I have suffered, that I am unable to face any new danger. Two or three years' patience will at last crown us with happiness.

HASTINGS: Such a tedious delay is worse than inconstancy. Let us fly, my charmer. Let us date our happiness from this very moment. Perish fortune. Love and content will increase what we possess beyond a monarch's revenue. Let me prevail.

MISS NEVILLE: No, Mr. Hastings; no. Prudence once more comes to my relief, and I will obey its dictates. In the moment of passion, fortune may be despised, but it ever produces a lasting repentance. I'm resolved to apply to Mr. Hardcastle's compassion and justice for redress.

HASTINGS: But though he had the will, he has not the power to relieve you.

MISS NEVILLE: But he has influence, and upon that I am resolved to rely.

HASTINGS: I have no hopes. But since you persist, I must reluctantly obey you. [*Exeunt.*

Scene changes.

Enter SIR CHARLES *and* MISS HARDCASTLE.

SIR CHARLES: What a situation am I in. If what you say appears, I shall then find a guilty son. If what he says be true, I shall then lose one that, of all others, I most wished for a daughter.

MISS HARD.: I am proud of your approbation, and, to show I merit it, if you place yourselves as I directed, you shall hear his explicit declaration. But he comes.

SIR CHARLES: I'll to your father, and keep him to the appointment. [*Exit Sir Charles.*

Enter MARLOW.

MARLOW: Though prepared for setting out, I come once more to take leave, nor did I, till this moment, know the pain I feel in the separation.

MISS HARD.: (*In her own natural manner.*) I believe sufferings cannot be very great, sir, which you can so easily remove. A day or two longer, perhaps, might lessen your uneasiness, by showing the little value of what you think proper to regret.

MARLOW: (*Aside.*) This girl every moment improves upon me. (*To her.*) It must not be, madam. I have already trifled too long with my heart. My very pride begins to submit to my passion. The disparity of education and fortune, the anger of a parent, and the contempt of my equals, begin to lose their weight; and nothing can restore me to myself but this painful effort of resolution.

MISS HARD.: Then go, sir. I'll urge nothing more to detain you. Though my family be as good as hers you came down to visit, and my education, I hope, not inferior, what are these advantages without equal affluence? I must remain contented with the slight approbation of imputed merit; I must have only the mockery of your addresses, while all your serious aims are fixed on fortune.

Enter HARDCASTLE *and* SIR CHARLES *from behind.*

SIR CHARLES: Here, behind this screen.

HARD.: Ay, ay, make no noise. I'll engage my Kate covers him with confusion at last.

MARLOW: By heavens, madam, fortune was ever my smallest consideration. Your beauty at first caught my eye; for who could see that without emotion? But every moment that I converse with you, steals in some new grace, heightens the picture, and gives it stronger expression. What at first seemed rustic plainness, now appears refined simplicity. What seemed forward assurance, now strikes me as the result of courageous innocence, and conscious virtue.

SIR CHARLES: What can it mean! He amazes me!

HARD.: I told you how it would be. Hush!

MARLOW: I am now determined to stay, madam, and I have too good an opinion of my father's discernment, when he sees you, to doubt his approbation.

MISS HARD.: No, Mr. Marlow, I will not, cannot detain you. Do you think I could suffer a connection, in which there is the smallest room for repentance? Do you think I would take the mean advantage of a transient passion, to load you with confusion? Do you think I could ever relish that happiness, which was acquired by lessening yours!

MARLOW: By all that's good, I can have no happiness but what's in your power to grant me. Nor shall I ever feel repentance, but in not having seen your merits before. I will stay, even contrary to your wishes; and though you should persist to shun me, I will make my respectful assiduities atone for the levity of my past conduct.

MISS HARD.: Sir, I must entreat you'll desist. As our acquaintance began, so let it end, in indifference. I might have given an hour or two to levity; but, seriously, Mr. Marlow, do you think I could ever submit to a connection, where I must appear mercenary, and you imprudent? Do you think, I could ever catch at the confident addresses of a secure admirer?

MARLOW: (*Kneeling.*) Does this look like security? Does this look like confidence? No, madam, every moment that shows me your merit, only serves to increase my diffidence and confusion. Here let me continue—

SIR CHARLES: I can hold it no longer. Charles, Charles, how hast thou deceived me! Is this your indifference, your uninteresting conversation!

HARD.: Your cold contempt; your formal interview. What have you to say now?

MARLOW: That I'm all amazement! What can it mean!

HARD.: It means that you can say and unsay things at pleasure. That you can address a lady in private, and deny it in public; that you have one story for us, and another for my daughter!

MARLOW: Daughter! this lady your daughter!

HARD.: Yes, sir, my only daughter. My Kate, whose else should she be?

MARLOW: Oh, the devil!

MISS HARD.: Yes, sir, that very identical tall squinting lady you were pleased to take me for. (*Curtsying.*) She that you addressed as the mild, modest, sentimental man of gravity, and the bold, forward, agreeable Rattle of the Ladies' Club: ha, ha, ha.

MARLOW: Zounds, there's no bearing this; it's worse than death.

MISS HARD.: In which of your characters, sir, will you give us leave to address you? As the faltering gentleman, with looks on the ground, that speaks just to be heard, and hates hypocrisy: or the loud confident creature, that keeps it up with Mrs. Mantrap, and old Miss Biddy Buckskin, till three in the morning; ha, ha, ha!

MARLOW: Oh, curse on my noisy head. I never attempted to be impudent yet, that I was not taken down. I must be gone.   [*Going.*

HARD.: By the hand of my body, but you shall not. I see it was all a mistake, and I am rejoiced to find it. You shall not, sir, I tell you. I know she'll forgive you. Won't you forgive him, Kate? We'll all forgive you. Take courage, man.

> [*They retire, she tormenting him, to the back scene.*
> *Enter* MRS. HARDCASTLE, TONY.

MRS. HARD.: So, so, they're gone off. Let them go, I care not.

HARD.: Who gone?

MRS. HARD.: My dutiful niece and her gentleman, Mr. Hastings, from town. He who came down with our modest visitor here.

SIR CHARLES: Who, my honest George Hastings? As worthy a fellow as lives, and the girl could not have made a more prudent choice.

HARD.: Then, by the hand of my body, I'm proud of the connection.

MRS. HARD.: Well, if he has taken away the lady, he has not taken her fortune, that remains in this family to console us for her loss.

HARD.: Sure, Dorothy, you would not be so mercenary?

MRS. HARD.: Ay, that's my affair, not yours.

HARD.: But you know, if your son, when of age, refuses to marry his cousin, her whole fortune is then at her own disposal.

MRS. HARD.: Ah, but he's not of age, and she has not thought proper to wait for his refusal.

Enter HASTINGS *and* MISS NEVILLE.

MRS. HARD.: (*Aside.*) What, returned so soon! I begin not to like it.

HASTINGS: (*To Hardcastle.*) For my late attempt to fly off with your niece, let my present confusion be my punishment. We are now come back, to appeal from your justice to your humanity. By her father's consent, I first paid her my addresses, and our passions were first founded in duty.

MISS NEVILLE: Since his death, I have been obliged to stoop to dissimulation to avoid oppression. In an hour of levity, I was ready even to give up my fortune to secure my choice. But I'm now recovered from the delusion, and hope from your tenderness what is denied me from a nearer connection.

MRS. HARD.: Pshaw, pshaw, this is all but the whining end of a modern novel.

HARD.: Be it what it will, I'm glad they're come back to reclaim their due. Come hither, Tony boy. Do you refuse this lady's hand whom I now offer you?

TONY: What signifies my refusing? You know I can't refuse her till I'm of age, father.

HARD.: While I thought concealing your age, boy, was

likely to conduce to your improvement, I concurred with your mother's desire to keep it secret. But since I find she turns it to a wrong use, I must now declare, you have been of age these three months.

TONY: Of age! Am I of age, father?

HARD.: Above three months.

TONY: Then you'll see the first use I'll make of my liberty. (*Taking Miss Neville's hand.*) Witness all men by these presents, that I, Anthony Lumpkin, Esquire, of BLANK place, refuse you, Constantia Neville, spinster, of no place at all, for my true and lawful wife. So Constance Neville may marry whom she pleases and Tony Lumpkin is his own man again!

SIR CHARLES: O brave 'squire!

HASTINGS: My worthy friend!

MRS. HARD.: My undutiful offspring!

MARLOW: Joy, my dear George, I give you joy, sincerely. And could I prevail upon my little tyrant here to be less arbitrary, I should be the happiest man alive, if you would return me the favour.

HASTINGS: (*To Miss Hardcastle.*) Come, madam, you are now driven to the very last scene of all your contrivances. I know you like him, I'm sure he loves you, and you must and shall have him.

HARD.: (*Joining their hands.*) And I say so, too. And Mr. Marlow, if she makes as good a wife as she has a daughter, I don't believe you'll ever repent your bargain. So now to supper. To-morrow we shall gather all the poor of the parish about us, and the mistakes of the night shall be crowned with a merry morning; so boy, take her; and as you have been mistaken in the mistress, my wish is, that you may never be mistaken in the wife.

EPILOGUE

WELL, having stooped to conquer with success,
And gained a husband without aid from dress,
Still as a barmaid, I could wish it too,
As I have conquered him to conquer you:
And let me say, for all your resolution,
That pretty barmaids have done execution.
Our life is all a play, composed to please,
"We have our exits and our entrances."
The first act shows the simple country maid,
Harmless and young, of everything afraid;
Blushes when hired, and with unmeaning action,
"I hopes as how to give you satisfaction."
Her second act displays a livelier scene,—
Th' unblushing barmaid of a country inn,
Who whisks about the house, at market caters,
Talks loud, coquets the guests, and scolds the waiters.
Next the scene shifts to town, and there she soars,
The chop-house toast of ogling connoisseurs.
On squires and cits she there displays her arts,
And on the gridiron broils her lovers' hearts—
And as she smiles, her triumphs to complete,
Even common councilmen forget to eat.
The fourth act shows her wedded to the squire,
And madam now begins to hold it higher;
Pretends to taste, at Operas cries caro,
And quits her Nancy Dawson, for Che Faro.
Doats upon dancing, and in all her pride,
Swims round the room, the Heinel of Cheapside:
Ogles and leers with artificial skill,
Till having lost in age the power to kill,
She sits all night at cards, and ogles at spadille.
Such, through our lives, the eventful history—
The fifth and last act still remains for me.
The barmaid now for your protection prays,
Turns female Barrister, and pleads for Bayes.

POEMS

THE DESERTED VILLAGE

SWEET Auburn! loveliest village of the plain,
Where health and plenty cheered the labouring swain,
Where smiling spring its earliest visit paid,
And parting summer's lingering blooms delayed:
Dear lovely bowers of innocence and ease,
Seats of my youth, when every sport could please,
How often have I loitered o'er thy green,
Where humble happiness endeared each scene;
How often have I paused on every charm,
The sheltered cot, the cultivated farm,
The never-failing brook, the busy mill,
The decent church that topped the neighbouring hill,
The hawthorn bush, with seats beneath the shade,
For talking age and whisp'ring lovers made;
How often have I blessed the coming day,
When toil remitting lent its turn to play,
And all the village train, from labour free,
Led up their sports beneath the spreading tree;
While many a pastime circled in the shade,
The young contending as the old surveyed;
And many a gambol frolicked o'er the ground,
And sleights of art and feats of strength went round;
And still as each repeated pleasure tired,
Succeeding sports the mirthful band inspired;
The dancing pair that simply sought renown,
By holding out to tire each other down;
The swain mistrustless of his smutted face,
While secret laughter tittered round the place;
The bashful virgin's side-long looks of love,
The matron's glance that would those looks reprove,
These were thy charms, sweet village; sports like these,
With sweet succession, taught e'en toil to please;
These round thy bowers their cheerful influence shed.
These were thy charms—But all these charms are fled.

Sweet smiling village, loveliest of the lawn,
Thy sports are fled, and all thy charms withdrawn;
Amidst thy bowers the tyrant's hand is seen,
And desolation saddens all thy green:
One only master grasps the whole domain,
And half a tillage stints thy smiling plain:
No more thy glassy brook reflects the day,
But choked with sedges, works its weedy way.
Along thy glades, a solitary guest,
The hollow-sounding bittern guards its nest;
Amidst thy desert walks the lapwing flies,
And tires their echoes with unvaried cries.
Sunk are thy bowers in shapeless ruin all,
And the long grass o'ertops the mould'ring wall;
And trembling, shrinking from the spoiler's hand,
Far, far away, thy children leave the land.

Ill fares the land, to hast'ning ills a prey,
Where wealth accumulates, and men decay:
Princes and lords may flourish, or may fade;
A breath can make them, as a breath has made;
But a bold peasantry, their country's pride,
When once destroyed, can never be supplied.

A time there was, ere England's griefs began,
When every rood of ground maintained its man;
For him light labour spread her wholesome store,
Just gave what life required, but gave no more:
His best companions, innocence and health;
And his best riches, ignorance of wealth.

But times are altered; trade's unfeeling train
Usurp the land and dispossess the swain;
Along the lawn, where scattered hamlets rose,
Unwieldy wealth, and cumbrous pomp repose;
And every want to opulence allied,
And every pang that folly pays to pride.
Those gentle hours that plenty bade to bloom,
Those calm desires that asked but little room,

Those healthful sports that graced the peaceful scene,
Lived in each look, and brightened all the green;
These, far departing, seek a kinder shore,
And rural mirth and manners are no more.

Sweet Auburn! parent of the blissful hour,
Thy glades forlorn confess the tyrant's power.
Here as I take my solitary rounds,
Amidst thy tangling walks, and ruined grounds,
And, many a year elapsed, return to view
Where once the cottage stood, the hawthorn grew,
Remembrance wakes with all her busy train,
Swells at my breast, and turns the past to pain.

In all my wand'rings round this world of care,
In all my griefs—and God has given my share—
I still had hopes my latest hours to crown,
Amidst these humble bowers to lay me down;
To husband out life's taper at the close,
And keep the flame from wasting by repose.
I still had hopes, for pride attends us still,
Amidst the swains to show my book-learned skill,
Around my fire an evening group to draw,
And tell of all I felt, and all I saw;
And, as a hare, whom hounds and horns pursue,
Pants to the place from whence at first she flew,
I still had hopes, my long vexations passed,
Here to return—and die at home at last.

O blest retirement, friend to life's decline,
Retreats from care, that never must be mine,
How happy he who crowns in shades like these,
A youth of labour with an age of ease;
Who quits a world where strong temptations try
And, since 'tis hard to combat, learns to fly!
For him no wretches, born to work and weep,
Explore the mine, or tempt the dangerous deep;

No surly porter stands in guilty state
To spurn imploring famine from the gate;
But on he moves to meet his latter end,
Angels around befriending Virtue's friend;
Bends to the grave with unperceived decay,
While resignation gently slopes the way;
And, all his prospects bright'ning to the last,
His Heaven commences ere the world be passed!

Sweet was the sound, when oft at evening's close
Up younder hill the village murmur rose;
There, as I passed with careless steps and slow,
The mingling notes came softened from below;
The swain responsive as the milk-maid sung,
The sober herd that lowed to meet their young;
The noisy geese that gabbled o'er the pool,
The playful children just let loose from school;
The watchdog's voice that bayed the whisp'ring wind,
And the loud laugh that spoke the vacant mind;
These all in sweet confusion sought the shade,
And filled each pause the nightingale had made.
But now the sounds of population fail,
No cheerful murmurs fluctuate in the gale,
No busy steps the grass-grown foot-way tread,
For all the bloomy flush of life is fled.
All but yon widowed, solitary thing
That feebly bends beside the plashy spring;
She, wretched matron, forced, in age, for bread,
To strip the brook with mantling cresses spread,
To pick her wintry faggot from the thorn,
To seek her nightly shed, and weep till morn:
She only left of all the harmless train,
The sad historian of the pensive plain.

Near yonder copse, where once the garden smiled,
And still where many a garden flower grows wild;
There, where a few torn shrubs the place disclose,
The village preacher's modest mansion rose.

A man he was to all the country dear,
And passing rich with forty pounds a year;
Remote from towns he ran his godly race,
Nor e'er had changed, nor wished to change his place;
Unpractised he to fawn, or seek for power,
By doctrines fashioned to the varying hour;
Far other aims his heart had learned to prize,
More skilled to raise the wretched than to rise.
His house was known to all the vagrant train,
He chid their wand'rings, but relieved their pain;
The long-remembered beggar was his guest,
Whose beard descending swept his aged breast;
The ruined spendthrift, now no longer proud,
Claimed kindred there, and had his claims allowed;
The broken soldier, kindly bade to stay,
Sat by his fire, and talked the night away;
Wept o'er his wounds, or tales of sorrow done,
Shouldered his crutch, and showed how fields were won.
Pleased with his guests, the good man learned to glow,
And quite forgot their vices in their woe;
Careless their merits, or their faults to scan,
His pity gave ere charity began.

Thus to relieve the wretched was his pride,
And e'en his failings leaned to virtue's side;
But in his duty prompt at every call,
He watched and wept, he prayed and felt, for all.
And, as a bird each fond endearment tries
To tempt its new-fledged offspring to the skies,
He tried each art, reproved each dull delay,
Allured to brighter worlds, and led the way.

Beside the bed where parting life was laid,
And sorrow, guilt, and pain, by turns dismayed,
The reverend champion stood. At his control,
Despair and anguish fled the struggling soul;
Comfort came down the trembling wretch to raise,
And his last falt'ring accents whispered praise.

At church, with meek and unaffected grace,
His looks adorned the venerable place;
Truth from his lips prevailed with double sway,
And fools, who came to scoff, remained to pray.
The service passed, around the pious man,
With steady zeal, each honest rustic ran;
E'en children followed with endearing wile,
And plucked his gown, to share the good man's smile.
His ready smile a parent's warmth expressed,
Their welfare pleased him, and their cares distressed;
To them his heart, his love, his griefs were given,
But all his serious thoughts had rest in Heaven.
As some tall cliff, that lifts its awful form,
Swells from the vale, and midway leaves the storm,
Though round its breast the rolling clouds are spread,
Eternal sunshine settles on its head.

Beside yon straggling fence that skirts the way,
With blossomed furze unprofitably gay,
There, in his noisy mansion, skilled to rule,
The village master taught his little school;
A man severe he was, and stern to view;
I knew him well, and every truant knew;
Well had the boding tremblers learned to trace
The day's disasters in his morning face;
Full well they laughed, with counterfeited glee,
At all his jokes, for many a joke had he;
Full well the busy whisper, circling round,
Conveyed the dismal tidings when he frowned;
Yet he was kind; or if severe in aught,
The love he bore to learning was in fault;
The village all declared how much he knew;
'Twas certain he could write, and cypher too;
Lands he could measure, terms and tides presage,
And e'en the story ran that he could gauge.
In arguing too, the parson owned his skill,
For e'en though vanquished, he could argue still;
While words of learned length and thund'ring sound
Amazed the gazing rustics ranged around,

And still they gazed, and still the wonder grew,
That one small head could carry all he knew.

But past is all his fame. The very spot
Where many a time he triumphed, is forgot.
Near yonder thorn, that lifts its head on high,
Where once the sign-post caught the passing eye,
Low lies that house where nut-brown draughts inspired,
Where grey-beard mirth and smiling toil retired,
Where village statesmen talked with looks profound,
And news much older than their ale went round.
Imagination fondly stoops to trace
The parlour splendours of that festive place;
The white-washed wall, the nicely sanded floor,
The varnished clock that clicked behind the door;
The chest contrived a double debt to pay,
A bed by night, a chest of drawers by day;
The pictures placed for ornament and use,
The twelve good rules, the royal game of goose;
The hearth, except when winter chilled the day,
With aspen boughs, and flowers, and fennel gay;
While broken tea-cups, wisely kept for show,
Ranged o'er the chimney, glistened in a row.

Vain, transitory splendours! Could not all
Reprieve the tottering mansion from its fall!
Obscure it sinks, nor shall it more impart
An hour's importance to the poor man's heart;
Thither no more the peasant shall repair
To sweet oblivion of his daily care;
No more the farmer's news, the barber's tale,
No more the wood-man's ballad shall prevail;
No more the smith his dusky brow shall clear,
Relax his pond'rous strength, and lean to hear;
The host himself no longer shall be found
Careful to see the mantling bliss go round;
Nor the coy maid, half willing to be pressed,
Shall kiss the cup to pass it to the rest.

Yes! let the rich deride, the proud disdain,
These simple blessings of the lowly train;
To me more dear, congenial to my heart,
One native charm, than all the gloss of art;
Spontaneous joys, where Nature has its play,
The soul adopts, and owns their first-born sway;
Lightly they frolic o'er the vacant mind,
Unenvied, unmolested, unconfined:
But the long pomp, the midnight masquerade,
With all the freaks of wanton wealth arrayed,
In these, ere triflers half their wish obtain,
The toiling pleasure sickens into pain;
And, e'en while fashion's brightest arts decoy,
The heart distrusting asks, if this be joy.

Ye friends to truth, ye statesmen, who survey
The rich man's joys increase, the poor's decay,
'Tis yours to judge, how wide the limits stand
Between a splendid and a happy land.
Proud swells the tide with loads of freighted ore,
And shouting Folly hails them from her shore;
Hoards, e'en beyond the miser's wish abound,
And rich men flock from all the world around.
Yet count our gains. This wealth is but a name
That leaves our useful products still the same.
Not so the loss. The man of wealth and pride
Takes up a space that many poor supplied;
Space for his lake, his park's extended bounds,
Space for his horses, equipage, and hounds;
The robe that wraps his limbs in silken sloth
Has robbed the neighbouring fields of half their growth,
His seat, where solitary sports are seen,
Indignant spurns the cottage from the green;
Around the world each needful product flies,
For all the luxuries the world supplies:
While thus the land adorned for pleasure, all
In barren splendour feebly waits the fall.

As some fair female unadorned and plain,
Secure to please while youth confirms her reign,
Slights every borrowed charm that dress supplies,
Nor shares with art the triumph of her eyes:
But when those charms are passed, for charms are frail,
When time advances, and when lovers fail,
She then shines forth, solicitous to bless,
In all the glaring impotence of dress.
Thus fares the land, by luxury betrayed,
In nature's simplest charms at first arrayed;
But verging to decline, its splendours rise,
Its vistas strike, its palaces surprise;
While scourged by famine from the smiling land,
The mournful peasant leads his humble band;
And while he sinks, without one arm to save,
The country blooms—a garden, and a grave.

Where then, ah! where, shall poverty reside,
To 'scape the pressure of contiguous pride?
If to some common's fenceless limits strayed,
He drives his flock to pick the scanty blade,
Those fenceless fields the sons of wealth divide,
And e'en the bare-worn common is denied.

If to the city sped—What waits him there?
To see profusion that he must not share;
To see ten thousand baneful arts combined
To pamper luxury, and thin mankind;
To see those joys the sons of pleasure know
Extorted from his fellow creature's woe.
Here, while the courtier glitters in brocade,
There the pale artist plies the sickly trade;
Here, while the proud their long-drawn pomps display,
There the black gibbet glooms beside the way.
The dome where Pleasure holds her midnight reign
Here, richly decked, admits the gorgeous train;
Tumultuous grandeur crowds the blazing square,
The rattling chariots clash, the torches glare.

Sure scenes like these no troubles e'er annoy!
Sure these denote one universal joy!
Are these thy serious thoughts?—Ah, turn thine eyes
Where the poor houseless shiv'ring female lies.
She once, perhaps, in village plenty bless'd,
Has wept at tales of innocence distress'd;
Her modest looks the cottage might adorn,
Sweet as the primrose peeps beneath the thorn;
Now lost to all; her friends, her virtue fled,
Near her betrayer's door she lays her head,
And, pinched with cold, and shrinking from the shower,
With heavy heart deplores that luckless hour,
When idly first, ambitious of the town,
She left her wheel and robes of country brown.

Do thine, sweet Auburn, thine, the loveliest train,
Do thy fair tribes participate her pain?
E'en now, perhaps, by cold and hunger led,
At proud men's doors they ask a little bread!

Ah, no. To distant climes, a dreary scene,
Where half the convex world intrudes between,
Through torrid tracts with fainting steps they go,
Where wild Altama murmurs to their woe.
Far different there from all that charmed before,
The various terrors of that horrid shore;
Those blazing suns that dart a downward ray,
And fiercely shed intolerable day;
Those matted woods where birds forget to sing,
But silent bats in drowsy clusters cling;
Those pois'nous fields with rank luxuriance crowned,
Where the dark scorpion gathers death around;
Where at each step the stranger fears to wake
The rattling terrors of the vengeful snake;
Where crouching tigers wait their hapless prey,
And savage men more murd'rous still than they;
While oft in whirls the mad tornado flies,
Mingling the ravaged landscape with the skies.

Far different these from every former scene,
The cooling brook, the grassy-vested green,
The breezy covert of the warbling grove,
That only sheltered thefts of harmless love.

Good heaven! what sorrows gloomed that parting day,
That called them from their native walks away;
When the poor exiles, every pleasure passed,
Hung round their bowers, and fondly looked their last,
And took a long farewell, and wished in vain
For seats like these beyond the western main;
And shudd'ring still to face the distant deep,
Returned and wept, and still returned to weep.
The good old sire, the first prepared to go
The new-found worlds, and wept for others' woe;
But for himself, in conscious virtue brave,
He only wished for worlds beyond the grave.
His lovely daughter, lovelier in her tears,
The fond companion of his helpless years,
Silent went next, neglectful of her charms,
And left a lover's for a father's arms.
With louder plaints the mother spoke her woes,
And bless'd the cot where every pleasure rose
And kissed her thoughtless babes with many a tear,
And clasped them close, in sorrow doubly dear;
Whilst her fond husband strove to lend relief
In all the silent manliness of grief.

O Luxury! thou curs'd by Heaven's decree,
How ill exchanged are things like these for thee!
How do thy potions, with insidious joy
Diffuse their pleasures only to destroy!
Kingdoms, by thee, to sickly greatness grown,
Boast of a florid vigour not their own;
At every draught more large and large they grow,
A bloated mass of rank unwieldy woe;
Till sapped their strength, and every part unsound,
Down, down they sink, and spread a ruin round.

E'en now the devastation is begun,
And half the business of destruction done;
E'en now, methinks, as pond'ring here I stand,
I see the rural virtues leave the land:
Down where yon anchoring vessel spreads the sail,
That idly waiting flaps with every gale,
Downward they move, a melancholy band,
Pass from the shore, and darken all the strand.
Contented toil, and hospitable care,
And kind connubial tenderness, are there;
And piety, with wishes placed above,
And steady loyalty, and faithful love.
And thou, sweet Poetry, thou loveliest maid,
Still first to fly where sensual joys invade;
Unfit in these degenerate times of shame,
To catch the heart, or strike for honest fame;
Dear charming nymph, neglected and decried,
My shame in crowds, my solitary pride;
Thou source of all my bliss, and all my woe,
That found'st me poor at first, and keep'st me so;
Thou guide by which the nobler arts excel,
Thou nurse of every virtue, fare thee well!
Farewell, and Oh! where'er thy voice be tried,
On Torno's cliffs, or Pambamarca's side,
Whether where equinoctial fervours glow,
Or winter wraps the polar world in snow,
Still let thy voice, prevailing over time,
Redress the rigours of th' inclement clime;
Aid slighted truth; with thy persuasive strain
Teach erring man to spurn the rage of gain;
Teach him, that states of native strength possess'd,
Though very poor, may still be very bless'd;
That trade's proud empire hastes to swift decay,
As ocean sweeps the laboured mole away;
While self-dependent power can time defy,
As rocks resist the billows and the sky.

THE HAUNCH OF VENISON
A Poetical Epistle to Lord Clare

THANKS, my Lord, for your venison, for finer or fatter
Never ranged in a forest, or smoked in a platter;
The haunch was a picture for painters to study,
The fat was so white, and the lean was so ruddy.
Though my stomach was sharp, I could scarce help
   regretting
To spoil such a delicate picture by eating;
I had thoughts, in my chambers, to place it in view,
To be shown to my friends as a piece of *virtu*;
As in some Irish houses, where things are so so,
One gammon of bacon hangs up for a show:
But for eating a rasher of what they take pride in,
They'd as soon think of eating the pan it is fried in.
But hold—let me pause—Don't I hear you pronounce
This tale of the bacon a damnable bounce?
Well, suppose it a bounce—sure a poet may try,
By a bounce now and then, to get courage to fly.

But, my Lord, it's no bounce: I protest in my turn,
It's a truth—and your Lordship may ask Mr. Byrne.
To go on with my tale—as I gazed on the haunch,
I thought of a friend that was trusty and staunch;
So I cut it, and sent it to Reynolds undressed,
To paint it, or eat it, just as he liked best.
Of the neck and the breast I had next to dispose;
'Twas a neck and a breast—that might rival M—r—'s:
But in parting with these I was puzzled again,
With the how, and the who, and the where, and the when.
There's H—d, and C—y, and H—rth, and H—ff,
I think they love venison—I know they love beef;
There's my countryman H—gg—ns—Oh! let him alone,
For making a blunder, or picking a bone.
But hang it—to poets who seldom can eat,
Your very good mutton's a very good treat;

Such dainties to them, their health it might hurt,
It's like sending them ruffles, when wanting a shirt.
While thus I debated, in reverie centred,
An acquaintance, a friend as he called himself, entered;
An under-bred, fine-spoken fellow was he,
And he smiled as he looked at the venison and me.
"What have we got here?—Why, this is good eating!
Your own, I suppose—or is it in waiting?"
"Why, whose should it be?" cried I with a flounce,
"I get these things often";—but that was a bounce:
"Some lords, my acquaintance, that settle the nation,
Are pleased to be kind—but I hate ostentation."

"If that be the case, then," cried he, very gay,
"I'm glad I have taken this house in my way.
To-morrow you take a poor dinner with me;
No words—I insist on 't—precisely at three:
We'll have Johnson, and Burke; all the wits will be
   there;
My acquaintance is slight, or I'd ask my Lord Clare.
And now that I think on 't, as I am a sinner!
We wanted this venison to make out the dinner.
What say you—a pasty? it shall, and it must,
And my wife, little Kitty, is famous for crust.
Here, porter!—this venison with me to Mile-end;
No stirring—I beg—my dear friend—my dear friend!"
Thus snatching his hat, he brushed off like the wind,
And the porter and eatables followed behind.
   Left alone to reflect, having emptied my shelf,

"And nobody with me at sea but myself";
Though I could not help thinking my gentleman hasty,
Yet Johnson, and Burke, and a good venison pasty,
Were things that I never disliked in my life,
Though clogged with a coxcomb, and Kitty his wife.
So next day, in due splendour to make my approach,
I drove to his door in my own hackney coach.

When come to the place where we all were to dine,
(A chair-lumbered closet just twelve feet by nine:)
My friend bade me welcome, but struck me quite dumb,
With tidings that Johnson and Burke would not come;
"For I knew it," he cried, "both eternally fail,
The one with his speeches, and t'other with Thrale;
But no matter, I'll warrant we'll make up the party
With two full as clever, and ten times as hearty.
The one is a Scotchman, the other a Jew,
They['re] both of them merry and authors like you;
The one writes the *Snarler*, the other the *Scourge*;
Some think he writes *Cinna*—he owns to *Panurge*."
While thus he described them by trade, and by name,
They entered, and dinner was served as they came.

At the top a fried liver and bacon were seen,
At the bottom was tripe in a swinging tureen;
At the sides there was spinach and pudding made hot;
In the middle a place where the pasty—was not.
Now, my Lord, as for tripe, it's my utter aversion,
And your bacon I hate like a Turk or a Persian;
So there I sat stuck, like a horse in a pound,
While the bacon and liver went merrily round.
But what vexed me most was that d—'d Scottish rogue,
With his long-winded speeches, his smiles and his
    brogue;
And, "Madam," quoth he, "may this bit be my poison,
A prettier dinner I never set eyes on;
Pray a slice of your liver, though may I be cursed,
But I've eat of your tripe till I'm ready to burst."
"The tripe," quoth the Jew, with his chocolate cheek,
"I could dine on this tripe seven days in the week:
I like these here dinners so pretty and small;
But your friend there, the Doctor, eats nothing at all."
"O—Oh!" quoth my friend, "he'll come on in a trice,
He's keeping a corner for something that's nice:
There's a pasty"—"A pasty!" repeated the Jew,
"I don't care if I keep a corner for 't too."

"What the de'il, mon, a pasty!" re-echoed the Scot,
"Though splitting, I'll still keep a corner for thot."
"We'll all keep a corner," the lady cried out;
"We'll all keep a corner," was echoed about.
While thus we resolved, and the pasty delayed,
With looks that quite petrified, entered the maid;
A visage so sad, and so pale with affright,
Waked Priam in drawing his curtains by night.
But we quickly found out, for who could mistake her?
That she came with some terrible news from the baker:
And so it fell out, for that negligent sloven
Had shut out the pasty on shutting his oven.
Sad Philomel thus—but let similes drop—
And now that I think on 't, the story may stop.
To be plain, my good Lord, it's but labour misplaced
To send such good verses to one of your taste;
You've got an odd something—a kind of discerning—
A relish—a taste—sickened over by learning;
At least, it's your temper, as very well known,
That you think very slightly of all that's your own:
So, perhaps, in your habits of thinking amiss,
You may make a mistake, and think slightly of this.

THE DOUBLE TRANSFORMATION

Secluded from domestic strife,
Jack Book-worm led a college life;
A fellowship at twenty-five
Made him the happiest man alive;
He drank his glass and crack'd his joke,
And Freshmen wonder'd as he spoke:

Such pleasures unallay'd with care,
Could any accident impair?
Could Cupid's shaft at length transfix,
Our swain arrived at thirty-six?
O had the archer ne'er come down
To ravage in a country town!
Or Flavia been content to stop
At triumphs in a Fleet-street shop.
O had her eyes forgot to blaze!
Or Jack had wanted eyes to gaze.
O!—But let exclamation cease,
Her presence banish'd all his peace.
So with decorum all things carry'd;
Miss frown'd, and blush'd, and then was—married.

Need we expose to vulgar sight
The raptures of the bridal night?
Need we intrude on hallow'd ground,
Or draw the curtains clos'd around?
Let it suffice, that each had charms;
He clasp'd a goddess in his arms;
And, tho' she felt his usage rough,
Yet in a man 'twas well enough.

The honey-moon like light'ning flew,
The second brought its transports too.
A third, a fourth, were not amiss,
The fifth was friendship mix'd with bliss:

But, when a twelvemonth pass'd away,
Jack found his goddess made of clay;
Found half the charms that deck'd her face,
Arose from powder, shreds, or lace;
But still the worst remain'd behind,
That very face had robb'd her mind.

　　Skill'd in no other arts was she,
But dressing, a patching, repartee;
And, just as humour rose or fell,
By turns a slattern or a belle:
'Tis true she dress'd with modern grace,
Half naked at a ball or race;
But when at home, at board or bed,
Five greasy night-caps wrap'd her head.
Could so much beauty condescend
To be a dull domestic friend?
Could any curtain-lectures bring
To decency so fine a thing?
In short, by night, 'twas fits or fretting;
By day, 'twas gadding or coquetting.
Fond to be seen she kept a bevy
Of powder'd coxcombs at her levy;
The 'squire and captain took their stations,
And twenty other near relations;
Jack suck'd his pipe, and often broke
A sigh in suffocating smoke;
While all their hours were pass'd between
Insulting repartee or spleen.

　　Thus as her faults each day were known,
He thinks her features coarser grown;
He fancies every vice she shews
Or thins her lip, or points her nose:
Whenever rage or envy rise,
How wide her mouth, how wild her eyes!
He knows not how, but so it is,
Her face is grown a knowing phyz;

And, tho' her fops are wond'rous civil,
He thinks her ugly as the devil.

Now, to perplex the ravell'd nooze,
As each a different way pursues,
While sullen or loquacious strife
Promis'd to hold them on for life,
That dire disease, whose ruthless power,
Withers the beauty's transient flower:
Lo! the small-pox, whose horrid glare,
Levell'd its terrors at the fair;
And, rifling ev'ry youthful grace,
Left but the remnant of a face.

The glass, grown hateful to her sight,
Reflected now a perfect fright:
Each former art she vainly tries
To bring back lustre to her eyes.
In vain she tries her paste and creams,
To smooth her skin, or hide its seams;
Her country beaux and city cousins,
Lovers no more, flew off by dozens:
The squire himself was seen to yield,
And even the captain quit the field.

Poor Madam, now condemn'd to hack
The rest of life with anxious Jack,
Perceiving others fairly flown
Attempted pleasing him alone.
Jack soon was dazzl'd to behold
Her present face surpass the old;
With modesty her cheeks are dy'd,
Humility displaces pride;
For taudry finery is seen,
A person ever neatly clean:
No more presuming on her sway
She learns good nature every day;
Serenely gay, and strict in duty,
Jack finds his wife a perfect beauty.

*This book
designed by William B. Taylor
is a production of
Heron Books, London*

*Published by arrangement with
William Collins Sons and Company Limited
© 1974, Illustrations, Heron Books, London
Introductions © William Collins Sons and Company Limited, Glasgow
© Heron Books, London*

*Printed in England by
Hazell Watson & Viney Limited
Aylesbury, Bucks*